HIGH-RISK
INFANTS AND CHILDREN

Adult and Peer Interactions

DEVELOPMENTAL PSYCHOLOGY SERIES

SERIES EDITOR
Harry Beilin

Developmental Psychology Program
City University of New York Graduate School
New York, New York

HIGH-RISK
INFANTS AND CHILDREN
Adult and Peer Interactions

Editor

TIFFANY MARTINI FIELD

Mailman Center for Child Development
University of Miami Medical School
Miami, Florida

Co-Editors

SUSAN GOLDBERG

Department of Psychology
Brandeis University
Waltham, Massachusetts

DANIEL STERN

Department of Psychiatry
Cornell University Medical Center
New York, New York

ANITA MILLER SOSTEK

Division of Newborn Medicine
Georgetown University School of Medicine
Washington, D.C.

1980

ACADEMIC PRESS

A Subsidiary of Harcourt Brace Jovanovich, Publishers

New York   London   Toronto   Sydney   San Francisco

ACADEMIC PRESS, INC.
111 Fifth Avenue, New York, New York 10003

United Kingdom Edition published by
ACADEMIC PRESS, INC. (LONDON) LTD.
24/28 Oval Road, London NW1 7DX

Library of Congress Cataloging in Publication Data

Main entry under title:

High—risk infants and children.

(Developmental psychology series)
Includes bibliographies and index.
1. Infant psychiatry. 2. Child psychiatry.
3. Children and adults. I. Field, Tiffany.
II. Series.
RJ502.5.H54   155.4   80—11870
ISBN 0—12—255550—3

PRINTED IN THE UNITED STATES OF AMERICA

80 81 82 83   9 8 7 6 5 4 3 2 1

Contents

Infant and Child Interactions with Parents

PART **I**

INFANTS OR CHILDREN EXPERIENCING FAILURE TO THRIVE, ABUSE, OR FAMILY DISRUPTION

CHAPTER **1**

PART **II**

INFANTS AT RISK FOR DEVELOPMENT OF AUTISTIC DISTURBANCES

CHAPTER **5**

CHAPTER **6**

PART **III**

INFANTS AND CHILDREN AT RISK FOR DEVELOPMENTAL DELAYS

PART **IV**

INFANTS AND CHILDREN WITH PERCEPTUAL–MOTOR HANDICAPS

CHAPTER **10**

Stages of Early Behavioral Organization: The Study of a Sighted Infant and a Blind Infant in Interaction with Their Mothers

181

H. ALS, E. TRONICK, AND T. B. BRAZELTON

CHAPTER **11**

Prelinguistic Communication Skills in Down's Syndrome and Normal Infants

205

OLWEN H. M. JONES

CHAPTER **12**

Interaction Systems between Preschool Handicapped or Developmentally Delayed Children and Their Parents

227

KATE L. KOGAN

Peer and Teacher Interactions of Children at Risk

CHAPTER **13**

**Peers, Play, and Pathology: Considerations in
the Growth of Social Competence**   **251**

WILLARD W. HARTUP

CHAPTER **14**

Structures of Interaction between Two Autistic Children   **257**

MARY MARTINI

CHAPTER **15**

Abused Children: Their Rejection of Peers and Caregivers   **293**

CAROL GEORGE AND MARY MAIN

List of Contributors

Numbers in parentheses indicate the pages on which the authors' contributions begin.

HEIDELEISE ALS (181), Child Development Unit, The Children's Hospital Medical Center and Department of Pediatrics, Harvard Medical School, Boston, Massachusetts 02115

WILLIAM A. ALTEMEIER (5), Department of Pediatrics, Vanderbilt University, School of Medicine, Nashville, Tennessee 37232

LEILA BECKWITH* (155), Department of Pediatrics, Harvard University, Boston, Massachusetts 02115

SHEILA BRACHFELD (133), Department of Psychology, Brandeis University, Waltham, Massachusetts 02138

T. B. BRAZELTON (181), Child Development Unit, The Children's Hospital Medical Center, Harvard Medical School, Boston, Massachusetts 02115

ROBERT L. BURGESS (43), College of Human Development, Pennsylvania State University, University Park, Pennsylvania 16802

SARALE E. COHEN (155), Department of Pediatrics, University of California at Los Angeles, Los Angeles, California 90032

RAND D. CONGER (43), Department of Psychology, Pennsylvania State University, University Park, Pennsylvania 16802

*PRESENT ADDRESS: Department of Pediatrics, University of California at Los Angeles, Los Angeles, California 90024

KIM N. DIETRICH (25), Department of Psychology, Wayne State University, Detroit, Michigan 48202

BARBARA DIVITTO (133), Early Intervention Program, Child Development Center, Providence, Rhode Island 02906

SUSAN FALSEY (5), National Education Association, Washington, D.C.

TIFFANY MARTINI FIELD (113, 313), Departments of Pediatrics and Psychology, Mailman Center for Child Development, University of Miami Medical School, Miami, Florida 33101

CAROL GEORGE (293), Department of Psychology, University of California at Berkeley, Berkeley, California 94720

SUSAN GOLDBERG (133), Department of Psychology, Brandeis University, Waltham, Massachusetts 02154

FAE HALL (61), London Hospital Medical College, Family Research Unit, London, E1, England

WILLARD W. HARTUP (251), Institute of Child Development, University of Minnesota, Minneapolis, Minnesota 55455

OLWEN H. M. JONES (205), Queen Mary's Hospital, Roehampton Health District, Roehampton, London SW15 5PN

MELISSA G. KAPLAN (25), Department of Family and Consumer Resources, Wayne State University, Detroit, Michigan 48202

DEBORAH S. KEARNEY (327), Department of Psychology, University of Massachusetts, Amherst, Massachusetts 01003

WILLIAM H. KIMBALL* (43), Department of Psychology, Pennsylvania State University, University Park, Pennsylvania 16802

KATE L. KOGAN (227), Department of Psychiatry and Behavioral Sciences, University of Washington, School of Medicine, Seattle, Washington, 98195

LORRAINE F. KUBICEK (99), Committee on Cognition and Communication, Department of Behavioral Sciences, The University of Chicago, Chicago, Illinois 60637

MARY MAIN (293), Department of Psychology, University of California at Berkeley, Berkeley, California 94720

MARY MARTINI (257), Committee on Human Development, University of Chicago, Chicago, Illinois 60637

HENRY N. MASSIE (79), Child Psychiatry Training, St. Mary's Hospital and Medical Center, McAuley Neuropsychiatric Institute, San Francisco, California 94117

MELINDA A. NOVAK (327), Department of Psychology, University of Massachusetts, Amherst, Massachusetts 01003

*PRESENT ADDRESS: CMHC, Mercy Hospital, 218 Stone Street, Watertown, New York 13601

SUSAN O'CONNOR (5), Department of Pediatrics, School of Medicine, Vanderbilt University, Nashville, Tennessee 37232

J. GREGORY OLLEY (327), Division TEACCH, Department of Psychiatry, University of North Carolina, Chapel Hill, North Carolina 27514

SUSAN J. PAWLBY (61), London Hospital Medical College, Family Research Unit, London, E1, England

HOWARD SANDLER (5), John F. Kennedy Center, Peabody College of Vanderbilt University, Nashville, Tennessee 37203

KATHRYN B. SHERROD (5), John F. Kennedy Center, Peabody College of Vanderbilt University, Nashville, Tennessee 37203

RAYMOND H. STARR, JR. (25), Department of Psychology, University of Maryland Baltimore County, Baltimore, Maryland 21228

ROBERT B. STEWART (43), Department of Psychology, Pennsylvania State University, University Park, Pennsylvania 16802

EDWARD TRONICK (181), Department of Psychology, University of Massachusetts, Amherst, Massachusetts 01003

PETER M. VIETZE (5), NICHD, Child and Family Research Branch, Bethesda, Maryland 20205

BARBARA NOTKIN WHITE (347), Research Institute for Educational Problems, Inc., Cambridge, Massachusetts 02138

Preface

A growing literature describes the early social interaction patterns of normal infants and children. Recently, several researchers following the development of infants and children at risk have noted interaction patterns that are different from those of normal children and have speculated a circular relationship between disturbances in early interactions and developmental problems. This volume presents empirical studies describing interactions between infants and children at risk and their parents, teachers, and peers.

These studies were conducted largely by psychologists, psychiatrists, and pediatricians, and they focus on infants and children who are considered at risk due to handicapping conditions and/or due to unfavorable caretaking environments. Included in these studies are infants with later diagnosed psychiatric problems, failures to thrive, victims of abuse, infants and children experiencing family disruptions, children of parents who come from disrupted families, infants who experienced premature birth or perinatal complications and are at risk for developmental delays, and those who have diagnosed perceptual-motor handicaps such as blindness or Down's syndrome.

The first part of this volume concerns studies of the early interactions of these infants and children with their parents, and the second part centers on their interactions with their teachers and peers. Some of the contributors present individual case studies; others present group data. Most chapters are based on careful analyses of films, videotapes, or time-sampling observations of interactions in naturalistic situations. The interaction data are often related to sensorimotor, cognitive, or language development. Thus, a picture emerges of the ways in which social interaction skills relate to other facets of development and the ways in which the at-risk child and his or her social environment interact. In addition, several chapters are concerned with attempts to modify behaviors of the child and the child's social partners to facilitate more harmonious interaction patterns.

We hope that these studies will provide perspectives for students of normal interaction patterns as well as for researchers, teachers, clinicians, and parents who are studying, working with, and relating to infants and children at risk.

Infant and Child Interactions
with Parents

PART I

INFANTS OR CHILDREN
EXPERIENCING FAILURE TO THRIVE,
ABUSE, OR FAMILY DISRUPTION

PETER M. VIETZE
SUSAN FALSEY
SUSAN O'CONNOR
HOWARD SANDLER
KATHRYN SHERROD
WILLIAM A. ALTEMEIER

CHAPTER **1**

Newborn Behavioral and Interactional Characteristics of Nonorganic Failure-to-Thrive Infants

INTRODUCTION

Earlier in this century, concern for the continuing health and welfare of children during infancy focused on occasions when infants were separated either permanently or for long periods of time from their mothers. Investigations of infants who were being raised in institutions without their biologic mothers suggested that absence of the mother, per se, was the cause of the infants' depressed motor, social, emotional, and intellectual development (Spitz, 1945). The implications of these findings suggested that if maternal deprivation led to such dire consequences for the infant, then maternal presence must provide an infant with the necessary ingredients to insure healthy development.

This early perspective [i.e., that the mother herself was the agent of social stimulation for the young infant] came under attack from a number of sources. Casler (1968), Yarrow (1963), and others suggested that the importance of the mother for the adequate development of her infant resides in the care-giving activities in which she engaged with her infant. Bakwin (1949) noted that infants hospitalized for long periods showed depressed behavior similar to that shown by the infants observed by Spitz (1945). Bakwin further noted that provision of a variety of extra stimulation experiences in the hospital such as that provided by mothers led to great improvement among these hospitalized infants.

5

HIGH-RISK INFANTS AND CHILDREN:
Adult and Peer Interactions

The interest in the effects of maternal deprivation as a mediator of general stimulus deprivation in infancy has had far-reaching consequences for both research and practice. Its effects on research have been realized in the vast number of studies on mother–infant separation as well as the formulation of theories on infant-to-mother attachment (Ainsworth, 1973; Bowlby, 1969). Practically, there has been an increased awareness of the important environmental ingredients necessary for healthy infant development in day-care settings, hospital wards, and programs for handicapped and retarded children. Nevertheless, much of these emphases are based on interpretations of one of two unidirectional models of caregiver–infant influence.

Early conceptions of behavioral development viewed the infant as being shaped by the parent so that the direction of effect was from parent to infant with the infant making little or no contribution to its own socialization and development. More recently, Bell (1971) and others (Lewis & Rosenblum, 1974) suggested that the infant's behavior and characteristics can have powerful effects on the caregiver's behavior in interaction with the infant. However, implicit in this change of perspective from one unidirectional model to another was the warning that models that fall short of acknowledging the bidirectional nature of Caregiver–Infant interaction were not considering parent and child behavior in a sufficiently broad context. It should be noted that over 25 years ago a bidirectional view of Parent–Infant interaction and socialization was proposed by Sears (1951) but not implemented or recognized widely in the research or child welfare literature. These changing perspectives in the research literature on Parent–Infant interaction—specifically Mother–Infant interaction—have made it possible to consider interactional disorders in families where parents and infants are not necessarily physically separated. The attempt to identify potential precursors of children's treatment by their parents was brought about partly by these shifts in the understanding of parental influences on child development.

Interest in explaining the early origins and social context of variations in child development, including developmental retardation, behavior disorders, and infant mortality and morbidity, has incorporated the view of bidirectional parent–infant influences. In the area of child development, researchers have begun to construe child outcomes as having multiple historical and causal determinants, rather than single factor causes. Sameroff and Chandler (1975) have proposed a model that views the multiple transactions between environmental forces, caregiver characteristics, and infant attributes as continuing, reciprocal contributions to the events and outcomes of child development. This transactional view of child development suggests that, in order to understand the progression of a child's development in terms of those factors influencing it, single events cannot have the salient effects once thought to exist. Instead, the ways in which the environment responds to particular infant characteristics must be considered in a dynamic way. Therefore, the continuing interactions of the infant and its environment, as well as the characteristics of both infant and context, must be measured. Sameroff and Chandler (1975) propose that the care-giving environment exists along a continuum which will influence how particular characteristics of a child are expressed. The transactional developmental perspective makes possible consideration of the child maltreatment phenomena as disorders of Parent–Infant interaction, rather than viewing them as resulting from parent psychopathology. In the present chapter, we have selected a form of child maltreatment, nonorganic failure to thrive, to illustrate one application of the transactional model to the understanding of disturbances in Mother–Infant interaction.

Nonorganic failure to thrive is a syndrome characterized by failure to gain weight in accordance with accepted guidelines for growth and inability to attribute this depressed weight gain to any organic disease process. Often, the absence of adequate weight gain is accompanied by retardation of cognitive, social, and emotional processes as well. This phenomenon is not unlike the "hospitalism" syndrome studied by Spitz (1945) and Bakwin (1949) cited earlier. However, several investigators report instances of noninstitutionalized infants who have retarded growth and development for no apparent reason. Coleman and Provence (1957) discussed a number of such cases in infants living at home with their natural mothers. Elmer (1960) presents several examples of failure to thrive and discusses the mother's psychological condition during the child's early months as an important contributor to the child's retarded growth. Although these cases ranged from preterm and low birthweight to term, full-size infants, they all seemed to have mothers who were psychologically preoccupied with matters other than the psychological care of their infants. In addition, the role of the father was discussed by Elmer in relation to the mother's psychological condition. In some of these cases the father's lack of support may have contributed to the mother's inability to provide adequately for her baby. Other research reports have suggested that the mother's failure to nurture her infant is a result of some personality defect, socioeconomic stress, or other factors (e.g., Barbero & Shaheen, 1967; Fischoff, Whitten, & Pettit, 1971; Koel, 1969; Leonard, Rhymes, & Solnit, 1966; Togut, Allen, & Lelchuck, 1969).

Although nonorganic failure to thrive is considered to result from a mother's failure to provide an appropriately nurturing environment in which her infant can develop normally, the exact way in which specific maternal actions (or lack thereof) and how they affect the infant have not been identified in the research literature. We do recognize that failure to thrive is a symptom of early disturbance in Mother–Infant and perhaps Family interaction. Most of the extant research on failure-to-thrive infants suffers from methodological weaknesses. Either the studies are retrospective analyses, in which the evaluations of the infants and families are done with the knowledge of the presenting symptoms, or there are no adequate comparison groups evaluated in a similar manner. Thus, the associations made between the infant's poor growth and family background and history may be spurious. There may be many ways in which parents, especially mothers, may be labeled as having character defects leading to infants' failure to thrive with none of these labeling factors being justified scientifically. Labeling prior to assessment without adequate control procedures may seriously confound the results and interpretation of these prior studies.

The effects of a diagnosis of nonorganic failure to thrive may have a variety of consequences for both mother and infant. After a diagnosis has occurred, an attempt is usually made by the physician to help the mother accelerate the weight gain of the infant. If the symptom is severe and the attempts to influence are not successful, the infant is hospitalized and treated under more controlled conditions than exist in the infant's own home environment. This hospitalization usually results in a rapid weight gain to normative levels. Although the hospitalizations of failure-to-thrive infants have not been carefully evaluated, the transactional model suggests that early behavioral patterns established between mother and child that may have contributed to nonorganic failure to thrive, as well as the effects of labeling and possible temporary separation of mother and infant, may serve as later obstacles to normal development.

In this chapter, we evaluate the use of different types of variables in discriminating between infants later diagnosed as nonorganic failure to thrive and a comparison group of infants not so diagnosed. The first group of maternal variables examined related to the mothers' own upbringing, personality, general attitudes toward childrearing, knowledge of child development, the presence of environmental and life stresses, and general demographic characteristics. Infant developmental variables included the infants' status at birth (weight, Apgar score, and presence of delivery, nursery, or pregnancy complications) and an assessment of infant states and motor and social maturity. The mother and infant were also observed together in the hospital soon after birth, permitting the derivation of variables indicative of mother, infant, and dyadic behavior during interaction.

Studies of mother–infant behavior have indicated the reciprocal nature of the interaction in the mother–infant dyad (Brazelton, Tronick, Adamson, Als, & Wise, 1975). Although most studies have focused on describing the attributes of normative development, others have examined the nature of Mother–Infant interactions for dyads in which one member is labeled with a disability. Vietze, Abernathy, Ashe, and Faulstich (1978) observed mothers interacting with their developmentally delayed infants and compared the patterns of contingent interactions with dyads in which the infants were not delayed. They found similar patterns of interaction between the two groups, though the dyads with delayed infants were older than those with no developmental delays. Brazelton *et al.* (1975) explored the sequence of interaction in a few mother–infant dyads in which some physical handicap existed. They concluded that both blind infants and their mothers must accomodate to the restrictions on interaction placed on the dyad by the disability of one member. Thoman, Miamo, and Freese (1977) noted markedly abnormal behavioral-state patterns in an infant who later died of sudden, infant death syndrome. Their study represents a departure from earlier studies as it examines the behaviors of interest prior to the occurrence of a problem or the establishment of a diagnosis.

Our study permits the examination of possible precursors of nonorganic failure to thrive that were obtained prior to diagnosis. In order to eliminate some of the sources of error in understanding the multiple factors related to child maltreatment in general, a study was initiated by us in which the transactional approach, briefly outlined previously, was applied. A prospective longitudinal design was used in which a cohort of 1400 women were interviewed during the first trimester of pregnancy using an interview developed to identify families most likely to contain an infant later identified as maltreated (Altemeier, Vietze, Sherrod, Sandler, Falsey, & O'Connor, 1979). About a third of these women and their infants were followed until the infants were 18 months of age. After the infant's first 2 weeks, a subsample of these mother–infant dyads were diagnosed as having nonorganic failure-to-thrive infants. This chapter reports the results of analyses comparing these dyads to dyads with normally growing infants. The model used in this study was based on comparisons of multiple factors which included initial stable characteristics of mother and infant as well as measures of Mother–Infant interaction. The use of interactional variables may permit a greater comprehension of the process by which infant development is interrupted by the infant's failure to thrive. Rather than simply relating the initial configuration to outcome, the focus here is on the dynamics through which the outcome might be created.

METHOD

Subjects

The subjects for the present analysis were selected from a sample of 498 mothers and infants participating in an ongoing research project, the Early Screening Project. Pregnant women at Nashville General Hospital, a hospital serving a predominantly low-income population, were approached initially by members of the research project team during the first visit to the prenatal clinic. These women were informed about the procedures and the general purpose of the study and were considered potential subjects for the longitudinal follow-up study if they agreed to participate (6% of those asked refused to participate). The 1400 consenting women were administered a prenatal interview covering aspects of the woman's own childhood, her present attitudes toward the pregnancy, availability of social support systems, recent stressful events, and knowledge of child development. Women were selected as active subjects for continuing follow-up in the Early Screening Project if they met one of two criteria: (a) selection by a random process, or (b) scores on the interview extreme enough to be considered warning signs of potential later problems for the mother–infant relationship (Altemeier et al., 1979).

All dyads with infants later diagnosed as having nonorganic failure to thrive and who had been observed at birth were selected for the present analysis. There were 18 dyads with male infants and 17 dyads with female infants. Nonorganic failure to thrive was diagnosed according to the criteria in Table 1.1. If an infant did not gain a specific number of ounces per day, the medical record was examined by two pediatricians. Those infants judged to be without severe growth retardation or without an organic abnormality that could account for the failure to thrive were eliminated from the classification. One third of the infants diagnosed as growth failures in the Early Screening Project were hospitalized for intervention in feeding and caretaking. These infants gained weight rapidly in the hospital at an average of 2.3 oz per day. A comparison group was selected from the remaining dyads in which infants were judged to be growing well and who were observed at birth. This comparison group was selected randomly from the larger sample and consisted of 25 males and 25 females.

Procedures

MATERNAL HISTORY AND ATTITUDES

During the first prenatal visit, the Maternal History Interview was administered. The women also provided information regarding their age, educational

TABLE 1.1
Definition of Nonorganic Failure to Thrive

0	—	14 days	—	Re-gain birthweight
15	—	60 days	—	.66 oz/day
61	—	270 days	—	.42 oz/day
271	—	360 days	—	.27 oz/day
361	—	540 days	—	.18 oz/day

Over at least 10 days, the infant's rate of weight gain was less than two-thirds of the Harvard fiftieth percentile curve, and this growth failure was not caused by illness or a congenital anomaly.

level, number of children, number of previous pregnancies, race, and marital status. These data are presented in Table 1.2 according to the infant's diagnostic status and gender. The Maternal History Interview (Altemeier et al., 1979) is divided into six areas assessing the woman's history, attitudes, and environmental conditions: (a) feelings about the pregnancy, (b) availability of support from her family and friends, (c) her own nurturance as a child, (d) personality characteristics, (e) stressful aspects of home life, and (f) skills in parenting. After the interview was completed, the interviewer made a global judgment of the women's potential risk for subsequent disorders in the mother–infant relationship.

Two additional questionnaires were administered during this initial contact. The first one, the Life Stress Inventory (Holmes & Rahe, 1967), determines the number of recent stressful events that have occurred for the woman and the father of the index child. Such events as death of a parent or loss of job, as well as household moves, are listed in this inventory. The second questionnaire, an inventory assessing the woman's knowledge of child development milestones, was also administered. This inventory, Knowledge of Developmental Norms, is based on a similar inventory reported by DeLissovoy (1973) and provides an index of the woman's accuracy of expectations about child development in the average normal child.

In addition, women selected for inclusion in the longitudinal follow-up study of themselves and their infants were administered a short version of the Maternal Attitude Scale (Cohler, Weiss, & Grunebaum, 1970), prenatally in their homes by one of the interviewers. This questionnaire provides information regarding the mother's attitudes toward childrearing according to the following five areas: (a) control of the child's aggression, (b) encouraging reciprocity with the child, (c) physical closeness toward the child, (d) acceptance of emotional complexity in the child, and (e) feelings of competence in caring for the child.

BIRTH INFORMATION

After delivery, the birth records for the selected infants and mothers were obtained and the following information was extracted from them: pregnancy

TABLE 1.2
Demographic Characteristics

	Nonorganic failure to thrive	Normal growth
Mean maternal age (in years)	20.71	20.62
Mean number of years of school	9.97	10.24
Mean number of children	1.03	.98
Percentage white	65.7	60.0
Percentage married	60.0	46.0

course, delivery and nursery complications, birthweight, gestational age, Apgar ratings at 1 min, and the mother's intention to breast- or bottle-feed her infant. These data are summarized in Table 1.3.

The Neonatal Assessment Scale (Brazelton, 1973) was administered to each selected infant 48 hr after delivery by trained, project personnel. The scale was summarized according to the a priori scoring technique devised by Als, Tronick, Lester, and Brazelton (1977). The infant's initial and predominant states and four subscales involving social, motor control, state control, and response to stress, were thus derived.

MOTHER–INFANT INTERACTION

The mother and her infant were observed simultaneously in the hospital during a scheduled feeding period before they were discharged. The observational system employed was developed by Anderson, Vietze, Faulstich, and Ashe (1978). An Electro General Datamyte (Minnetonka, Mn.) was used by trained observers to enter predetermined codes relating to the type of caretaking setting, infant state, mother–infant proximity, and mother and infant behaviors. As each code was entered, the time (in seconds) from the beginning of the observation was automatically inserted in the record. Following initial entry of the codes appropriate to the observational session, the observers entered codes only as changes occurred. After the observational session was terminated, the record was transmitted to a PDP 11/40 computer, edited, and made available for data reduction and retrieval.

The codes for the mother and the infant each consisted of nine mutually exclusive and exhaustive combinations of four basic behavior categories and one code to represent none of the other coded behaviors. The four basic maternal behaviors were visual attention, vocalization, smile, and tactile play; those for the infant included visual attention, vocalization, and crying. The total list of behavioral codes is presented in Table 1.4. Information concerning

TABLE 1.3
Birth Information

	Nonorganic failure to thrive	Normal growth
Percentage with pregnancy complications	25.0	26.0
Percentage with delivery complications	23.5	32.0
Percentage with nursery complications	41.2	34.0
Percentage breast-fed	11.4	18.0
Mean birthweight (in gm)	3001.57	3244.6
Mean gestational age (in weeks)	38.67	39.52
Mean gravidity	2.38	2.1
Mean parity	2.05	1.96
Mean Apgar at 1 min	6.79	7.33

TABLE 1.4
Outline of Observation Categories[a,b]

Infant behavior patterns
    Vocalize
    Look at mother
    Look/Smile
    Vocalize/Look
    Vocalize/Look/Smile
    Vocalize/Smile
    Smile
    Cry
    Cry/Look
    No signaling behavior

Maternal behavior patterns
    Vocalize to infant
    Look at infant
    Look/Smile
    Vocalize/Look
    Vocalize/Look/Smile
    Vocalize/Tactile play
    Look/Smile/Tactile play
    Vocalize/Look/Smile/Tactile play
    Tactile play
    No behavior to infant

Caregiving
    Feed
    Bathe/Diaper/Dress
    Put to sleep
    No caregiving

Infant state
    Active awake
    Quiet awake
    Drowsy
    Asleep

Maternal proximity
    Holds infant
    Within 3 ft
    Greater than 3 ft
    Out of room

[a] SOURCE: Adapted from Vietze, Abernathy, Ashe & Faulstich, 1978.
[b] Mean reliability of mother and infant categories, based on 23 reliability observations during project:

Mother categories	Correlation	Percentage agreement
Visual	.728	.923
Vocal	.742	.767
Smile	.586	.544
Tactile play	.797	.675
No signal	.675	.661

Infant categories	Correlation	Percentage agreement
Visual	.756	.731
Vocal	.660	.644
Smile	.613	.523
Cry	.882	.777
No signal	.786	.887

inter-observer reliability was obtained throughout the duration of the project and at different ages. Reliability estimates, computed both as a proportion of agreement within 10-sec intervals and as a correlation of seconds occurring during 10-sec intervals, are also presented in Table 1.4.

The system of continuous recording permitted the computation of the duration as well as frequency of occurrence of both individual mother and infant behaviors, and dyadic behavior. Additionally, the proportion of total session time for each of the five maternal and five infant behavior categories (including no response) were computed.

Measures of dyadic behavior were also obtained from the observational records. The presence of any response (excluding no response) was scored as a response for the mother or infant in 1-sec intervals. Four dyadic states were established: (a) mother-only responding, (b) infant-only responding, (c) both responding, and (d) neither responding. A transition matrix with 1-sec intervals was derived using these four states. The conditional probability of state change, as well as the total probability of occurrence for each state, were obtained from this matrix. The coding system permitted the entry of only one change at a time and the datamyte recorder was limited to entries greater than or equal to 1 sec apart. Because of these limitations, those cells of the transition matrix representing simultaneous change by the mother and infant could never be entered when using a 1-sec lag. However, observers rarely reported simultaneous changes and did not consider this restriction as a serious limitation of the coding system. (See Bakeman & Brown, 1977, for details of this scheme for evaluating behavioral interactions.)

RESULTS

The results of the present study were analyzed and are presented in distinct sections to represent the varying aspects of the mother and infant that may be construed as factors contributing to nonorganic failure to thrive. Rather than combining these aspects, the present report attempted to distinguish between the interpretation of result when viewed from these independent perspectives.

The major analyses involved 2-way analyses of variance, with Diagnosis (nonorganic failure to thrive, and not diagnosed) and Infant Gender as between-subjects factors. Single factor analyses of variance using Diagnosis as the between-subjects factor were conducted separately for each gender if an interaction occurred.

Demographic Variables

Using χ^2 to compare the two diagnosis groups, the mothers of infants later diagnosed as having failure to thrive did not differ significantly from the mothers in the comparison group according to race or marital status. Analyses of variance indicated no differences by diagnosis or infant gender for maternal age, level of education, parity, or gravidity.

Maternal Characteristics Prior to Birth

Analyses of variance on the six scales of the Maternal History Interview, the Knowledge of Developmental Norms, and the Life Stress Inventory revealed no significant differences between mothers of infants later diagnosed as nonorganic failure to thrive and the mothers in the comparison group. The mothers also did not differ by later infant gender on any prenatal variables except for the personality subscale of the Maternal History Interview. Mothers of male infants demonstrated more positive personality characteristics than did mothers of female infants ($F [1,81]) = 6.32, p < .05$) with a mean score of -1.28 for males and -4.26 for females. No significant effects by diagnosis or infant gender were found in the analysis of the Maternal Attitude Scale which assessed the mother's general attitudes toward childrearing. Using χ^2 analysis, no significant effects were found for diagnosis group in the mother's intention to breast or bottle feed her infant.

Infant Developmental Status at Birth

Infants later diagnosed as nonorganic failure to thrive had significantly lower birthweights ($F [1,81] = 4.27, p < .05$) and had shorter gestational ages ($F [1,80] = 4.37, p < .05$) than did the infants in the comparison group. As the criterion for nonorganic failure to thrive was based on weight gain from the infant's own birthweight, the lower birthweight in the nonorganic failure-to-thrive group was not directly confounded with the diagnosis.

The analyses of the Neonatal Assessment Scale did not reveal any main effects or interactions of diagnosis or infant gender for either infant states or the a priori dimensions of infant developmental status. The groups also did not differ significantly on 1-min Apgar scores or on the presernce of prenatal, delivery, or neonatal complications.

Mother–Infant Interaction

MATERNAL BEHAVIOR

No effects of infant gender were found for the five maternal behavioral variables (i.e., vocalization, visual attention, smile, tactile play, and no response). However, mothers of infants who were later diagnosed as nonorganic failure to thrive spent less time in visually attending to their infants than did the mothers of infants in the comparison group (F [1,72] = 6.45, p < .05). The mothers did not differ significantly by diagnosis group for the four other maternal behavioral variables (Table 1.5).

INFANT BEHAVIOR

Infants later diagnosed as nonorganic failure to thrive did not differ significantly from the comparison group on the four infant behaviors that were analyzed (i.e., vocalization, visual attention, cry, and no response). In addition, there were no effects of infant gender or any statistical interactions in these analyses (Table 1.5).

DYADIC BEHAVIOR

Joint mother and infant behavior was examined as four dyadic states (i.e., mother only, infant only, both responding, and neither responding). Both the simple probability of each state and the conditional probability of movement between states were analyzed.

Although there were no significant effects or interactions on the measures that reflected the total proportion of time spent in each of the four states, there were significant interactions of diagnosis group and gender for three of the conditional probability measures. The sub-analyses by infant gender indicated that the effects of the diagnosis group were significant only for dyads with male infants. The significant interactions involved the transitions of mother-only to

TABLE 1.5
Mother and Infant Behaviors

	Nonorganic failure to thrive	Normal growth
Maternal		
Vocalize to infant	18.15	19.48
Visual attention to infant	78.06	89.26
Smile at infant	3.78	6.51
Touchplay	2.12	2.00
None of above	13.81	10.62
Infant		
Vocalize	1.18	1.31
Visual attention to mother	14.96	12.48
Cry	1.95	1.06
None of above	81.81	85.02

mother-only (F [1,72] $= 8.00$, $p < .01$) and mother-only to neither responding (F [1,72] $= 7.23$, $p < .05$).

Given that the mother was responding in isolation (mother only), there was a greater probability for mothers of male infants later diagnosed as nonorganic failure to thrive to terminate their response than for mothers of male infants not diagnosed (F [1,36] $= 19.33$, $p < .01$). Inversely, there was a greater probability for mothers of male infants in the comparison group to maintain their responding when the infant was not responding than for mothers of male infants later diagnosed (F [1,72] $= 17.02$, $p < .01$). Given maternal responding alone, there was no difference between groups for infant joining the interaction (mother-alone to both).

The third interaction indicated that, given both mother and infant responding, mothers of male infants later diagnosed as nonorganic failure to thrive had a greater probability of dropping out of the interaction than did mothers of male infants in the comparison group (F [1,36] $= 4.3$, $p < .05$). There were no other differences in the probability of moving to other states after being in both responding. There were no significant differences in the conditional probabilities involving the initial states of either infant-only responding or neither responding.

DISCUSSION

Failure to thrive represents one of the most extreme examples of a deficient mother–infant relationship early in a child's life. It is a condition that is readily noticed by an attending physician if frequent measurement of the infant's growth is taken. On the one hand, the health professionals who are most likely to have primary contact with infants and their families take very seriously the indicators of growth failure because it is an index of many potentially serious problems threatening the health of the child. Nevertheless, it has been unclear up to now whether failure to thrive that cannot be traced to some medical problem can be attributed to failure on the part of the mother to provide psychological and, hence, nutritional stores in order to maintain her infant. As mentioned earlier, it has frequently been suggested that nonorganic failure to thrive is suffered by infants with mothers who have personality defects (e.g., Fischoff, Whitten, & Pettit, 1971; Hufton & Oates, 1977). However, these investigations, like other studies of failure-to-thrive infants, suffer from a variety of methodological problems—the major ones being failure to include adequate comparison groups and having retrospective designs.

In the present investigation, a prospective longitudinal approach was taken beginning before the birth of the index children. The Early Screening Project was based in a hospital serving primarily low-income patients, and, in which, alarming numbers of infants had been seen in recent years for various forms of child maltreatment. The possibility of following a cohort of mother–infant dyads, only some of whom would contain failure-to-thrive infants, allowed us to test a variety of notions about the precursors of this condition of infancy. Strengthening the importance of our findings is the fact that we were able to collect our data prior to the diagnosis of the failure-to-thrive outcome and include nondiagnosed infants and mothers from the same population.

Using a transactional perspective suggested by Sameroff and Chandler (1975), we attempted to collect and evaluate data relating to the different levels of the infant's early environment. We included maternal historical factors that represented the mother's social situation, developmental history, and attitudinal background relating to childrearing. Also included were measures that represented the infant's biologic and temperamental constitution in order to evaluate how the infant itself, or the conditions surrounding birth, might affect early growth and development. Finally, we sought to take into account the ways in which the infant and mother related to one another during their earliest encounters by observing them together while they were still in the hospital in which the infant was born. These different factors have been analyzed separately to see how they are implicated as antecedent conditions to nonorganic failure to thrive. No attempt was made in the analyses to examine individual differences or cases in order to understand how the variables might conspire in unique ways leading to growth failure. In addition, the analyses are prefatory to efforts in which the interrelationships among the variables in predicting failure to thrive are examined.

The results of our analyses are noteworthy for the differences found between the mothers and their infants with growth failure and those who grew adequately, as well as the variables for which no differences were found. No significant differences were found between mothers whose infants were later diagnosed with nonorganic failure to thrive and those in the comparison group with regard to their age, number of years in school, number of previous children, race, or marital status. In addition, there were no significant differences found for the results of the Maternal Attitude Scales, Maternal History Interview, Knowledge of Developmental Norms, or Life Stress Events. It should be noted that in an earlier report we did indicate that, based on the Maternal History Interview as a whole, we were able to predict better than chance which women were going to have infants with nonorganic growth failure (Altemeier et al., 1979). In that report we found that 77% of the infants with nonorganic failure to thrive had been identified as being at risk for child maltreatment, based on the prenatal interview. Nevertheless, the individual factors that comprised the interview did not show significant differences in the present analysis. This points to the importance of multivariate analyses of these data in the future.

The findings of no differences in the maternal attributes examined contradict the assumptions and findings in the literature relating deviant maternal attributes to subsequent nonorganic failure to thrive. The fact that this study was prospective rather than retrospective may be one way of accounting for the conflict in findings. The infants had not been identified at the time the data were being collected, and, thus, the mothers were not subject to the search for pathology which might occur once the diagnosis of growth failure was made. Also, the inclusion of an appropriate comparison group drawn from the same population at the same time probably accounts for our results being at odds with the prevalent findings in the literature regarding maternal characteristics.

Among the theories prevalent in the child maltreatment literature is the assertion that maltreated children somehow coerce the poor treatment which befalls them (Belsky, 1978; Milowe & Lourie, 1964; Parke & Collmer, 1975). This assumption has led to investigations in which, retrospectively, children who have been abused or neglected are evaluated and classified in order to find something atypical about them which would explain the fact of their abuse. This exercise is well intentioned but amounts to what has been called "blaming the victim [Ryan, 1971]." In the present investigation, we were able to examine a number of biologically dependent characteristics of the infant, as well as behavioral variables identified on the Newborn Behavioral Assessment Scales. In addition, infant behavior, emitted during interaction with the mother soon after birth, was observed. The analyses revealed that there were no differences between the two study groups in infant behavior observed on the Newborn exam or in the interaction behaviors observed for the infant alone. However, it was found that the infants diagnosed as growth failures were significantly lighter in weight at birth and had significantly shorter gestational ages. Because the computation of growth failure was based on weight gain calculated from birthweight, it is not possible that this is merely a spurious finding. Previous research has reported an association among low birthweight and preterm infants and child abuse (Elmer & Gregg, 1967; Hunter, Kilstrom, Kraybill, & Loda, 1978; Klein & Stern, 1971; Lynch & Roberts, 1977; ten Bensel, 1977). However, only the latter two are prospective studies. There are no previous prospective studies of failure to thrive reporting that this diagnosis is related to birthweight and gestational age. Typically, the explanation offered for the finding that abused or neglected children were underweight or born before term is that these conditions are often themselves associated with atypicality. We suggest that, in the present analyses, we could find no behavioral differences between our two groups, and so we are less likely to accept such an explanation. However, others have suggested (e.g., ten Bensel, 1977) that the low birthweight and preterm infant is typically placed in a special care nursery. This increases the chances that the mother and infant do not have much opportunity to interact in the early days following birth. This raises an issue which has been addressed by Klaus and Kennel (1976) and confirmed by us elsewhere (O'Connor, Altemeier, Sherrod, Sandler, & Vietze, 1978), namely, that early mother–infant contact may serve to decrease the likelihood of child maltreatment in certain populations. Thus, although it is true that the range of birthweights and gestational ages in the two groups studied here was quite broad, it is conceivable that the infants with growth failure spent longer periods of time separated from their mothers right after birth than the infants who grew normally. This might account for the differences in birthweight and gestational age between the two groups.

In examining individual maternal behaviors observed while the infants and mothers were together in the lying-in period, only one difference was found between the failure-to-thrive and the normal-growing infants. The mothers in the growth failure group tended to spend significantly less time looking at their babies than the other group of mothers. It is clear from the range of behaviors here that there is sufficient overlap among the mothers in the two groups so that it would not be possible to use this measure alone to predict growth failure. However, maternal visual gaze may be a subtle indicator of early interest in the baby. Maternal visual attention may index some component of maternal bonding to the infant. Brown, Bakeman, Snyder, Frederickson, Morgan, and Hepler (1975) found less maternal attending to female than to male infants, and one interpretation of this finding related to the greater birthweight of male than female infants. Although we found no gender differences in birthweight, the finding of lower birthweight in infants diagnosed as nonorganic failure to thrive suggests that the relationship between birthweight and maternal attention should be explored further.

The results of the analyses of dyadic interactional measures complement those for maternal visual attention in indicating the context in which mothers were less active. Although the infant's initiation or termination of dyadic interaction was not differentiated by diagnostic category, the analysis of the mother's contribution to the interchange did show significant differences. However, these findings only held for male infants. Mothers of male infants with later nonorganic failure to thrive were more likely to drop out of a simultaneous interaction than were mothers of male infants not diagnosed for growth failure. Furthermore, mothers of male growth failures were less likely to maintain a behavior in isolation and inversely more likely to terminate their isolated behavior than were mothers of male infants not diagnosed. There were no differences in the probability of mothers to join the infants responding or to initiate a behavior when neither of them was responding. It is conceivable that the male infants were identified as growth failures earlier and that the interactional behavior of the mothers preceded the subsequent poor weight gain for these infants. If this were the case, then we might expect that infant girls diagnosed as growth failures later than 1 month might have mothers who showed interactional patterns at 1 month similar to the ones just described. Unfortunately, the size of the samples did not permit our testing of this hypothesis.

The present results have been examined separately in order to provide a profile of the infant diagnosed as nonorganic failure to thrive. The foregoing discussion has attempted to explicate the findings in the light of some of the extant literature on child abuse and neglect. It should be emphasized that in order to understand these phenomena from a transactional perspective, the framework in which the study was conceived, multivariate analyses will have to be carried out. The picture we have of some of the precursers of failure to thrive indicate that although the infant's contribution to the interference with its growth is evident in lower birthweight and earlier birth, there are no behavioral consequences of these differences manifest in the infant's behavior. However, the finding that the mothers who have infants with growth failure do not seem to differ along a number of dimensions from their peers with nondiagnosed infants suggests that perhaps the differences in birth condition lead to immediate consequences for the Mother–Infant interaction that set up a chain of events resulting in poorly growing infants. Such a chain of events would illustrate the transactional viewpoint. Specific events (e.g., small or early baby), in the context of environmental pressures experienced by families in both groups, may lead to greater difficulty in the mother's forming a sufficiently strong attachment to her infant to provide adequate psychological stores to insure healthy development. Individual cases must be examined in detail in order to provide support for this interpretation of the results presented here. Subsequent reports will focus on such detailed individual analyses.

REFERENCES

Ainsworth, M. D. S. The development of mother–infant attachment. In B. M. Caldwell & H. N. Ricciuti (Eds.), *Review of child development research: Child development and social policy* (Vol. 3). Chicago: Univ. Chicago Press, 1973.

Als, H., Tronick, E., Lester, B. M., & Brazelton, T. B. The Brazelton Neonatal Behavioral Assessment Scale (BNBAS). *Journal of Abnormal Child Psychology,* 1977, *5,* 215–231.

Altemeier, W. A., Vietze, P. M., Sherrod, K. B., Sandler, H. M., Falsey, S., & O'Connor, S. Prediction of maltreatment during pregnancy. *Journal of the American Academy of Child Psychiatry,* 1979, 18, 205–218.

Anderson, B. J., Vietze, P. M., Faulstich, G., & Ashe, M. L. Observational manual for assessment of behavior sequences between infant and mother: Newborn to 24 months. *JSAS Catalog of Selected Documents in Psychology,* 1978, *8,* 31.

Bakeman, R., & Brown, J. V. Behavior dialogues: An approach to the assessment of mother–infant interaction. *Child Development,* 1977, *48,* 195–203.

Bakwin, H. Emotional deprivation in infants. *Journal of Pediatrics,* 1949, *35,* 512.

Barbero, G. J., & Shaheen, E. Environmental failure to thrive: A clinical view. *Journal of Pediatrics,* Nov. 1967, *71*(5), 639–644.

Bell, R. Q. Stimulus control of parent or caretaker behavior by offspring. *Developmental Psychology,* 1971, *4,* 63–72.

Belsky, J. Three theoretical models of child abuse: A critical review. *International Journal of Child Abuse,* 1978, *2.*

Bowlby, J. *Attachment.* New York: Basic Books, 1969.

Brazelton, T. B. *Neonatal Behavioral Assessment Scale.* Philadelphia: Lippincott, 1973.

Brazelton, T. B., Tronick, E., Adamson, L., Als, H., & Wise, S. Early mother–infant reciprocity. In *Parent–Infant interaction.* Ciba Foundation Symposium 33. New York: American Elsevier, 1975.

Brown, J. V., Bakeman, R., Snyder, P. A., Frederickson, W. T., Morgan, S. T., & Hepler, R. Interactions of black inner-city mothers with their newborn infants. *Child Development,* 1975, *46,* 477–686.

Casler, L. Perceptual deprivation in institutional settings. In G. Newton & S. Levine (Eds.), *Early experience and behavior.* Springfield, Illinois: C. C Thomas, 1968.

Cohler, B. J., Weiss, J. L., & Grunebaum, H. U. Child care attitudes and emotional disturbance among mothers of young children. *Genetic Psychology Monographs,* 1970, *82,* 3–47.

Coleman, R. W. & Provence, S. Environmental retardation (hospitalism) in infants living in families. *Pediatrics,* 1957, *19,* 285.

DeLissovoy, V. Child care by adolescent parents. *Children Today,* 1973, 2, 22–25.

Elmer, E. Failure to thrive: role of the mother. *Pediatrics,* 1960, *25,* 717–725.

Elmer, E., & Gregg, G. S. Developmental characteristics of abused children. *Pediatrics,* 1967, *40,* 596–602.

Fischoff, J., Whitten, C. F., & Pettit, M. G. A psychiatric study of mothers of infants with growth failure secondary to maternal deprivation. *Journal of Pediatrics,* August, 1971, *79*(2), 209–215.

Holmes, T., & Rahe, R. The social readjustment rating scale. *Journal of Psychosomatic Research,* 1967, *11,* 213–218.

Hufton, I. W., & Oates, K. R. Nonorganic failure to thrive: A long-term follow-up. *Pediatrics,* 1977, *59,* 73–77.

Hunter, R. S., Kilstrom, N., Kraybill, E. N., & Loda, F. Antecedents of child abuse and neglect in premature infants: A prospective study in a newborn intensive care unit. *Pediatrics,* 1978, *61,* 629–635.

Klaus, M., & Kennell, J. *Maternal-infant bonding.* St. Louis, Missouri: Mosby, 1976.

Klein, M., & Stern, L. Low birth weight and the battered child syndrome. *American Journal of Diseases of Children,* 1971, *122,* 15.

Koel, B. S. Failure to thrive and fetal injury as a continuum. *American Journal of Diseases of Children,* 1969, *118,* 565–567.

Leonard, M. F., Rhymes, J. P., & Solnit, A. J. Failure to thrive in infants. *American Journal of Diseases of Children,* 1966, *111,* 600–612.

Lewis, M., & Rosenblum, L. A. (Eds.) The effect of the infant on its caregiver. In *The origins of behavior series* (Vol. 1). New York: Wiley, 1974.

Lynch, M. A., & Roberts, J. Predicting child abuse: Signs of bonding failure in the maternity hospital. *British Medical Journal,* 1977, *1,* 624–236.

Milowe, I., & Lourie, R. The child's role in the battered child syndrome. *Journal of Pediatrics,* 1964, *65,* 1079–1081.

O'Connor, S., Altemeier, W. A., Sherrod, K. B., Sandler, H. M., & Vietze, P. M. The effect of extended postpartum contact on problems with parenting: A controlled study of 301 families. *Birth and the Family Journal,* 1978, *5,* 231–234.

Parke, R., & Collmer, C. Child Abuse: An interdisciplinary analysis. In E. M. Hetherington (Ed.), *Review of Child Development Research* (Vol. 5). Chicago: Univ. Chicago Press, 1975.

Ryan, W. *Blaming the victim.* New York: Pantheon, 1971.

Sameroff, A. J., & Chandler, J. J. Reproductive risk and the continuum of caretaking casualty. In F. D. Horowitz, M. Hetherington, S. Scarr-Salapatek, & G. Siegel (Eds.), *Review of child development research* (Vol. 4). Chicago: Univ. Chicago Press, 1975.

Sears, R. R. A theoretical framework for personality and social behavior. *American Psychologist,* 1951, *6,* 476–482.

Spitz, R. A. Hospitalism: An inquiry into the genesis of psychiatric conditions in early childhood. *Psychoanalytic Study of the Child,* 1945, *1,* 53–74.

ten Bensel, R. W. Child abuse following early postpartum separation. *Journal of Pediatrics,* 1977, *90,* 490.

Thoman, E. B., Miano, V. N., & Freese, M. P. The role of respiratory instability in the sudden infant death syndrome. *Developmental Medicine and Child Neurology,* 1977, *19,* 729–738.

Togut, M. R., Allen, J. E., & Lelchuck, L. A psychological exploration of the nonorganic failure-to-thrive syndrome. *Developmental Medicine and Child Nuerology,* 1969, *11,* 601–607.

Vietze, P., Abernathy, S. B., Ashe, M. L., & Faulstich, G. Contingent interaction between mothers and their developmentally delayed infants. In G. P. Sackett (Ed.), *Observing Behavior.* Baltimore: Univ. Park Press, 1978.

Yarrow, L. J. Research in dimensions of early maternal care. *Merrill-Palmer Quarterly,* 1963, *9,* 101–114.

KIM N. DIETRICH
RAYMOND H. STARR, JR.
MELISSA G. KAPLAN

CHAPTER **2**

Maternal Stimulation and Care of Abused Infants

INTRODUCTION

Researchers on child abuse would like to believe that we have come a long way during the last quarter century toward understanding the problem. Certainly the pioneering efforts of Caffey (1946), Woolley and Evans (1955), and Kempe, Silverman, Steele, Droegemueller, and Silver (1962) did much to wipe out the explanatory panacea of the "easily bruised child." Although these efforts have made us nationally more sensitive to the problem, and pediatricians and social service agencies are more likely to report and act on such cases, much controversy still exists as to the relative effects of child maltreatment. The issue is particularly opaque when we look at research on the critical interpersonal variable—Parent–Infant interaction.

Much has been written about abnormalities of Parent–Infant interaction in cases of child abuse. However, as one recent review of the literature concluded, "[T]he amount of discussion . . . exceeds by a considerable degree the amount of well controlled research on the subject [Herner, 1976, p. 38]." A number of studies, mostly based on parental interview, have cited role reversal as creating pathological conditions within the parent–infant dyad leading to abuse. For example, the parent, wanting to be loved and "taken care of" by his or her child is ultimately disappointed and assaults the child as a result of these frustrated dependency needs. Alternatively, abusive parents have often been

25

HIGH-RISK INFANTS AND CHILDREN:
Adult and Peer Interactions

described as having a childhood history of severe physical discipline. It is suggested that they have internalized this practice and now deal with their own children in a similar manner. What too often easily escapes the reader in reviewing these studies is that they do not *directly* examine the Parent-Infant interaction (the actual ongoing exchange occurring in presumably disturbed families).

Several recent studies have directly examined Parent-Infant interaction in relation to abuse. Gray, Cutler, Dean, and Kempe (1976) observed maternal behavior during and immediately after birth. Particular abnormalities in maternal behavior were related to the later occurrencè of child abuse or neglect. A review of their methodology reveals, however, that the observations were not systematized or quantified and therefore may not be replicable. In a task-oriented setting, Disbrow, Doerr, and Caulfield (1977) found clearer differences in their observations of Mother-Infant interaction. Four factors were developed from an initial 25-item observation scale. Abusive and control dyads differed on three factors: perceived communication, child's readiness to learn, and parent-facilitating behavior. Finally, a third study by Burgess and Conger (1977) further demonstrates the presence of interactional differences, finding less verbal and physical interaction in abusive compared with control families. Furthermore, when the abusive families interacted, their behavior was more negative and less positive than that of control families.

However, none of these studies carefully examined the variety of maternal behaviors that occur during the course of normal interaction. Maternal behavior becomes more critical when one considers the results of years of research on the importance of stimulation of the developing infant by the caretaker. Early studies by Spitz (1945) and Dennis and Najarian (1957) clearly illustrated the effects of maternal deprivation and neglect—effects such as delays in intellectual, motor, and social functioning. The primary caretaker has come to be viewed as an important source of stimulation for the infant. For example, White and Castle (1964) found that the amount of visual attention in infants was related to levels of physical handling. White, LaCrosse, Litman, and Ogilvie (1969) reported that mothers who were sensitive to their child's levels of stimulus tolerance, and needs in general, had infants who were developmentally advanced. Further, Lewis and Goldberg (1969) suggest that contingent responsiveness by the mother both reinforces stimulus-response bonds for specific behaviors and develops infants' expectancies that their behavior affects the environment. Clarke-Stewart (1973) similarly reports that measures of cognitive development in the infant were associated with the mother's response to the child's social behaviors. This maternal responsiveness was related to the child's mental development quotient, speed of information processing, and schema development. Language, social, and emotional indices of development were also related to maternal stimulation in response to infant cues.

Additionally, Greenberg (1962, 1963, 1964, 1965) has illustrated the importance of the caregiver in the mother-infant relationship. Through physiological measurements and state descriptions, he has demonstrated how maternal activities call into use and facilitate the development of specific sensorimotor mechanisms in the infant.

Results of prior research indicate that abused children are behaviorally similar to children deprived of normal caretaker stimulation (Elmer, 1977; MacCarthy, 1977; Ramey, Starr, Whitten, Pallas & Reed, 1975). The fact that the abused infant or child is compromised in his or her cognitive and motor development is well documented in the literature (Martin, 1976). However, the extent to which this is directly the result of a pattern of physical assault is not clear. Naturally, in cases of subdural and subarachnoid hematomas, degradation of the central nervous system would clearly explain lower developmental quotients in the abused. However, in cases of less severe injuries, the lower scores may reflect the overall quality of the environment in which the child develops, rather than any physiological manifestations. That is, the abusive home may not provide adequate amounts of stimulation to promote motivation in the infant to explore or learn. No study to date has clearly separated out this very important factor. Also, many children who have been abused physically are reported to be undernourished as well (Elmer & Gregg, 1967; Helfer & Pollock, 1968; Koel, 1969; Martin, Beezley, Conway, & Kempe, 1974; Smith, 1975). This constitutes an additional factor to be considered when determining the major factors contributing to cognitive and motor delays.

Over the last decade many studies have described the developmental characteristics of abused children. In 1967, Elmer and Gregg found that 50% of their sample were mentally retarded upon evaluation. Birrel and Birrel (1968) described 10 of their 35 children as mentally deficient. Martin et al. (1974) similarly found 33% of a sample of 42 abused children had language difficulties and were mentally retarded. Using the Griffiths scales, Smith (1975) reported his sample of abused children scored significantly lower than a control group. However, as all of these studies used retrospective designs, it is not clear whether developmental delays preceded the abuse or were a consequence of it.

There is also evidence that the effects of an abusive environment interact with other factors such as physical neglect. Elmer and Gregg (1967), Martin et al. (1974), and Smith (1975) all report considerable differences in intellectual functioning when children diagnosed as both abused and neglected are compared to those that were only subject to physical assault. The abused and neglected children have greater developmental delays. These data tend to cast aspersions on Steele and Pollock's (1968) conclusion that abuse and neglect are mutually exclusive. It appears that in some cases abusive parents may both injure their child physically and fail to provide adequate nourishment.

As was stated above, it is of interest that the developmental characteristics of the abused infant or child approximate that of the maternally deprived young. It is the contention of this chapter that it is much more than the physical assault of an infant or child that may contribute to the developmental delays observed. Rather, it is the overall quality of the abusive environment in a number of dimensions that contribute to the "at risk" situations of these infants.

The developmental similarities between stimulus deprived and abused infants led us to suspect that mothers of abused infants would be significantly less stimulating in interactions with their children than mothers of infants not diagnosed as abused. In conjunction with this hypothesis, it is predicted that such lower levels of stimulation would be reflected in cognitive and motor developmental delays in the abused infants. We also predicted that the abuse sample would be delayed in their physical development and suffer from nutritional inadequacy as well.

METHOD

Sample

Two groups of mother–infant dyads were evaluated. The abuse sample consisted of dyads residing in the Detroit area on whom a report of suspected or actual child abuse had been filed by the medical staff of Children's Hospital of Michigan in Detroit. The control sample contained infants who had been admitted through the emergency room of the hospital for nontrauma illness and their mothers. Note that both abused and control groups experienced emergency room admissions. This was done based on the intuitively valid assumption that the degree of stress placed on the control children and their families by an emergency room experience is as similar as possible to that present in families when the emergency admission is for suspected abuse. Also, in the control sample only nontrauma cases were selected for study. This was done to prevent the possible inclusion of a case of undetected child abuse.

The subjects, a subset from a larger investigation (Starr, 1978), consisted of 28 mother–infant dyads with 10 Black and 4 White dyads in each group. The mean age of the abused infants was 5.1 months with a range of 3–8.5 months. The control group infnats were similar in age with a mean of 5.4 months and a range of 3–9.1 months. There were 6 boys and 8 girls in each group. Only one family in each group was above social class V according to the Hollingshead (1957) Two Factor Index (level V is the lowest social class on the scale).

The abused infants had, in general, suffered severe injuries with multiple injuries in 71.4% of the cases. Specific injuries were bruises and abrasions (42.8%), surface wounds (42.8%), fractures other than to the skull (42.8%), internal injuries other than to the central nervous system (21.1%), skull fractures (21.1%), subdural hematoma (14.2%), and second degree burns (7.1%). Discharge diagnoses for control infants were upper respiratory infections (28.5%), asthma (21.4%), gastrointestinal disorders (42.8%), and pneumonia (7.1%).

The groups were quite similar with regard to maternal gravidity and parity, infant 1- and 5-min Apgar scores, and infant birthweight. The means for the abuse and control groups, respectively, are: (a) gravidity, 2.6 and 2.4; (b) parity, 1.2 and 0.9; (c) 1-min Apgar, 8.2 and 8.0; (d) 5-min Apgar, 8.9 and 8.7; and (e) birthweight, 3093 gm and 2835 gm. None of these values were significantly different.

All subjects were recruited during home visits by project social workers who explained the study in detail and assured the parents that the data to be collected would be confidential. Families were paid a total of $60 for participating in five interview sessions. The bulk of the data for this study was collected during the last of these five sessions, allowing the families ample time to become familiarized with project staff members and offices.

Procedure

Anthropometric and laboratory data were taken by the authors from each infant's hospital chart for the day of admission. Growth statistics of weight, height, and head circumference were converted to percentiles using norms developed by Reed and Stuart (in Watson, 1962). Laboratory data consisted of hemoglobin concentrations satisfactorily recorded upon admission.

Each infant was examined by Dietrich who used both the mental and psychomotor scales of the Bayley Scales of Infant Development. Prior to the initiation of this research, Deitrich was trained in the administration of both scales. In every case, the biologic mother was present during all phases of testing. Care was taken to insure that the infant was fed, rested, and in reasonably good health when examined.

The situation for assessment of maternal behaviors was a relatively unstructured free-play context in which the mother interacted with her infant for about 10 min. First, a familiar social worker escorted the pair into a 9-ft. × 10-ft. room where a table, infant seat, and chair for the mother were present. Because some mothers were apparently unfamiliar with the use of infant seats, some of them were allowed to hold their infants or sit them on the table or their lap during the interaction. Although this decreases situational uniformity between dyads and changes the nature of the situation, it did make the mothers and probably the infants more comfortable and natural.

Each dyad was instructed to perform two tasks. First, the mother was asked to feed her child a jar of strained fruit, a spoon and bib having been placed on the table. Data from this activity are not considered here. After about 7-10 min, the social worker returned and said, "Now we would like you to talk or play with (child's name) for a few minutes. I'll be back in a short while." The worker then left the room. This type of situation has been used successfully before to study maternal-infant dyadic behaviors (e.g., Lewis & Goldberg, 1969). For the most part, mothers in both groups did not appear intimidated or uncomfortable.

Behaviors were recorded using videotape recording equipment. The fleeting character of some maternal behaviors made this necessary. Two cameras were used in conjunction with a split-screen generator to enable viewing of both mother and infant behavior. One camera was focused on the child and another, placed behind a one-way mirror, was focused on the mother. The mothers were aware that the session was being recorded.

A continuous 5 min segment of the free-play interaction was analyzed. To allow time for the mother and infant to adjust to the transition from the feeding situation, coding of the present interaction began at 1 min into the activity. Data were coded using an event sampling procedure, the Measure of Maternal Stimulation (MMS) (Dietrich, 1977). The behaviors which were coded are listed in the Appendix.

Four categories of maternal activity (auditory, tactile, vestibular, and visual) were coded for duration of stimulating contact and variety of stimulation *within* each of the four modes. The coding system allowed for an assessment of all the maternal behaviors displayed in the interaction situation. Inter-rater reliability was 82% for the auditory, 91% for the visual, 85% for the vestibular, and 86% for the tactile modes.

RESULTS

Analysis of interactional data will be reported first. Data for the duration of maternal stimulation in each of the four modes was analyzed using t tests, which revealed significant group differences (see Table 2.1). Control group mothers engaged in significantly more tactile and auditory stimulation. There were no significant differences in the visual and vestibular modes. However, for the vestibular mode, 93% of the control group mothers engaged in vestibular stimulation compared to only 57% of the abuse group mothers.

Significant differences were similarly found when the number of different forms of stimulation each mother used *within* each of the four modes was calculated as an index of the variety of stimulation (see Table 2.2). The control mothers used a greater variety of tactile and vestibular strategies. Results for the auditory and visual modes showed nonsignificant trends in the predicted direction.

TABLE 2.1
Means, Standard Deviations, and *t* Values for Duration of Maternal Stimulation by Mode

Mode	Group	Mean (sec)	SD	t (26 df)
Tactile	Abuse	134.50	95.10	2.71*
	Control	220.80	65.96	
Auditory	Abuse	169.21	68.78	3.69**
	Control	246.78	34.05	
Vestibular	Abuse	21.10	32.09	.87
	Control	31.10	26.83	
Visual	Abuse	114.20	65.88	.30
	Control	107.30	60.72	

*p < .02
**p < .01

The relatively larger and more distinct number of coding categories contained in the tactile and auditory observation format allowed for a more detailed examination of maternal behavior in these two areas. Considering the tactile mode first, data were further analyzed by dividing the coding categories into two sets, resulting in multi-item factors of passive and active contact. *Passive* contact included activities in which the mother held the infant or restrained any parts of the infant's body by holding. *Active* contact events included patting, touching, kissing, mouthing, grooming, tactile play, and other similar activities. The control group mothers used significantly more active

TABLE 2.2
Means, Standard Deviations, and *t* Values for Maternal Stimulation Variety by Mode

Mode	Total categories	Group	(Mean)	SD	t (26 df)
Tactile	13	Abuse	5.14	1.88	2.78**
		Control	7.92	1.43	
Auditory	10	Abuse	4.42	1.79	1.38
		Control	5.42	1.95	
Vestibular	6	Abuse	1.11	1.26	2.68*
		Control	2.42	1.11	
Visual	5	Abuse	2.21	.66	.46
		Control	2.35	.89	

*p < .02
**p < .01

strategies. They spent a mean of 103.28 sec (SD = 51.85) in active stimulation compared with a mean of 45.28 sec (SD = 40.92) for the abuse-group mothers (t [26] = 3.20, p < .01). Not only did the control mothers spend more overall time in active stimulative strategies, a greater proportion of their time was devoted to such behaviors. They spent 67.15% of the time devoted to the tactile mode in active stimulation of their infants compared to 28.14% of the time devoted to active stimulation by the abuse-group mothers.

Mothers in the two samples also differed in the variety of tactile stimulation strategies used. The control group mothers engaged in more intimate behaviors such as kissing, mouthing, nuzzling, and allowing their baby to play with their face, hair, etc. Abuse-group mothers averaged 32.37 sec (SD = 14.25) whereas controls spent a mean of 131.48 sec (SD = 32.42) in this activity (t [26] = 9.83; p < .001).

Turning now to the auditory mode, differences in the delivery of the mother's speech proved to be a significant discriminator between samples. Mothers of the control group engaged in significantly more "baby talk." This involved the well-known pattern of soft or medium volume, elongation of vowels, and an exaggeration of syllabic enunciation. Abuse mothers spent a mean of 101.07 sec (SD = 68.35) whereas controls averaged 184.92 sec (SD = 65.60) in this behavior (t [26] = 3.23, p < .01).

Because the prognosis of the abused infant is worse if physical neglect is present, we examined the anthropometric data available at the time of admission. Rates of growth below the tenth percentile are often used in hospitals as clinical indications of possible nutritional deficiency, maternal neglect, or as indicative of some physiological growth problem. The two samples were surprisingly similar in terms of this measure. For height, 11% of the abused infants were at or below the tenth percentile and 22% of the controls were within this range. For weight (the major anthropometric parameter utilized in diagnosing failure to thrive or neglect) *both* samples had 49% of their respective members at or below the tenth percentile. The greatest difference between the groups was found in fronto-occipital circumference. One third of the abuse sample were at or below the tenth percentile, whereas only 9% of the controls were distributed toward that portion of the growth curve.

The apparent inefficiency of anthropometric data and global ratings for discriminating between our two groups led us to search for another index of the child's general development and physical care. Hemoglobin is the iron-containing pigment protein of the red blood cells whose function is to carry oxygen from lungs to tissues. Some investigators have linked low hemoglobin concentrations to insufficient dietary intake (Provisor, 1976). Significant differences were found between the groups on this variable. The abused infants had a mean concentration of 9.9 gm per 100 c.c. (SD = 1.07); controls had a mean level of 12.07 gm per 100 c.c. (SD = 1.10). This difference was statistically significant (t [26] = 5.16, p < .001).

Finally, the results of infant developmental exams revealed some significant differences. Although mean scores for both samples were within the normal range, deviations below these limits were found in both groups on both the mental and motor index (e.g., 42% of the abuse sample were more than one standard deviation below the mean according to published norms; this was the case in only 14% of the control group). The mean score on the mental development index for the abuse group was 90.00 (SD = 16.30) compared to the control group mean of 106.28 (SD = 26.64; t [26] = 2.07; p < .05). Mean scores on the psychomotor index were 88.85 (SD = 15.91) for the abuse group and 99.71 (SD = 15.71) for control infants. Though in the predicted direction, the difference was not statistically significant (t [26] = 1.77, p < .10).

Further analyses of the data involved correlations across groups between parameters of the maternal stimulation measure and the infant's developmental quotient (see Table 2.3). The duration of the mother's auditory and vestibular

TABLE 2.3
r and t Values of Correlations of Stimulation Parameters of Duration and Variety in Mode and Mental and Motor Development

Test	Mode	Parameter	r	t (26 df)
Mental	Tactile	Duration	+.15	.66
	Auditory	Duration	+.42	2.35*
	Vestibular	Duration	+.45	2.56**
	Visual	Duration	+.03	.15
Motor	Tactile	Duration	+.33	1.74
	Auditory	Duration	+.48	2.78***
	Vestibular	Duration	+.54	3.26***
	Visual	Duration	−.12	.61
Mental	Tactile	Variety	+.52	3.36***
	Auditory	Variety	+.17	.92
	Vestibular	Variety	+.40	2.22*
	Visual	Variety	+.07	.35
Motor	Tactile	Variety	+.91	10.92****
	Auditory	Variety	+.06	.30
	Vestibular	Variety	+.40	2.20*
	Visual	Variety	+.13	.66

*p < .05
**p < .02
***p < .01
****p < .001

stimulation of her child was significantly related in a positive direction to her infant's level of mental development. The relationship between duration of visual and tactile stimulation and the infant's developmental quotient was not significant. Similarly, duration of stimulation in the vestibular and auditory modes was positively related to motor development. This relationship did not hold for the tactile and visual modes.

When the variety of stimulation was examined, positive relationships were found between tactile and vestibular stimulation and mental development. Variety within the auditory and visual modes did not significantly correlate with the level of mental development. Additionally, results for motor development were similar to those for mental development and stimulation variety, with significant correlations for the tactile and vestibular modes.

The literature suggests that the developmental delays found in abused children are exacerbated if physical neglect is present. Because of this, we correlated hemoglobin concentration and cognitive and motor development. Although the correlation between hemoglobin and Bayley Mental Scale scores were not significant, there was a significant correlation between hemoglobin and the Bayley Psychomotor Development Scale ($r = +.53$; $t [26] = 3.18$; $p < .01$).

DISCUSSION

These findings tend to support the general view that mothers in the abuse dyad are less stimulating. In terms of duration, the abuse-group mothers were significantly less stimulating in two of the four modes measured. These mothers also engaged in significantly less overall variety of stimulation in two of the four modes measured.

There is also some evidence in our examination of interactive quality that abuse mothers were less involved with their infants. In addition to engaging in less quantity and variety of stimulation, the abuse mothers were more passive. In the tactile mode, for example, control mothers engaged in more active stimulative strategies. Overall, these mothers were more involved, engaging in more touching, rubbing, mouthing, nuzzling, and other typically gregarious maternal behaviors. Abuse mothers, instead, engaged in more holding and restraining of the infant. The abuse-group mothers were also less physically intimate with their infants. Control-group mothers were observed to frequently kiss, mouth, and nuzzle their infants. They displayed no aversion to physically proximal interaction. Also, as a more or less anecdotal addition, when control infants initiated play with their mothers' hair or face, the control mother typically allowed this activity to continue. However, in several abuse dyads, some mothers would quickly draw back, wanting no part of this sort of interaction.

In terms of involvement, it is also interesting that the abuse-group mothers engaged in significantly less baby talk. This typical pattern of higher pitch, elongation of vowels, and exaggeration of syllabic enunciation has been considered as both important for language development and as an index of the mother's ability to adjust her behavior to the developmental level of her child (Ferguson, 1964).

The results of these observations indicate that the abuse mothers were less stimulating than matched controls. Note, however, that the term "less stimulating" is used rather than "understimulating." It was not our overall impression that these mothers were grossly depriving in the setting in which we observed them. With a few notable exceptions, as a group these mothers interacted in a suitable manner with their children. In fact, additional data indicate that professional and lay groups have great difficulty differentiating a subsample of identified abusers and their children from their matched control dyads when the videotapes are viewed in an unstructured manner. The differences found in this study show that, when coding of observations is structured; differences in both quantity and type of interaction appear.

In terms of physical growth, this study did not find differences between index and control groups on this variable. Indeed, for the major parameter used in diagnosing failure to thrive—weight—both samples had an equal number of cases below the tenth percentile. The fact that 50% of the infants in each group possessed rates of physical development this slow is of critical importance. Recall that both groups were in the very lowest echelons of socioeconomic class. In fact, by matching our groups so exactly we have two samples of infants that may both be subject to the same degree of neglect. This conclusion is supported by Elmer (1977). Results of her longitudinal follow-up study of abused and accidentally injured children indicate that lower social-class membership and the often resulting neglect were more critical factors than the abuse per se in the development of the children in her sample. Few group differences were found. Indeed, multiple developmental problems were common characteristics of children in both samples.

Hemoglobin concentrations were analyzed as another probable index of the quality of physical care the infant was receiving. Abused infants were found to have significantly lower mean hemoglobin levels. This result agrees with that of Ebbin, Gollub, Stein, and Wilson (1969). In addition, 79% of the abused infants had hemoglobin concentrations low enough to indicate a condition of iron deficiency anemia. No case in the control sample possessed levels this low. In an indirect manner, these data may indicate something more about the interactions between caretakers and abused infants. Provisor (1976) suggests that iron deficiency anemia in infancy may reflect a dietary history of excessive milk intake to the exclusion of iron-rich solid foods. Perhaps our abuse sample mothers prolonged the period of time that their infants were bottle fed. The transition to solid foods can sometimes be a difficult one for both the mother and the infant, and this negotiation may require a level of involvement that our abuse-sample mothers lacked.

The present study also found abused infants significantly compromised in relationship to controls on evaluations of mental development. Furthermore, a considerably higher proportion of abused infants were below normal limits according to norms for the Bayley scales. For motor development, the differences found were in the predicted direction but did not quite achieve statistical significance.

The quality of the maternal–infant relationship has often been cited as a factor affecting the infant's development. In recent years the primary caregiver has come to be described as a significant source of stimulation for the infant. This investigation found that some parameters of the observation measure were related to the infant's cognitive and motor development. However, the extent to which scores for a particular mode of stimulation correlated with Bayley scores depended on whether we measured its duration or the variety of maternal stimulative strategies within categories. Mental development was correlated with *duration* of stimulation in the auditory and vestibular modes and *variety* of stimulation in the tactile and vestibular modes. Similarly, motor development was positively correlated with *duration* of auditory and vestibular stimulation and with *variety* of tactile and vestibular stimulation strategies. For both mental and motor development, duration in the auditory and vestibular modes and variety in the tactile and vestibular modes seemed consistently important.

It is interesting to note that both duration and variety of vestibular stimulation was related to cognitive and motor functioning. Some have suggested (notably Korner & Thoman, 1970) that this type of stimulation is particularly effective in quieting infants and bringing them to a level of arousal that is facilitative of interaction with the environment. It is also possible that infants who get more practice in making postural adjustments on these occasions receive more muscular feedback and develop superior motor coordination. The critical importance of this type of stimulation has been demonstrated in several investigations (Ainsworth, 1964; Held & Hein, 1963).

The literature on abused children has stressed the point that the developmental prognosis is poorer if the infant or child is physically neglected. Because the usual anthropometric measures failed to discriminate between these two samples, the authors used blood hemoglobin as an additional index of each child's physical status. This variable was not correlated with the infant's level of mental development but was significantly correlated with motor development. As much of what we describe as "infant intelligence" is motor as well as perceptual in nature, we might suppose that deficits in motor functioning, resulting from poor nutrition, may later extend to perceptual-cognitive functioning as well.

OVERVIEW

This study has focused on two aspects of maternal attention—stimulation and physical care. What emerges is the description of two groups that possess both differences and similarities. Having discussed the differences, let us now review some of the similarities between the groups and their implications. The most striking statistic which comes to mind is the admission weights of the infants. *Both* groups had 50% of their respective members at or below the tenth percentile. The implication here is that there is some inadequacy in the infant care occurring in both groups. Also, in terms of the maternal stimulation measure, it would *not* be fair to conclude that all the abuse-group mothers stimulated their infants less than controls. In fact, several of the abuse-group mothers would seem like model maternal figures on the level of casual observation of our tapes. In addition, at least one case comes to mind in the control sample in which the mother did practically nothing while her infant made strong overtures for attention.

These similarities do not diminish the importance of the group differences that the statistics indicate. They are clear and meaningful. However, we also want to realistically evaluate what the results of our abuse and control samples tell us. What Sameroff and Chandler (1975) have termed a "continuum of caretaking casualty" is a useful concept here. As we have stated earlier, the effects of lower social-class membership are applicable to both abuse and control groups. Our control sample is in somewhat "better shape" because they are presumably exposed only to inadequate caregiving, whereas the abused infants are subject to assault, inadequate physical care, and, as a group, less stimulation. The more factors deleterious to normal growth and development that enter the picture, the poorer the prognosis. In short, when studying abused and nonabused infants in the types of families we investigated, what emerges is not two entirely distinct groups but so many infants at different points along this continuum as a function of different, maternal-care practices.

This investigation suggests that knowing the interactive characteristics of the abusive mother–infant dyad may provide an additional diagnostic tool for the physician in cases of abuse. Because early stimulation has been shown to be essential for normal infant development, intervention should be available for families having difficulties in forming positive interaction. We also need to be sensitive to the effects of poor physical care on both the abused *and* nonabused infant. The usefulness of parent training-programs in educating parents and potential parents in the needs of children and strategies of child-rearing has been demonstrated and is recommended as one major method effective in preventing child abuse and neglect (Education Commission of the States, 1976).

ACKNOWLEDGMENT

This research is based on a thesis submitted by Kim N. Dietrich, to Wayne State University in partial fulfillment of the requirements for the M.A. degree. This research was supported by National Center on Child Abuse and Neglect, Administration for Children, Youth, and Families, DHEW grant No. 90-C-426 awarded to Raymond H. Starr, Jr.

APPENDIX: MEASURE OF MATERNAL STIMULATION

Auditory Mode

A1	Mother talks to infant, soft or medium volume, elongated vowels
A2	Mother talks to infant, soft or medium volume, adult speech
A3	Mother talks to infant, loud volume, adult speech
A4	Sings
A5	Whistles
A6	Gutteral sounds
A7	Clucks tongue
A8	Smacks lips
A9	Claps hands or snaps fingers
A10	Bangs table or object

Tactile Mode

T1	Pats
T2	Touches
T3	Kisses
T4	Mouths
T5	Rubs or caresses
T6	Nuzzles
T7	Tickles
T8	Inspects
T9	Grooms
T10	Tactile play
T11	Elicits grasp reflex

T12   Holds
T13   Mother allows child to play with face, hair, etc.

Vestibular Mode

L1   Mother rocks infant in seat, knees, or arms
L2   Mother bounces or jiggles infant
L3   Mother lifts infant up and down
L4   Mother pushes infant seat back and forth
L5   Mother twirls infant around in seat or on table
L6   Mother leans infant forward or backward, side to side

Visual Mode

V1   Mother presents face in front of infant's eyes
V2   Mother slowly moves face across visual field of infant
V3   Mother presents object in front of infant's eyes
V4   Mother slowly moves object across visual field of infant
V5   Mother engages infant in visual play (peek-a-boo)

REFERENCES

Ainsworth, M. D. Patterns of attachment behavior shown by the infant in interaction with his mother. *Merrill-Palmer Quarterly,* 1964, *10,* 51–58.

Birrel, R. G., & Birrel, J. H. W. The maltreatment syndrome in children: A hospital survey. *Medical Journal of Australia,* 1968, *55,* 1023–1029.

Burgess, R. L., & Conger, R. D. *Family interaction in abusive, neglectful and normal families.* Paper presented at the meeting of the Society for Research in Child Development, New Orleans, March, 1977.

Caffey, J. Multiple fractures in the long bones of infants suffering from chronic subdural hematoma. *American Journal of Roentgenology,* 1946, *56,* 163–173.

Clarke-Stewart, K. A. Interactions between mothers and their young children: characteristics and consequences. *Monographs of the Society for Research in Child Development,* 1973, *38* (6–7, Whole No. 153).

Dennis, W., & Najarian, P. Infant development under environmental handicap. *Psychological Monographs,* 1957, *71* (Whole No. 436).

Dietrich, K. N. *The abused infant: Developmental characteristics and maternal handling.* Unpublished master's thesis, Wayne State University, Detroit, 1977.

Disbrow, M. A., Doerr, H. O., & Caulfield, C. *Measures to predict abuse.* (Final report on Maternal and Child Health Grant MC-R 530351). Seattle, Washington: Univ of Washington, 1977.

Ebbin, A. J., Gollub, M. H., Stein, A. M., & Wilson, M. G. Battered child syndrome at the Los Angeles County Hospital. *American Journal of Diseases of Childhood,* 1969, *118,* 660–667.

Education Commission of the States. *Education for parenthood: A primary prevention strategy for child abuse and neglect.* Denver, Colorado: Author, 1976.

Elmer, E. A follow-up study of traumatized children. *Pediatrics*, 1977, *59*, 273-279.
Elmer, E., & Gregg, G. S. Developmental characteristics of abused children. *Pediatrics*, 1967, *40*, 596-602.
Ferguson, C. A. Baby talk in six languages. *American Anthropologist*, 1964, *66*, 103-114.
Gray, J. D., Cutler, C. A., Dean, J. G., & Kempe, C. H. *Prediction and prevention of child abuse and neglect*. Paper presented at the meeting of the Society for Pediatric Research, St. Louis, Missouri 1976.
Greenberg, N. H. Studies in psychosomatic differentiation during infancy. *Archives of General Psychiatry*, 1962, *7*, 389-401.
Greenberg, N. H., Cekan, P., & Loesch, J. G. *Some cardiac rate and behavioral characteristics of sucking in the neonate*. Paper presented at the meeting of the American Psychosomatic Society, Atlantic City, New Jersey, 1963.
Greenberg, N. H. Origins of head rolling (Spasmus-nutans) during early infancy. *Psychosomatic Medicine*, 1964, *26*, 2.
Greenberg, N. H. Developmental effects of stimulation during early infancy. *Annals of the New York Academy of Science*, 1965, *118*, 831-859.
Held, R., & Hein, A. Movement-produced stimulation in the development of visually guided behavior. *Journal of Comparative and Physiological Psychology*, 1963, *56*, 872-876.
Helfer, R. E., & Pollock, E. B. The battered child syndrome. *Advances in Pediatrics*, 1968, *15*, 9-27.
Herner & Co. *Analysis and status of child abuse and neglect research*. Washington, D.C.: Author, 1976.
Hollingshead, A. B. *Two-factor index of social position*. Unpublished manuscript, 1957. (Available from Yale Station, New Haven, Connecticut).
Kempe, C. H., Silverman, F. N., Steele, B. F., Droegemueller, W., & Silver, H. K. The battered child syndrome. *Journal of the American Medical Association*, 1962, *181*, 17-24.
Koel, B. S. Failure to thrive and fatal injury as a continuum. *American Journal of Diseases of Children*, 1969, *118*, 565-567.
Korner, A. F., & Thoman, E. B. Visual alertness in neonates as evoked by maternal care. *Journal of Experimental Child Psychology*, 1970, *10*, 67-78.
Lewis, M., & Goldberg, S. Perceptual-cognitive development in infancy: A generalized expectancy model as a function of the mother-infant interaction. *Merrill-Palmer Quarterly*, 1969, *15*, 81-100.
MacCarthy, D. Deprivation dwarfism viewed as a form of child abuse. In A. W. Franklin (Ed.), *The challenge of child abuse*. New York: Grune & Stratton, 1977.
Martin, H. P. (Ed.). *The abused child: A multidisciplinary approach to developmental issues and treatment*. Cambridge, Massachusetts: Ballinger, 1976.
Martin, H. P., Beezley, P., Conway, E. F., & Kempe, C. H. The development of abused children. *Advances in Pediatrics*, 1974, *21*, 25-73.
Provisor, A. J. Childhood anemia. *Practical Therapeutics*, 1976, *14*, 125-134.
Ramey, C., Starr, R. H., Jr., Pallas, J., Whitten, C. F., & Reed, V. Nutrition, response contingent stimulation, and the Maternal Deprivation Syndrome: Results of an early intervention program. *Merrill-Palmer Quarterly*, 1975, *21*, 45-54.
Sameroff, A. J., & Chandler, M. J. Reproductive risk and the continuum of caretaking casualty. In F. D. Horowitz (Ed.), *Review of child development research*. Vol. 4. Chicago: Univ. Chicago, 1975.
Smith, S. M. *The battered child syndrome*. London: Butterworths, 1975.
Spitz, R. A. Hospitalism: An inquiry into the genesis of psychiatric conditions in early childhood. *Psychoanalytic Study of the Child*, 1945, *1*, 323-342.

Starr, R. H., Jr. The controlled study of the ecology of child abuse and drug abuse. *Child Abuse and Neglect*, 1978, *2*, 19-28.

Steele, B. F., & Pollock, C. G. A psychiatric study of parents who abuse infants and small children. In R. E. Helfer & C. H. Kempe (Eds.), *The battered child.* Chicago: Univ. Chicago, 1968.

Watson, E. H., & Lowrey, G. H. *Growth and development of children* 4th ed. Chicago: Yearbook Medical Publishers, 1962.

White, B. L., & Castle, P. W. Visual exploratory behavior following postnatal handling of human infants. *Perceptual and Motor Skills*, 1964, *18*, 497-502.

White, B. L., LaCrosse, E. R., Litman, F., & Ogilvie, D. M. *The Harvard Preschool Project: An etho-ecological study of the development of competence.* Symposium presented at the meeting of the Society for Research in Child Development, Santa Monica, California, 1969.

Woolley, P. A., Jr., & Evans, W. A., Jr. Significance of skeletal lesions in infants resembling those of traumatic origin. *Journal of the American Medical Association*, 1955, *158*, 539-543.

WILLIAM H. KIMBALL
ROBERT B. STEWART
RAND D. CONGER
ROBERT L. BURGESS

CHAPTER **3**

A Comparison of Family Interaction in Single- versus Two-Parent Abusive, Neglectful, and Control Families

INTRODUCTION

Three reviews (Herzog & Sudia, 1973; Hetherington, Cox, & Cox, 1977; Marino & McCowan, 1976) have pointed out the complexity of the relationship between father absence and child development. Although generalizations abound with respect to the adverse consequences of father absence for such problems as juvenile delinquency, intellectual defects, and psychological maladjustment, these reviewers suggest that the relationships are much more equivocal than is often assumed. Inconsistent findings from studies of the correlation between father absence and aberrant behavior point to the fact that many researchers have not adequately controlled for such factors as income level, race, and type of parent absence. A much clearer relationship appears to exist between such factors as the quality of parenting and general family climate and harmony than the presence or absence of the father (Herzog & Sudia, 1973). Consequently, it is essential to examine family processes and functioning rather than to assume that father absence or presence will necessarily have a particular effect.

To this end, Hetherington, Cox, and Cox (1976) have recently conducted a 2-year longitudinal investigation of families having lately experienced divorce as well as families that had not. These authors used laboratory observational

43

HIGH-RISK INFANTS AND CHILDREN:
Adult and Peer Interactions

measures as well as self-report and questionnaire methods to measure family functioning and climate. The observational measures indicated significant differences between the intact and divorced families, particularly during the first year following the divorce. Divorced mothers exhibited fewer positive and more negative behaviors to their children, while their children were less compliant. By the end of the second year, significant improvements, as defined by a greater number of positive parent behaviors and more child compliance, had occurred within the families having divorced parents. The observational measures provide an excellent way to measure family climate and the quality of parenting.

Another observational methodology for objectively assessing family processes and functioning has been devised by Burgess and Conger (1978). They attempted to explore the reciprocal nature of everyday interactions within families that might contribute to child abuse or neglect. In their work with two-parent families, they found striking differences between abusive, neglectful, and control families when all were intact. The parents in the abusive families, particularly the mothers, initiated fewer overall contacts, fewer positive contacts, and considerably more negative contacts than the control parents. Similarly, the neglectful parents displayed fewer positive and more negative behaviors than did the controls.

Recently, Burgess and his colleagues have extended their research to the examination of interaction patterns within mother-headed, single-parent abusive, neglectful, and control families. This work represents an opportunity to compare the family functioning of single- and two-parent families and to determine whether any differences in the style of interaction between single-parent (i.e., mother) and two-parent families are peculiar to abusive, neglectful, or control families. It also provides an opportunity to determine whether the differences between intact abusive, neglectful, and control families are replicated in families in which one parent—the father—was absent.

METHOD

Sample

Three single-parent family types were selected for study on the basis of (a) those in which there were authenticated occurrences of nonaccidental injury (abuse) to one or more children by a caretaker; (b) those in which one or more children experienced a lack of parental attention (neglect) so severe that it reached the attention of legal authorities; and (c) families with no official records of abuse or neglect (control) but that were similar to the first two types on a number of dimensions (e.g., age of mother and children, number of children, income, and educational levels).

Single-parent families classified as abusive ($N = 8$) or neglectful ($N = 9$) were recruited through the Commonwealth of Pennsylvania's Department of Public Welfare. The control single-parent families ($N = 10$) were contacted by the Pennsylvania Field Research Laboratory. All families participated in the study voluntarily. The families resided in a generally rural environment in central Pennsylvania and all families were Caucasian. In order to attract subjects, as well as to assure continued participation in the study, the mothers were paid $10 for each of two visits.

Single-parent families were included in these analyses if there was no male figure living in the home on a routine basis. Unfortunately, because of sampling restrictions, it was not possible to control for the type of parent absence. Reasons for father absence included: divorce or separation ($N = 20$); death ($N = 5$); never married ($N = 1$); and husband in jail ($N = 1$). Within the abusive families, the absent father was the identified abuser in 4 cases. The two-parent families (17 abuse, 17 neglect, and 19 control) are the same families described by Burgess and Conger (1978). They were recruited the same way as the above families and had similar demographic characteristics.

Procedure

All families were contacted by the project supervisor who obtained written, informed consent, gathered information concerning the family background, and arranged an observation schedule. Two observers, uninformed as to whether the family was abusive, neglectful, or control, were scheduled to see each family at home for 6 hr during a given week or consecutive weeks. Observations were typically taken in the evening between 6 and 10 P.M., however, only 4 of the 6 hr were spent in actual observation. Each observation session was separated into three types of distinct tasks as follows: (a) cooperative task (e.g., building blocks, tinker toys, Lincoln logs); (b) competitive tasks (e.g., throwing bean bags through a hoop or tossing rings over a wooden post); and (c) discussion tasks (e.g., "What would your family like to do on a vacation?"). These tasks, assigned to all families, were designed to facilitate interaction among family members. The observations took 15–20 min per task, depending on family size, and there was a short break between tasks. The order of tasks was standardized across families.

Within each task, a particular family member was the focal subject twice for a minimum of 1 and 1.5 min. Thus, each family member was a focal subject for at least 36 min over the 4 hr of observation. The order of focal subjects was determined with a table of random numbers before each session began. The

additional 2 hr in the home were used by the two research assistants to administer questionnaires dealing with such topics as perceived health, social
stress, and parental perceptions of each child.

Response Definition

The principal dependent variable in this study was the observed pattern of
interaction between family members. The observation code was recorded
through the Behavior Observation Scoring System (BOSS). BOSS consists of a
10-digit keyboard, a stopwatch, and an especially modified cassette tape recorder. When a particular behavior occurs, the observer depresses a key and an
electrical impulse is transmitted onto a magnetic tape inside the attached recorder. Special computer programs decipher the impulses from the magnetic
tape.

The behavior code consists of five column entries as follows:

Column 1: *Type of interaction:* verbal give or receive, physical give or
       receive
Column 2: *Affect of interaction:* neutral, positive, negative, or mixed
Column 3 and 4: *Person interacting with the focal subject*
Column 5: *Commands or complies:* prescriptive command, proscriptive
       command, comply, refuse, none of the above.

Observer Reliability

The observers operated in pairs that were shifted in composition every 2–3
weeks to prevent the development of unique definitions of the behavior code.
In order to check on observer reliability, both observers coded family interactions over all sessions. One observer's tapes were randomly selected for complete analysis. Then a "probe" tape was randomly selected from the second
observer's coding, one from each session, to compare with the data from the
other observer. Observer reliability was estimated by computing correlation
coefficients, slopes, and intercepts among the rates of a particular behavior
scored for each family member by the two observers. That is, for each observer
a matrix was produced showing rates of a given behavior from each member to
every other, and it was these matrix entries that were correlated. If the correlation coefficient was high, the intercept close to zero and the slope approximately 1.00, the agreement between the observers would be high. If the intercept either exceeded or was less than zero, a high correlation with a slope close
to unity would suggest a persistent positive or negative bias in the data.

For the code as a whole, observer agreement was quite high, the lowest
coefficient being .85. Moreover, the slopes were all close to 1.00, the most

disparate being .98. The intercepts were close to the expected value of zero with apparently random fluctuations ranging from .00 to .03.

RESULTS

Rates of behavior per minute were considered to be the most appropriate unit of analysis rather than frequencies because individual family members were not always observed for equivalent time periods. When rates are examined, it must be remembered that a small difference in rate per minute can reflect a large difference in total amounts of behavior over the 4 hr observation period.

Comparisons will be presented between the two-parent (to be called "intact") and single-parent families within each of the abusive, neglectful, and control family types. In addition, all intact families combined will be compared to all single-parent families combined.[1] The single-parent mothers' data will be compared to both the intact mothers' data and to the intact parents' (mothers' and fathers' combined) data. The first comparison was conducted by computing both univariate and multivariate analyses of variance for nine major measures of intrafamilial interaction. These nine measures include the following: (a) total family interaction, (b) mothers' interaction, (c) childrens' interaction, (d) parents' interaction, (e) mothers to children exchange, (f) parents to children exchange, (g) children to mothers exchange, (h) children to parents exchange, and (i) children to children exchange. Each of these measures was further qualified by noting whether the exchange was verbal or physical and of a positive or negative nature. Thus, a total of 36 dependent variables were considered as 16 separate MANOVA procedures were performed.

These first comparisons were made to determine whether the single and two-parent mothers interact with their children in similar ways. It might be expected, for example, that a single-parent mother would interact more with her children as there is no husband present. The latter comparison, the single-

[1]The single-parent data were collected after two-thirds of the two-parent data had already been collected. Because the observers were more experienced with the code during the single-parent data collection, analyses were conducted to determine if the differential rates, particularly for emotional affect, in the single-parent data could be due to changes in the observers' behavior. These analyses were conducted by comparing the first half of the two-parent families within each family type with the second half of the two-parent families within each family type. These latter two-parent families were observed at the same time and by the same observers as were the single-parent families. No consistent pattern of differences emerged. Although we cannot completely rule out the possibility that the observers' behavior changed over time, we are reasonably confident of our findings. We also compared the patterns of interaction in those single-parent families in which the mother was the identified abuser with those in which the absent father was the official perpetrator of the abuse. The interaction patterns were remarkably similar and displayed no consistent differences.

parent mother versus the intact parents, was made to examine whether the single-parent mothers adjust (i.e., increase) their rates of interaction to offset the absence of the father.

A 3 × 2 (Type—abusive, neglectful, control) by Family Structure (single, intact) MANOVA was performed for each qualitative behavior type (verbal, physical, positive, negative) to describe further the effects due to family structure, type, and the interaction thereof. Univariate two-way analyses of variance were also computed for each of the 36 dependent measures.

Verbal Contacts

Table 3.1 summarizes the group means and statistical tests for all the verbal contact measures. The Type × Structure MANOVA indicated only a significant main effect of family structure ($F[9,16] = 38.09$; $p < .0001$). The one-way MANOVAs indicated that there was a significant effect of family structure for each family type ($F[9,15] = 15.12$; $p < .0001$ for abusive families; $F[9,16] = 10.22$; $p < .0001$ for neglecting families; and $F[9,19] = 19.92$, $p < .0001$ for control families). As Table 3.1 indicates, the univariate analyses suggest that the primary source of these differences is found in the rate of *parent* behaviors, the rate of *mother to child* contacts, and the *child to mother contacts*. In each case, mother- and children in single-parent families made more verbal contacts with each other than those in the intact families.

It might be expected that single mothers, because they did not have a husband as a potential recipient of their behavior, might interact more often with their children than mothers in intact families. Indeed, across all groups, this tendency was demonstrated, especially by abusive mothers (F-1,23] = 17.66, $p < .001$ for abuse; $F[1,24]$ 3.37, $p < .08$ for neglect; F-1,27] =6.59, $p < .02$ for control; overall, $F[1,78] = 23.66$, $p \leq .0001$). Combining all family types, the single-parent mothers directed approximately 54% more verbal behavior to their children than did the mothers from the intact families. In fact, mothers in the single-parent, abusive families directed over twice as many verbal contacts to their children as the mothers in intact abusive families. However, combining all family types, the children received approximately 70 fewer parental contacts per hour as a result of being in a single-parent home ($F[1,78] = 5.98$, $p < .02$). This tendency was largely accounted for by the single-parent control families ($F[1,27] = 6.18$, $p < .02$). With the exception of the control families, the mothers in the single-parent families almost succeeded in compensating for the fathers' absence in terms of the sheer frequency of Parent–Child interaction.

When the children's behavior was examined, we found that, overall, children in single-parent families displayed over twice the rate of verbalization to their mothers then did children in the intact families ($F[1,78] = 80.07$, $p <$

TABLE 3.1
Mean Rate of Verbal Contacts

Variable	Abuse 2 parent (N = 17)	Abuse 1 parent (N = 8)	Abuse F (df = 1,23)	Neglect 2 parent (N = 17)	Neglect 1 parent (N = 9)	Neglect F (df = 1,24)	Control 2 parent (N = 19)	Control 1 parent (N = 10)	Control F (df = 1,27)	All 2 parent (N = 53)	All 1 parent (N = 27)	All F (df = 1,78)	Two-way MANOVA[a] T: df = 2,74	S: df = 1,74	TS: df = 2,74
Total family	19.479	19.349	.00	19.608	16.770	2.36	20.768	15.971	11.99**	19.983	17.238	6.97**	T: 6.13*	S: .51	TS: 1.67
Mother	4.469	6.446	6.63*	5.423	5.570	.03	5.892	5.993	.03	5.285	5.986	2.64	T: 3.05	S: .56	TS: 2.03
Children	10.223	12.901	.98	10.063	11.202	.38	10.033	9.978	.00	10.104	11.252	1.01	T: 1.15	S: .60	TS: .46
Parent[b]	9.256	6.446	7.62**	9.544	5.570	18.83***	10.734	5.993	37.29****	9.878	5.986	55.56****	T: 54.72****	S: .87	TS: 1.16
Mother to children	2.979	6.116	17.66***	3.899	5.374	3.37	4.084	5.557	6.59*	3.670	5.662	23.66****	T: 24.70****	S: .16	TS: 1.71
Parents to children	6.340	6.116	.06	6.734	5.374	2.53	7.376	5.557	6.18*	6.838	5.662	5.98*	T: 5.45*	S: .25	TS: .93
Children to mother	2.112	5.210	34.64****	2.723	5.318	21.18****	2.801	4.815	26.62****	2.555	5.100	80.07****	T: 81.48****	S: .52	TS: 1.22
Children to parents	4.410	5.210	1.98	4.372	5.318	2.45	5.021	4.815	.25	4.617	5.100	2.54	T: 2.84	S: .04	TS: 1.50
Children to children	2.867	5.612	2.01	2.834	4.581	1.17	2.394	3.444	1.33	2.687	4.666	4.34*	T: 4.57*	S: .80	TS: .32
Multivariate F ratio (Hotelling-Lawley Trace)	F_S = 15.12****	df = 9, 15		F_S = 10.22****	df = 9,16		F_S = 19.92****	df = 9,19		F_S = 37.26****	df = 9,70		F_T = .67 df = 18,130	F_S = 38.09**** df = 9,16	F_{TS} = .88 df = 18,130

[a] T refers to type effect (abuse, neglect, control); S refers to structure effect (2 parent, 1 parent).
[b] Data in the row compare rates of both parents combined.
*$p < .05$
**$p < .01$
***$p < .001$
****$p < .0001$

.0001). Indeed, the single mothers received contacts from their children equivalent to those directed to both parents combined in the intact families.

Physical Contacts

Table 3.2 lists the comparisons for physical interactions. Once again, the Type × Structure MANOVA yields a significant main effect of family structure ($F[9,66] = 27.41$; $p < .0001$) which is supported by a significant effect for family structure within each family type ($F[9,15] = 8.55$, $p < .001$ for the abuse group; $F[9,16] = 10.96$, $p < .0001$ for the neglect group; $F[9,19] = 11.64$, $p < .0001$ for the controls).

Further examination of Table 3.2 indicates that the two parents in intact families displayed approximately 25 more physical contacts per hour than did the single mothers alone ($F[1,78] = 7.37$, $p < .01$). As was seen in the verbal interaction data, the single mothers displayed a substantially higher rate of physical contacts than the mothers in intact families ($F[1,78] = 4.89$, $p < .03$). When the recipients of the physical contacts were examined, patterns similar to the verbalization data again emerged. The single mothers, especially the mothers in abusive families, exhibited a significantly higher rate of physical contacts toward their children than the mothers in the intact families ($F[1,23] = 13.90$, $p < .001$ for abuse; $F[1,78] = 9.56$, $p < .003$ overall). In fact, single mothers' rate clearly resemble the parents' rate of physical contact with children in intact families ($F[1,78] = 2.19$, n.s.). Thus, children in single-parent families did not differ from those in intact families in patterns of physical contact received.

The overall rate of childrens' physical responses did not differ as a function of family structure ($F[1,78] = 1.43$, n.s.). Significant differences appeared when the recipients of the physical behavior were examined. Combining all family types, the children in single-parent families directed 36% more physical behavior to their mothers than the children in intact families ($F[1,78] = 9.82$, $p < .002$). Most of this difference is accounted for by the children in the single-parent abusive families ($F[1,23] = 10.46$, $p < .004$). The children in single-parent families directed fewer physical contacts to their mothers than did those in intact families directed to the two-parent combined ($F[1,78] = 10.07$, $p < .002$). The children in single-parent families directed more physical behavior to each other than those in intact families ($F[1,78] = 6.80$, $p < .01$). These differences were primarily manifested in the control families. In short, although children in the single-parent families did not receive fewer physical contacts than those in intact families, they did receive a greater proportion of their physical contacts from each other. The significant MANOVA for family structure with the neglect families must be viewed with caution as no univariate measure revealed a significant difference. Further analysis indicated that the

TABLE 3.2
Mean Rate of Physical Contacts

Variable	Abuse 2 parent (N = 17)	Abuse 1 parent (N = 8)	Abuse F (df = 1,23)	Neglect 2 parent (N = 17)	Neglect 1 parent (N = 9)	Neglect F (df = 1,24)	Control 2 parent (N = 19)	Control 1 parent (N = 10)	Control F (df = 1,27)	All 2 parent (N = 53)	All 1 parent (N = 27)	All F (df = 1,78)	Two-way MANOVA[a] T (df = 2,74)	S (df = 1,74)	TS (df = 2,74)
Total family	4.190	4.600	.29	4.516	4.448	.01	4.576	4.289	.22	4.433	4.434	.00	T: .01	S: .00	TS: .25
Mother	.699	1.089	7.77**	.958	1.284	1.42	.947	1.068	.34	.871	1.146	4.89*	T: 1.05	S: 4.96*	TS: .43
Children	2.847	3.511	.79	2.897	3.163	.17	2.860	3.223	.55	2.868	3.288	1.43	T: .07	S: 1.42	TS: .10
Parent[b]	1.342	1.089	1.92	1.620	1.284	1.18	1.715	1.068	5.33*	1.565	1.146	7.37**	T: .80	S: 7.07**	TS: .62
Mother to children	.576	1.089	13.90***	.883	1.284	2.14	.822	1.061	1.44	.763	1.144	9.56**	T: 1.33	S: 9.70**	TS: .42
Parents to children	1.134	1.089	.06	1.454	1.284	.30	1.489	1.061	2.74	1.364	1.144	2.19	T: .97	S: 2.07	TS: .59
Children to mother	.728	1.176	10.46**	.919	1.140	1.12	.980	1.264	2.85	.880	1.197	9.82**	T: .94	S: 9.76**	TS: .42
Children to parents	1.495	1.176	2.32	1.545	1.140	2.68	1.850	1.264	5.30*	1.638	1.197	10.07**	T: 1.14	S: 9.80**	TS: .33
Children to children	1.348	2.334	1.83	1.338	2.021	1.32	1.004	1.955	4.43*	1.222	2.089	6.80**	T: .38	S: 6.58**	TS: .08
Multivariate F ratio (Hotelling-Lawley Trace)	F_s = 8.55*** df = 9,15			F_s = 10.96**** df = 9,16			F_s = 11.64**** df = 9,19			F_s = 27.45**** df = 9,70			F_T = .89 df = 18,130	F_s = 27.41**** df = 9,66	F_{TS} = .61 df = 18,130

[a]T refers to type effect (abuse, neglect, control); S refers to structure effect (2 parent, 1 parent).
[b]Data in the row compare rates of both parents combined.
*p < .05
**p < .01
***p < .001
****p < .0001

single-parent children in neglectful families consistently showed higher, though nonsignificant, rates of interaction than did their two-parent counterparts.

Positive Interaction (Verbal and Physical Combined)

The comparisons of positive contacts, both verbal and physical, are summarized in Table 3.1. The Type × Structure MANOVA showed a main effect of family structure ($F[9,66] = 12.24$, $p < .0001$) supported by a significant effect of structure within each family type ($F[9,15] = 4.00$, $p < .01$) in the abuse group; $F[9,16] = 4.54$, $p < .01$ for the neglect group; $f[9,19] = 5.85$, $p < .001$ for controls). One variable from the 2-way ANOVA, mother to child positives, yielded a Type × Structure interaction ($F[2,74] = 3.40$, $p < .05$). This interaction is explained by the finding that although family structure had no effect on Mother–Child positive interaction in the neglect or control groups, the mothers in the abuse group engaged in a higher rate of positive interactions in the single-parent group relative to intact families ($F[1,23] = 11.07$, $p < .01$).

The two parents in intact control families exhibited higher combined rates of positive contact than the single mothers in the control group ($F[1,27] = 5.05$, $p < .03$). Indeed, the two parents combined in the intact control families displayed more than twice as many positive interactions as the mothers in the single-parent control group. Mothers in the abusive and neglectful single-parent families exhibited rates of positive behaviors nearly identical to those of the abusive and neglectful parents combined in intact families.

In abusive and neglectful families, the rate of positive behavior for single mothers was 80% higher than that for mothers in intact families. In the control group, family structure did not affect the rate of positive behavior.

The findings for the recipients of the interactions exhibit a similar pattern (Table 3.3). Although intact and single control mothers did not differ in rates of positive contacts directed to their children ($F[1,27] = 0.14$), in abusive families, single mothers directed more positive behavior to their children than those in intact families ($F[1,23] = 11.07$, $p < .003$). Briefly, in the abusive and neglectful families, children received as many positive contacts from their single mothers as those children in the intact families received from both parents. On the other hand, the children in single-parent control families received only half as many positive contacts as those in the intact control families ($F[1,27] = 4.76$, $p < .05$).

Another suggestive finding was that the children in the intact families displayed significantly fewer positive behaviors (almost 20 fewer per hr) than those with single mothers, ($F[1,78] = 12.77$, $p < .001$). This tendency was manifested across all family types, although it was not statistically significant for the children from abusive families. The interesting differences shown by the

TABLE 3.3
Mean Rate of Positive Contact

Variable	Abuse 2 parent (N = 17)	1 parent (N = 8)	F (df = 1,23)	Neglect 2 parent (N = 17)	1 parent (N = 9)	F (df = 1,24)	Control 2 parent (N = 19)	1 parent (N = 10)	F (df = 1,27)	All 2 parent (N = 53)	1 parent (N = 27)	F (df = 1,78)	Two-way MANOVA[a] T: df = 2,74 / S: df = 1,74 / TS: df = 2,74		
Total family	.928	1.299	1.39	.733	.974	1.44	1.154	1.114	.03	.946	1.122	1.40	T: 1.50	S: 1.67	TS: .69
Mother	.273	.530	5.45*	.221	.346	1.62	.415	.334	.58	.307	.396	2.02	T: 1.35	S: 2.72	TS: 2.66
Children	.399	.769	3.14	.368	.628	4.54*	.426	.782	5.55*	.399	.727	12.77***	T: .49	S: 12.25***	TS: .14
Parent[b]	.532	.530	.00	.366	.346	.03	.728	.334	5.05*	.549	.396	2.55	T: 1.57	S: 12.21	TS: 1.91
Mother to children	.209	.516	11.07**	.182	.341	2.69	.351	.317	.14	.251	.384	5.68*	T: 1.21	S: 7.13**	TS: 3.40*
Parents to children	.413	.519	.67	.305	.341	.08	.633	.317	4.76*	.457	.384	.81	T: 1.59	S: .57	TS: 2.91
Children to mother	.094	.291	10.51**	.109	.286	10.22**	.114	.391	25.47****	.106	.326	45.24****	T: 1.42	S: 43.39****	TS: .92
Children to parents	.215	.291	.97	.176	.286	2.86	.233	.391	4.82*	.209	.326	8.14**	T: 1.43	S: 7.63**	TS: .33
Children to children	.085	.378	4.34*	.108	.234	4.34*	.087	.249	7.30**	.093	.288	12.92***	T: .73	S: 13.30***	TS: 1.02
Multivariate F ratio (Hotelling-Lawley Trace)	F_S = 4.00**	df = 9,15		F_S = 4.54**	df = 9,16		F_S = 5.85***	df = 9,19		F_S = 12.27****	df = 9,70		F_T = 1.02 / F_S = 12.24**** / F_{TS} = 1.07	df = 18,130 / df = 9,66 / df = 18,130	

[a] T refers to type effect (abuse, neglect, control); S refers to structure effect (2 parent, 1 parent).
[b] Data in the row compare rates of both parents combined.

*p < .05
**p < .01
***p < .001
****p < .0001

single-parent control families were also apparent when the recipients of the children's positive contacts were examined. In the control group, more positive acts were directed to single mothers than to mothers in intact families ($F[1,27] = 25.47$, $p < .0001$) or to both parents combined ($F[1,27] = 4.82$, $p < .05$). This same pattern was observed in both abusive and neglecting families, though only the comparisons for rate of contacts with mothers was significant in each case ($F[1,23] = 10.51$, $p < .01$ in the abuse group; $F[1,24] = 10.22$, $p < .01$ in the neglect group). Across all groups, children of single parents directed three times as many positive behaviors to each other as children in intact families ($F[1,78] = 12.92$, $p < .001$).

Negative Interactions (Verbal and Physical Combined)

Table 3.4 and Figure 3.1 present the findings for comparisons involving measures of negative interactions. The Type × Structure MANOVA yielded a highly significant main effect of family structure ($F[9,66] = 11.46$, $p < .0001$) as well as a moderately significant Type × Structure interaction ($F[18,130] = 1.70$, $p < .05$). As in the previous analyses, the main effect of structure was supported by a significant effect of structure within each group ($F[9,15] = 4.81$, $p < .01$ for abusive families; $F[9,16] = 7.54$, $p < .001$ for neglecting families; $F[9,19] = 4.26$, $p < .01$ for the controls). In all cases, there were more negative interactions in the single-parent families than in the intact families.

The univariate analyses suggest that the Type × Structure interaction is primarily accounted for by differing patterns of negative interactions. These patterns are initiated by children in families of different types as there are significant univariate main effects of type on children's total negative behaviors ($F[2,74] = 3.96$, $p < .05$), child-to-mother behavior ($F[2,74] = 3.97$, $p < .05$), child-to-parents behavior ($F[2,74] = 3.03$, $p < .05$), and child-to-child behavior ($F[2,74] = 4.17$, $p < .05$).

Combining all three family types, the single-parent families exhibited a rate of negative behavior over 70% higher than the intact families ($F[1,78] = 9.18$, $p < .003$). These differences appeared in all family types, although they were not statistically significant within the family types taken separately. The 2-way analysis of variance for the total family rate of negative interaction also revealed a significant effect for family structure ($F[1,74] = 9.74$, $p < .003$). The higher rate of negative contacts in the single-parent families appears to be accounted for as much by the mothers ($F[1,78] = 18.54$, $p < .0001$) as by their children ($F[1,78] = 8.46$, $p < .005$). The single mothers displayed over twice as many negative behaviors (almost 25 more per hr) as did the mothers in intact families for all family types combined. This difference was especially noticeable within the abusive ($F[1,23] = 6.71$, $p < .02$) and control ($F[1,27] = 11.46$, $p < .002$) families. Less pronounced differences appeared when the

TABLE 3.4
Mean Rate of Negative Contact

Variable	Abuse 2 parent (N = 17)	Abuse 1 parent (N = 8)	Abuse F (df = 1,23)	Neglect 2 parent (N = 17)	Neglect 1 parent (N = 9)	Neglect F (df = 1,24)	Control 2 parent (N = 19)	Control 1 parent (N = 10)	Control F (df = 1,27)	All 2 parent (N = 53)	All 1 parent (N = 27)	All F (df = 1,78)	Two-way MANOVA[a] T: df = 2,74; S: df = 1,74; TS: df = 2,74		
Total family	1.108	2.118	3.65	1.205	1.884	2.61	.738	1.315	3.43	1.006	1.742	9.18**	T: 2.44	S: 9.74**	TS: .28
Mother	.228	.512	6.71*	.334	.647	2.89	.130	.651	11.46**	.227	.608	18.54****	T: .68	S: 17.42****	TS: .73
Children	.709	1.609	4.11*	.660	1.236	5.44*	.488	.660	.80	.614	1.133	8.46**	T: 3.96*	S: 9.97**	TS: 1.49
Parent[b]	.396	.512	.54	.545	.647	.25	.248	.651	5.85*	.391	.608	4.47*	T: .87	S: 4.05*	TS: .96
Mother to children	.201	.499	8.19**	.309	.631	3.26	.117	.625	11.72**	.205	.590	20.23****	T: .73	S: 19.06****	TS: .62
Parents to children	.355	.499	.93	.495	.631	.46	.228	.625	6.17*	.354	.590	5.65*	T: .84	S: 5.18*	TS: .79
Children to mother	.100	.446	16.34***	.142	.592	13.86***	.089	.284	8.45**	.110	.435	34.67****	T: 3.97*	S: 38.01****	TS: 2.01
Children to parents	.168	.446	5.75*	.231	.592	5.74*	.145	.284	3.45	.180	.435	14.15***	T: 3.03*	S: 15.05***	TS: .99
Children to children	.439	1.082	3.31	.355	.592	2.89	.192	.346	.21	.359	.646	4.89*	T: 4.17*	S: 6.12*	TS: 1.88*
Multivariate F ratio (Hotelling-Lawley Trace)	F_s = 4.81** df = 9,15			F_s = 7.54*** df = 9,16			F_s = 4.26** df = 9,19			F_s = 10.49**** df = 9,70			F_T = 1.62 df = 18,130	F_S = 11.46**** df = 9,66	F_{TS} = 1.70* df = 18,130

[a]T refers to type effect (abuse, neglect, control); S refers to structure effect (2 parent, 1 parent)
[b]Data in the row compare rates of both parents combined.
*p < .05
**p < .01
***p < .001
****p < .0001

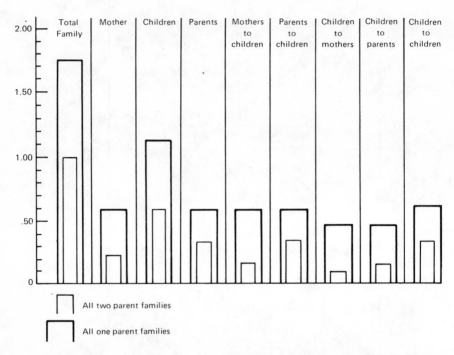

FIGURE 3.1.   The graph illustrates the mean rate of negative contacts within families.

single mothers were compared to the data of both parents combined in intact families, ($F[1,78] = 4.47$; $p < .05$). It is clear that there was a higher rate of negative contacts displayed by the single mothers, especially in abusive and control groups.

The children of single mothers also displayed a higher rate of negative interactions than those in intact families. Combining all family types, they produced about twice as many (approximately 30 more per hr) negative responses as the intact families. This difference was especially present in the abusive ($F[1,23] = 4.11$, $p < .06$) and neglect ($F[1,24] = 5.44$, $p < .03$) families. Children of single mothers in all groups directed more negative behaviors to their mothers ($F[1,78] = 34.67$, $p < .0001$) than children in intact families directed to their mothers or to their parents combined ($F[1,78] = 14.15$, $p < .001$). Again, this tendency was somewhat less dramatic in the control children.[2]

---

[2]Analyses were also conducted on the commands and comply data. Within the one-parent family types, no significant differences emerged. Some statistically significant differences were found between the single-parent and intact families. The intact parents displayed approximately 36 more commands per hr than did the single-parent mothers. This difference is statistically significant and is present across all family types, particularly within the neglectful families. The single-parent

SUMMARY AND DISCUSSION

In a previous paper, Burgess and Conger (1978) reported significant differences in patterns of family interaction between abusive and neglectful families, on the one hand, and matched control families on the other. In general, their findings indicated that in abusive and neglectful families interactions among members occur at a level lower than that of their controls. This pattern was especially the case for positive exchanges involving behaviors such as praise and affection. They also discovered that the abusive and the neglectful families had elevated rates of negative interactions involving threats, hits, and other forms of coercive behavior. These findings, however, were from families that had two adults living in the home. In the present chapter, we have attempted to make similar comparisons for families with only one parent in the home.

In the course of our analyses, we found that the differences reported by Burgess and Conger (1978) were overridden by the effects of family structure. For example, when we examined total verbal interaction, we found a lower frequency of Parent–Child interaction in the single-parent families—despite the fact that the single mothers, as a group, interact with their children more often than the mothers in the intact families. However, differences in the frequency of Parent–Child interaction is reduced somewhat by the fact that the children in the single-parent families direct interaction toward their mothers at a higher rate than do the children in the intact families to both of their parents combined. Whether these are qualitative or functional differences between child-to-parent versus parent-to-child contacts for the relationship as a whole is a matter that should be explored in further research.

A similar pattern is found when we examine physical contacts. For physical interaction, there is a lower frequency of Parent–Child interaction in the single-parent families, again despite the fact that single mothers make physical contact with their children at a higher rate than the mothers in the intact families. The children in the single-parent families direct physical behavior toward their mothers more often than children in the intact families. However, in contrast to verbal contacts, the absence of a second parent results in a lower rate of parent–child physical contacts when we consider simultaneously both parent directed as well as child directed interaction.

A somewhat different pattern is found for positive interaction. For positive

---

mothers tended to give slightly more commands to their children than did the intact mothers, but the intact parents combined tended to give slightly more commands than did the single-parent mothers. Intact families combined had a higher comply rate. This difference was present for all family types, but especially for the control families. It should be remembered that the higher rate of intact family compliance may be a function of the higher command rate by the intact parents.

exchanges, children in the single-parent families receive such parental behavior about as often as do children in intact families. Indeed, the single mothers actually display positive behavior toward their children more often than do mothers in the intact families. An exception to this pattern is exhibited by the single mothers in the control group whose rates of positive behavior, though similar that of the other single mothers, is, nonetheless, slightly lower than that of the mothers from the intact families and considerably lower than both parents combined in the intact control families. Interestingly, the rate of positive child-parent contact is higher in the single-parent families. When we examine the rates of positive interaction across abusive and neglectful families and combine both child-directed and parent-directed positive contacts, we find that there is a higher rate of Parent-Child positive interaction in the single-parent families. In contrast, the children in the single-parent control families receive only half as many positive parental contacts as do the children in the intact families. Combining child-directed and parent-directed positive contacts, we see that there is a lower rate of positive Parent-Child interaction in the single-parent control families than in the intact control families.

The greatest differences between the single and intact families are found, however, when we examine negative interaction. Across all family types, there is a strikingly higher frequency of negative behavior in the single-parent families. For example, the single mothers display rates of negative contacts with their children that are over twice those found in the intact families. Moreover, this twofold difference remains when we combine parent-directed and child-directed negative interactions. This means that, in 1 hr, there are 30 more coercive parent-child encounters in the single-parent than in two-parent families. In addition, children in the single-parent families also interacted negatively with each other at a higher rate than those in the intact families. Finally, across all three family types, there is a higher rate of positive than negative Parent-Child interaction in intact families. This pattern is reversed in the single-parent families where we find a higher rate of negative than positive interaction.

The data described in this study suggests that patterns of family interaction found to be typical of two-parent abusive and neglectful families (Burgess & Conger, 1978) are more likely given the absence of one parent. Admittedly, these data must be interpreted cautiously as the sample is not random and largely rural. Moreover, the patterns we have described may be more likely in lower socioeconomic status (SES) families, as these were (Burgess & Conger, 1978). Some may object that the sample was too small. On the other hand, given that tests of significance are a function of sample size and the strength of the relationship between variables, the large number of statistically significant differences that we found, given our relatively small sample, are all the more suggestive. In any event, the data reported in this chapter are consistent, in many respects, with the popular notion that the absence of the father (or mother) may place undue stress on the remaining parent and, thus, increase the likelihood of coercive behavior.

There are, undoubtedly, circumstances in which the departure of one of the parents could reduce tension and conflict within the home. Yet, it is equally true that there are factors that can exacerbate the potentially negative effects of having just one parent in the home. Such factors would include the number of children in the home (Burgess, 1978), spacing of births, physical or behavior abnormalities of the child, poor parental health, drug and alcohol abuse, financial difficulties, overcrowded or inadequate living conditions, isolation from effective social support systems, and a lack of effective and appropriate parenting skills (Burgess, 1979). The absence of these additional stress-producing factors could mitigate the negative consequences of single parenthood. In any case, these are clearly issues deserving of further observational research within the context of family structure and process.

ACKNOWLEDGMENTS

Preparation of this chapter was supported in part by Grant 90-C-445 from the National Center on Child Abuse and Neglect, Children's Bureau/Administration on Children, Youth and Families, Office of Human Development Services/Department of Health, Education and Welfare.

REFERENCES

Burgess, R. L. *Project Interact: A study of patterns of interaction in abusive, neglectful and control families.* Final Report to the National Center of Child Abuse and Neglect, Children's Bureau/ Administration on Children, Youth, and Families, Department of Health, Education and Welfare, August, 1978.

Burgess, R. L. Child Abuse: A social interactional analysis. In B. Lakey & A. Kazdin (Eds.), *Advances in clinical child psychology* (Vol. 2.). New York: Plenum, 1979.

Burgess, R. L., & Conger, R. D. Family interaction in abusive, neglectful and normal families. *Child Development,* 1978, *49,* 1163–1173.

Herzog, E., & Sudia, C. Children in fatherless homes. In B. M. Caldwell & H. Riccuti (Eds.), *Review of Child Development Research.* Chicago: Univ. Chicago Press, 1973.

Hetherington, E. M., Cox, M., & Cox, R. Divorced fathers. *The Family Coordinator,* 1976, *10,* 417–428.

Hetherington, E. M., Cox, M., & Cox, R. *The development of children in mother headed families.* Paper presented at the conference on Families in Contemporary America, George Washington University, June, 1977.

Marino, C., & McCowan, R. The effects of parent absence on children. *Child Study Journal,* 1976, *6,* 165–182.

SUSAN J. PAWLBY
FAE HALL

CHAPTER **4**

Early Interactions and Later Language Development of Children Whose Mothers Come from Disrupted Families of Origin

INTRODUCTION

Language acquisition has long been the subject of investigation by linguists, psychologists, and anyone concerned to know how children normally learn to speak so very rapidly. There now seems to be little doubt that children in some sense, may have an intrinsic knowledge of the universal rules of language (Chomsky, 1965). More recent research (Bruner, 1977) emphasizes that the study of language acquisition cannot be separated from the study of the social context in which it occurs. Long before the wave of current research describing the importance of the mother (or caregiver)–child relationship in providing the necessary base from which a child's communicative skills emerge, Lewis (1963) suggested that "the linguistic growth of the child moves forward as a result of the interaction of two factors, those that spring from within the child himself and those that impinge upon him from the community." It has been recognized increasingly that language derives its significance from its communicative function. Therefore, it is important to look at language development as a social skill. We are still far from reaching any firm conclusion about how the rules of language are mastered, but what has become more apparent is that words only take on meaning in the context of a young child's interactions with his or her caregivers.

61

HIGH-RISK INFANTS AND CHILDREN:
Adult and Peer Interactions

What happens when a young child is deprived of the opportunity of participating in interactions with a caregiver? Provence and Lipton (1962) have shown that infants in institutions were delayed in vocal and verbal development. Similarly, Brodbeck and Irwin (1946) compared frequency of and variety in the vocalizations of "well-mothered" babies with those of children cared for in orphanages and found significant differences between the two groups as early as the first 2 months of life. The discrepancies became more marked by the fourth and sixth months.

Bernstein's work (1965), as well as that of many others (Davie, Butler, & Goldstein, 1972; Douglas, 1964; Douglas, Ross, & Simpson, 1968) suggests that children of working-class mothers do less well when compared with children of middle-class mothers in linguistic competence and subsequent intellectual development and scholastic attainment. Other factors found to relate to a child's intellectual development are maternal age (Davie et al., 1972 Illsley, 1967; Oppel & Royston, 1971; Record, McKeown, & Edwards, 1969), illegitimacy (Crellin, Pringle, & West, 1971), birth order (Davie et al., 1972; Record et al., 1969), and family size (Davie et al., 1972). However, it is unlikely that any of these factors are proximal influences on the outcome for the child. The findings probably reflect differences in styles of maternal interaction or language use. Thus, for example, Snow (1976) found that differences in the quality of the mother's speech are somewhat class determined. Bernstein (1965) distinguished differences in a mother's style of speaking and suggests that the "elaborated code" used by middle-class mothers is much more effective for educational purposes than the "restricted code" of working-class mothers. This position is shared by Hess and Shipman (1966) who found that the flow of language between mother and child varies according to social class. Their findings suggest that the "teaching style" of lower-class mothers is far less explicit and less effective than that of middle-class mothers, and that teaching style is related to the cognitive functioning of the child. Dunn (1977) found that "acceptance" in a mother's speech to her child at 14 months was positively associated with IQ scores on the Stanford-Binet Intelligence Test at 4½ years.

As de Hirsch (1970) says, "It is impossible to over-rate the importance of language in children's development." Although a large proportion of children with delayed speech and language development at 3 years may catch up (Bax & Hart, 1976), it has also been shown that delay in language development tends in turn to be related to delays in other areas. In a total population of 3-year-olds, Richman and Stevenson (1977) found an association between language delay and behavior difficulties. Ingram (1970) has shown that 40% of the children who are not talking adequately at 3 years later show a delay in learning to read. The poor prognosis for children with reading delay and its associations with other difficulties has also been demonstrated by Rutter, Tizard, and Whitmore (1970).

From a clinical viewpoint, it is important for us not only to identify as early as possible those groups of children most at risk for delay in language development, but also to seek to understand why the delay occurs. Our study identified a group of children who were delayed in their language and speech development at the age of 27 months. Data collected earlier on the mother's interaction with her baby at 20 weeks provided some clue as to the mechanisms involved in promoting a child's language development.

METHOD

Sample

Subjects for the study formed a subsample of an ongoing, larger longitudinal epidemiological study of British-born mothers and their first-born babies from the London borough of Tower Hamlets.[1] Observations of the mothers and their first-born children were made when the children were 20-weeks old, 14-months old, and 27-months old. At 27 months, the stage to be described here, the sample consisted of 69 mother–child pairs, 56 of whom had been observed in the home when the baby was 20-weeks old. Of the 69 mothers, 53 were married or cohabiting at the time of the screening interview (i.e., first prenatal clinic visit) and 16 were single. Their median age was 21 years. As judged by their husband's (or in the case of the single girls, their father's) occupation, 62 of the women belonged to Class III manual or below according to the Registrar General's classification and only 7 to Class III nonmanual or above. Of the 69 children, 36 were boys and 33 girls. Their birthweights ranged from 1730 gm to 4150 gm (median = 3170 gm), and only 5 out of the 69 had a birthweight lower than 2500 gm.

As the focus of the study was an attempt to identify factors that may lead to early psychiatric disturbance in young children, the observational sample was selected with an unduly high proportion of women who were thought (on the basis of the initial interview data) to be susceptible to later difficulties in childrearing. One of the factors included in this assessment was whether or not the woman herself had come from a disrupted family. For the purpose of this study, women were included in this category if, before the age of 16, they had been in the care of a local authority, and/or they had parents who had divorced or separated, or they had experienced the death of a parent. Of the 69 mothers in this observational subsample, 25 (36%) came from a disrupted family. This will be referred to as *the disrupted group;* the remainder (N = 44) as *the nondisrupted group.*

[1]Details of this study may be found in Wolkind, Hall, and Pawlby, 1977.

Procedure

AT 20 WEEKS

Details of the observations made of mothers and their babies in the home at 20-weeks-old are given in Wolkind, Hall, and Pawlby (1977) and Hall, Pawlby, and Wolkind (in press). Briefly, our results were drawn from a 25-min period of continuous event recording (100 15-sec intervals) made during the baby's awake, nonfeeding time. Both maternal and child behaviors were recorded during this period, occurring in a continual stream. A decoded record of such events during one 15-sec interval might read as follows: "Baby lying on back, facing mother, and within touching distance. Baby vocalizes. Mother looks at baby's face and speaks to her, picks her up, holds her on her lap, facing toward her but with no trunk contact, smiles and speaks to her and kisses her."

AT 27 MONTHS

When the children were 27-months old, the mothers were invited in pairs to bring their children to a playroom where they were observed, and the Reynell Developmental Language Scales, both Comprehension and Expressive, (Reynell, 1969), were given to each child in turn. These scales were administered to each child by the same observer (SJP) who was unaware of the back-

TABLE 4.1
Mean Frequencies and Standard Deviations with Which Each Maternal Behavior Category Was Observed at 20 Weeks

Maternal behavior category	Nondisrupted group (N = 48)		Disrupted group (N = 20)		Mann-Whitney "u" test (one-tailed)
	M	SD	M	SD	
Vocal acts	75.3	31.3	49.1	29.6	$z = 2.88$ $p = .002$
Noncaretaking touching	30.6	15.9	14.4	12.9	$z = 4.55$ $p < .001$
Looking	77.3	27.9	50.7	25.5	$z = 3.49$ $p < .001$
Presentation of objects	9.7	9.0	6.5	7.3	$z = 1.52$ $p = .06$
Smiling	19.7	11.5	16.5	13.1	$z = 1.52$ $p = .06$

ground history of the mother. Wherever possible the test was given without the mother being present. However, in 20 cases, the child was unwilling to leave his mother, and she was therefore allowed to be present in the room. On such occasions, the mother sat away from the child and was discouraged from participating in the test.

Raw scores were calculated on the Comprehension scale and on the Expressive scale. From these, standard scores were derived for each child, using Reynell's (1969) own standardization based on deviations from the mean for the child's chronological age at the time of the test. Separate standards are given for boys and girls. The findings presented here are based on these standard scores. The findings for the Comprehension scale and the Expressive scale are presented separately, although there was a correlation between the two for both sexes of .78. The children's scores on both scales were normally distributed around the mean given by Reynell for their age level.

RESULTS

At 20 Weeks

We have already shown (Hall, Pawlby, & Wolkind, in press; Wolkind, Hall, & Pawlby, 1977) from the observations made of the mother and baby when the babies were 20-weeks old that women in the disrupted group interacted significantly less with their babies compared with the nondisrupted group. Based on simple frequency counts, the disrupted group talked to their babies less than the nondisrupted group; touched them less; smiled at them less; looked at them less; presented objects to them less; and spent less time holding them or within reach or sight of them (Tables 4.1 and 4.2).

Further analyses at 20 weeks were carried out in an attempt to examine the mother's behavior relative to that of her baby from an interactional standpoint. The first analysis looked at the proportion of baby's acts directed toward the mother that elicited an immediate maternal response. A second analysis examined the proportion of baby's vocalizations (cry, fret, play noise, laugh) to which the mother responded immediately; and a third analysis examined the proportion of baby's vocalizations (this time excluding cry and fret) to which the mother's immediate response was a vocal one. In each case, it was found that the mothers in the disrupted group acted less contingently toward the activities of their babies when compared with mothers from the nondisrupted group (Table 4.3). At this stage, we found no differences in the frequency with which the babies of mothers from the disrupted group vocalized, cried, fretted, moved, or sucked objects when compared with the babies of mothers from the nondisrupted group.

TABLE 4.2
Mean Frequencies and Standard Deviations of the Number of 15-Sec Intervals Spent by the
Mother at Different Distances from the Baby at 20 Weeks

Distance of mother from baby	Nondisrupted group (N = 48)		Disrupted group (N = 20)		Mann-Whitney "u" test (one-tailed)
	M	SD	M	SD	
Baby out of sight	13.3	13.7	25.2	16.6	$z = -3.05$ $p = .001$
Baby held	33.9	19.1	24.4	15.8	$z = 1.83$ $p = .03$
Baby held or within reach	72.2	18.6	54.0	18.3	$z = 3.38$ $p < .001$
Baby held, within reach, or within sight	85.0	18.3	74.8	16.6	$z = 3.05$ $p = .001$

At 27 Months

The standard scores on the Reynell Comprehension Scale and on the
Expressive scale of the children from the disrupted group were compared with
those from the nondisrupted group. Table 4.4 gives the mean standard scores
and the standard deviations for each group.

A significant difference was found between the scores of the disrupted
group and those of the nondisrupted group on both the Comprehension scale

TABLE 4.3
Proportion of Baby's Acts at 20 Weeks Responded to Contingently by Mother

Contingency measure	Nondisrupted group (N = 48)		Disrupted group (N = 20)		Mann-Whitney "u" test (one-tailed)
	M	SD	M	SD	
Proportion of baby's attributed acts responded to by mother	61.4	14.5	51.2	15.9	$z = 2.43$ $p < .01$
Proportion of baby's cry, fret, laugh, play noise responded to by mother	25.0	13.4	18.2	16.0	$z = 2.13$ $p < .02$
Proportion of baby's laugh, play noise responded to by mother's vocal act	25.2	13.9	17.9	18.1	$z = 2.52$ $p = .01$

TABLE 4.4
Standard Scores on the Reynell Language Scales

	Nondisrupted group (N = 44)		Disrupted group (N = 25)		t test (two-tailed) df = 67
	M	SD	M	SD	
Comprehension scale	1.0	1.42	−0.2	1.15	3.45*
Expressive scale	0.7	1.29	−0.3	1.41	2.76**

*p = .001
**p < .01

and the Expressive scale. In both cases, the disrupted group scored significantly lower than the nondisrupted group. Further examination, using χ^2 tests, revealed no significant difference between the disrupted group and the nondisrupted group in social class, marital status of the mother, complications of pregnancy, smoking during pregnancy, or attitude toward motherhood.

However, as in the larger epidemiological sample (Wolkind, 1977; Wolkind, Kruk, & Chaves, 1976) there was a relationship in this sample between disruption in a mother's family of origin and her age at the time of pregnancy. Those women in the disrupted group were more likely than those in the nondisrupted group to be under 20-years old at the time of the prenatal interview given when the women were 7-months pregnant ($X^2 = 4.49$; $p < .05$). Although not statistically significant, mothers in the disrupted group tended to have babies of lower birthweight than mothers in the nondisrupted group (3050 gm versus 3212 gm; $t(67) = 1.31$; $p < .20$). Because both age of the mother and the child's birthweight have been related in other studies to the child's later cognitive ability, an analysis of variance, controlling for the effect of maternal age and for birthweight, was performed. The results still show a significant difference, independent of maternal age and birthweight, between the scores of the disrupted group and the nondisrupted group on both the Comprehension scale ($F = 6.8$, $p = .01$) and on the Expressive scale ($F = 5.9$, $p < .02$). The effect of maternal age on the child's scores was less clear cut than that of whether or not the mother came from a disrupted family of origin.

A marginally significant difference, independent of disruption and birthweight, was found only for the Comprehension scale ($F = 3.5$, $p = .06$), showing that the children of mothers, who were under 20-years old at the time of the prenatal interview, scored less well on the Comprehension scale of the Reynell Test. However, on the Expressive scale, there was no significant difference, when disruption and birthweight were controlled for, between the scores of children of teenage mothers and those of mothers who were age 20 or over. There was no significant interaction between the factors of disruption and maternal age on either language scale. The results of the analysis of variance also show that, as in other studies, birthweight, in this case independent of family disruption and maternal age, was significantly related to the child's scores on both the Comprehension scale ($F = 5.4$, $p = .02$) and on the Expressive scale ($F = 5.8$, $p < .02$). The lower the birthweight, the lower the child's scores on both scales of the language test. As the results are based on Reynell's standard scores, which take account of the sex of the child, it is not surprising to find that sex had no significant effect on the child's scores on either scale of the language test.

Findings at 20 Weeks versus Findings at 27 Months

Of the 69 children who were successfully given the Reynell language test at 27 months, 56 had been observed in the home with their mothers at 20 weeks. Using Kendall's T, a number of significant positive correlations were found between the frequency with which the mother interacted with her baby at 20 weeks and the child's later scores on both the Comprehension and Expressive scales of the Reynell language test. The more frequently a mother touched,

TABLE 4.5
Correlations between Maternal Behavior at 20 Weeks and Child's Reynell Scores at 27 Months

	Reynell standard scores					
	Comprehension			Expression		
Behavior category at 20 weeks	Group (N = 56)	Girls (N = 27)	Boys (N = 29)	Group (N = 56)	Girls (N = 27)	Boys (N = 29)
Mothers' vocal acts	.10	.23*	−.09	.12	.34**	−.11
Mothers' noncaretaking touching	.17*	.24*	.06	.24***	.24*	.22*
Mothers' looking	.12	.33**	−.09	.15*	.35***	−.01
Mothers' presentation of objects	.15*	.24*	.05	.25***	.36***	.14
Mothers' smiling	.16*	.40***	−.07	.12	.34**	−.04
Proportion of baby's attributed acts responded to by mother	.12	.24*	.02	.09	.26**	−.08
Proportion of baby's cry, fret, laugh, play noise responded to by mother	.09	.24*	−.09	.01	.23*	−.17
Proportion of baby's laugh, play noise responded to by mothers vocal act	.12	.22	−.01	.04	.27**	−.14

*$p ⋜ .10$
**$p ⋜ .05$
***$p ⋜ .01$ (Kendall's T, two-tailed tests).

smiled at, or presented objects to her baby, the higher the child's scores on the Comprehension scale. Similarly, the more frequently a mother touched, looked at, or presented objects to her baby, the higher the child's scores on the Expressive scale. However, further analysis by sex shows that, although significant positive correlations exist between the frequency and contingency of *every* maternal interaction measure with her 20-week-old daughter and the child's later language scores, there is no overall pattern of correlation for mothers and their sons. Indeed, for boys there is only one weakly significant positive correlation between the frequency with which mothers touched their sons at 20 weeks and the son's later score on the Expressive scale of the Reynell language test (Table 4.5). There were no significant effects of sex in the frequency with which the mothers engaged in any of the activities measured at 20 weeks.

DISCUSSION

The findings presented suggest that, by simple questioning of a woman antenatally about her own family background, we may be able to identify a group of women whose children will show delays in language and speech development by the age of 27 months.

In our sample as a whole, equal numbers of children scored above and below the mean given by Reynell for their age level, despite the fact that ours is an almost totally working-class sample. However, of the children of mothers in the disrupted group, 18 of 25 (72%) scored below the mean for their age level (Reynell, 1969) on the Comprehension scale versus 11 of 44 (25%) children of mothers in the nondisrupted group. Similarly for the Expressive scale, 14 (56%) of the children of mothers in the disrupted group had scores below the mean for their age level, compared with only 9 (20%) of those of mothers in the nondisrupted group.

This finding is important because other studies suggest that language delays at 2–3 years are likely to be followed by delays in other areas later on. However, it is not sufficient merely to be aware that children of mothers from disrupted families are more likely to be delayed in language development at 2 years of age than those whose mothers do not come from such a background. It is also necessary to seek an explanation for the delay.

One clue is provided by our earlier findings, which showed that mothers in the disrupted group interact much less with their babies at 20 weeks than do mothers in the non-disrupted group. Further findings from the longitudinal study showed that a mother's level of interaction with her baby is, in turn, related to her child's later linguistic competence, though in our study this is primarily only true for girls. Significant positive correlations were found for girls between the frequency with which their mothers spoke to them, touched them, looked at them, presented objects to them, smiled at them, and acted contingently towards the girls' own activities at 20 weeks, and the girls' language and speech performance at 27 months. For boys, however, there was only one significant correlation between the frequency of maternal behavior toward the baby at 20 weeks and later language development. A positive relationship was found between the frequency with which mothers touched their sons at 20 weeks and the boys' scores on the Expressive scale of the language test at 27 months.

Several other reports from longitudinal studies have found specific relationships between various indices of maternal care and later intellectual development. Many of these have found sex-related differences most frequently with stronger correlations between mothers and their daughters than between mothers and their sons. Both Kagan (1971) and Moss (1967) suggest from their data that girls are more susceptible than boys to maternal or environmental influence. On the other hand, Clarke-Stewart's findings (1973) appear to show an opposite trend. Her figures show that, where there were sex-related differences in correlations between early maternal behavior and later cognitive, language, social, and emotional measures in the child, they tended to be lower for girls. However, the differences were slight, and she concluded that, at the age in her study (9–18 months), there were no real sex-related differences in the effect of maternal behavior. Yarrow, Goodwin, Manheimer, and Milow (1974) in a longitudinal study of adopted children, related several dimensions of maternal care by adoptive parents at 6 months to the child's WISC IQ score at 10 years. They found that physical contact, appropriateness of stimulation, responsiveness of the mother to the infants' attempts at communication, the degree to which she individualized the infant (i.e., saw him as a differentiated, unique person), the depth of emotional involvement of the mother with the child, and the degree to which she expressed positive affect toward the infant were all related to IQ at 10 years. However, although the correlations between the variables and IQ were positive for both boys and girls, they were only significant for boys. More recently, Blurton Jones, Ferreira, Brown, and Macdonald (in preparation), working with middle-class mothers, have also found that a child's performance on the Reynell language scales at 21 months and at 27 months, and on the Stanford-Binet IQ test at 39 months, was positively correlated with measures of maternal responsiveness to her child's vocalizations at 15 months. They found "similar" patterns of correlations for both boys and girls.

There seems to be little doubt from these studies that early maternal behavior is an important contributor to the cognitive development of the child. The precise nature of the relationship seems, however, to differ—depending to a large extent on the age under investigation and on the particular measures of maternal and infant functioning assessed. For example, Dunn (1977) found no relationship between her simple frequency measures of maternal responsiveness made during the first year and IQ as measured with the Stanford-Binet Test at 4½ years. It was only when she adopted a more subtle qualitative measure of maternal "acceptance" in response to the child's vocalizations that she found a positive correlation with IQ scores.

In our study, our initial analyses of maternal behavior toward the baby at 20 weeks were based on simple frequency counts of the number of times each mother engaged in each behavior item (Wolkind, Hall, & Pawlby, 1977). However, more detailed analyses, taking into account the appropriateness and the contingent nature of the mother's behavior toward her baby's behavior, did not prove to be any more sensitive in predicting either boys' or girls' language scores at 27 months (see Table 4.5).

Our results strongly support the view that, for girls, the low level of interaction provided by mothers from the disrupted group at 20 weeks is in some way related to poor language development at 27 months. However, for boys the picture is less clear as it seems unlikely that the one maternal behavior (that of noncaretaking touch at 20 weeks), which relates to Reynell scores, can be a principal determinant of the boys' language development at 27 months. It is, however, interesting to note that Moss (1967) found that mothers behave differently toward their 3-month-old boys and girls, tending to provide more "tactile and visual stimulation" for boys and tending to "imitate" girls more. Moss, Robson, and Pederson (1969) go on to show that a rating of the animation of the mother's voice during a pregnancy interview was associated mainly with providing "social affectionate stimulation" to boys at 3 months and "stimulation of the distance receptors (visual and auditory)" for girls. Similarly, Lewis (1972) found that mothers of 3-month-old boys held, touched, and rocked them more, whereas mothers of girls vocalized and looked at them more frequently. Not only did Lewis find sex-related differences in the frequency with which mothers interacted with their infants, but, in carrying out detailed interactional analyses, he revealed important differences in the pattern of interaction between mothers of girls versus boys. In particular, he suggests that a girl infant's vocalizations are more likely to be associated with maternal vocalization (i.e., when a boy is vocalizing, it is equally likely that his mother is holding him or vocalizing, whereas, when a girl is vocalizing, her mother is most likely vocalizing as well). As Lewis points out, the potential consequence of this difference for subsequent language and cognitive development is considerable. Such very detailed interactional analyses are unfortunately beyond the scope of our present study.

We found no significant sex-related differences in the overall frequency with which mothers engaged in the various behavior items at 20 weeks nor in the contingent nature of their behavior in relation to that of the baby. However, we did find that, whereas for girls, mothers in the disrupted group differed from the nondisrupted group on all 20-week behavior items, for boys, mothers in the disrupted group only differed from the nondisrupted group in the frequency of noncaretaking touching activities. It may be that this means of stimulation, as both Moss (1967) and Lewis (1972) found, is preferred by mothers of boys at 20 weeks, and that where such stimulation is lacking (as is the case for the mothers of boys in the disrupted group), it reflects a more general lack of appropriate responsiveness toward the baby. This is also illustrated in our questionnaire data. In response to the question asked at 20 weeks, "It takes a bit of time to begin to see a baby as a person—do you feel that yet?" the mothers of boys in the disrupted group were significantly less likely to answer positively than the mothers of boys in the nondisrupted group.

Although our findings do suggest that a mother's early level of interaction bears an important relationship to her daughter's later linguistic ability at 27 months, we are unable to show that the same relationship exists for boys. Nevertheless, in our study boys were not found to have disproportionately lower scores on the Language scale at 27 months. We are thus forced to conclude either that boys learn to talk by some different pathway from girls, or, alternatively, and probably more likely, that similar mechanisms are operative for both boys and girls. Our attempts have so far failed to pinpoint this. More detailed microanalytic interaction studies along the lines described by Lewis (1972), Stern, Beebe, Jaffe, and Bennett (1977) and Bruner (1977), with a follow-up from infancy into early and even later childhood, may help to shed light on the complex nature of the mechanisms involved in determining how a child learns to speak. We should also add here that our study only looks at the mother's interaction with her child. The critical variable for a boy's language development may be his *father's* level of interaction and contingent responsiveness.

Whatever factors prove to be important in determining a child's language skills, the finding from our study remains that both boys *and* girls whose mothers come from disrupted families tend to be delayed in their language development at 27 months. It is not yet possible to say from our study whether this delay in language will, in fact, persist, or whether it will be related to delays or difficulties in other areas of the child's development. Other research, however, points in this direction. Studies by Frommer and O'Shea found that among women who reported difficulties with their children during the first year (1973a), or whose children had been referred to a day center for disturbed preschool children (1973b), an unduly high proportion reported separations from one or both of their own parents, often in the context of family disharmony. These findings suggest, along with ours, that where a woman has herself been deprived of a stable, loving relationship within her family of origin, she, in turn, finds it difficult to provide her own child with the adequate mothering necessary for the emotional, social, and intellectual needs of a young child.

SUMMARY

As part of an ongoing study of British-born mothers and their first babies in a London Borough, a subsample was included in an observational study. Using ethological techniques, observations were made of mothers and their children in their homes when the children were aged 20 weeks, 14 months, and 27 months. At 27 months, 72 mothers were also invited, in pairs, to bring their children to a playgroup where they were again observed (69 of the children were successfully given the Reynell Developmental Language Scales). Earlier findings (Wolkind et al., 1977; Hall, Pawlby, Wolkind, in press) showed that those women who came from a disrupted family interacted much less with their babies at 20 weeks than those women without such a background. At 27 months, the children of those mothers from the disrupted group scored significantly lower than the children of mothers from the nondisrupted group on both the Comprehension and Expressive scales of the Reynell language test. Sex-related correlations were found between the frequency with which a mother interacted with her 20-week-old baby and the child's later language and speech development. Our findings suggest that knowledge of a women's background may be a useful factor in identifying a group of babies at risk for interaction deficits which may lead to poor language development for the child.

REFERENCES

Bax, M. C. O., & Hart, H. Health needs of pre-school children. *Archives of Disease in Childhood,* 1976, *51,* 848–852.

Bernstein, B. A sociolinguistic approach to social learning. In J. Gould, (Ed.), *Penguin Survey of the Social Sciences.* Baltimore, Maryland: Penguin, 1965.

Blurton Jones, N., Rosetti Ferreira, M. C., Brown, M. F., & Macdonald, L. *Language development and mother's response to child vocalisations: Influence of child's simultaneous behavior.* In preparation.

Brodbeck, A. J., & Irwin, O. C. The speech behaviour of infants without families. *Child Development,* 1946, *17,* 145.

Bruner, J. A. Early social interaction and language acquisition. In H. R. Schaffer (Ed.), *Studies in mother–infant interaction.* New York: Academic Press, 1977.

Chomsky, N. *Aspects of the theory of syntax.* Cambridge, Massachusetts: M.I.T. Press, 1965.

Clarke-Stewart, K. A. Interactions between mothers and their young children: characteristics and consequences. *Monographs of the Society for Research in Child Development,* 1973, *38* (No. 6–7).

Crellin, E., Pringle, M. L. K., & West, P. *Born illegitimate: Social and educational implications.* Windsor, England: National Foundation for Educational Research, 1971.

Davie, R., Butler, N., & Goldstein, H. *From birth to seven.* London: National Children's Bureau, 1972.

Douglas, J. W. B. *The home and the school.* London: MacGibbon & Kee, 1964.

Douglas, J. W. B., Ross, J. M., & Simpson, H. R. *All our future.* London: Peter Davies, 1968.

Dunn, J. B. Patterns of early interaction: Continuities and consequences. In H. R. Schaffer (Ed.), *Studies in mother–infant interaction.* New York: Academic Press, 1977.

Frommer, E. A., & O'Shea, G. The importance of childhood experience in relation to problems of marriage and family building. *British Journal of Psychiatry,* 1973, *123,* 157–160.

Frommer, E., & O'Shea, G. Antenatal identification of women liable to have problems managing their children. *British Journal of Psychiatry,* 1975, *123,* 149–156.

Hall, F., Pawlby, S. J., & Wolkind, S. N. Early life experiences and later mothering behavior: a study of mothers and their 20-week old babies. In D. Schaffer & J. B. Dunn (Ed.), *The first year of life.* New York: Wiley, in press.

Hess, R., & Shipman, V. C. *Influences upon early learning.* In R. D. Hess & R. M. Bear (Eds.), Chicago: Aldine, 1966.

Hirsch, K. de. A review of early language development. *Developmental Medicine and Child Neurology,* 1970, *12,* 87–97.

Illsley, R. Family growth and its effect on the relationship between obstetric factors and child functioning. In R. Platt & A. S. Parkes (Eds.), *Social and genetic influences on life and death.* Edinburgh: Oliver & Boyd, 1967.

Ingram, T. T. S. In F. A. Young & D. B. Lindsley (Eds.), *Early experience and visual information processing in perceptual and reading disorders.* Washington, D.C.: National Academy of Sciences, 1970.

Kagan, J. *Change and continuity in infancy.* New York: Wiley, 1971.

Lewis, M. State as an infant-environment interaction: An analysis of mother–infant interaction as a function of sex. *Merrill-Palmer Quarterly,* 1972, *18,* 95–121.

Lewis, M. M. *Language, thought and personality in infancy and childhood.* London: Harrap, 1963.

Moss, H. A. Sex, age and state as determinants of mother-infant interaction. *Merrill-Palmer Quarterly,* 1967, *13,* 19–36.

Moss, H. A., Robson, K. S., & Pedersen, F. Determinants of maternal stimulation of infants and consequences of treatment for later reactions to strangers. *Developmental Psychology,* 1969, *1,* 239–246.

Oppel, W. C., & Royston, A. E. Teenage births: Some social, psychological and physical sequelae. *American Journal of Public Health,* 1971, *61,* 751–756.

Provence, S., & Lipton, R. *Infants in institutions.* New York: International Univ. Press, 1962.

Record, R. G., McKeown, T., & Edwards, J. H. The relation of measured intelligence to birth order and maternal age. *Annals of Human Genetics,* 1969, *33,* 61–69.

Reynell, J. K. *Reynell Developmental Language Scales. Experimental Edition.* Windsor, England: National Foundation for Educational Research, 1969.

Richman, N., & Stevenson, J. Language delay in 3-year-olds: Family and social factors. *Acta Paediatrica Belgium,* 1977, *30,* 213–219.

Rutter, M., Tizard, J., & Whitmore, K. *Education, health and behaviour.* London: Longmans, 1970.

Snow, C. E. Mothers speech in three social classes. *Journal of Psycholinguistic Research,* 1976, *5,* 1–19.

Stern, D. N., Beebe, B., Jaffe, J., & Bennett, S. L. The infant's stimulus world during social interaction: a study of caregiver behavior with particular reference to repetition and timing. In H. R. Schaffer (Ed.), *Studies in mother–infant interaction.* New York: Academic Press, 1977.

Wolkind, S. N. Women who have been "in care"—psychological and social status during pregnancy. *Journal of Child Psychology and Psychiatry,* 1977, *18,* 179–182.

Wolkind, S. N., Kruk, S., & Chaves, L. P. Childhood separation experiences and psycho-social status in primiparous women: Preliminary findings. *British Journal of Psychiatry,* 1976, *128,* 391–396.

Wolkind, S. N., Hall, F., & Pawlby, S. J. Individual differences in mothering behaviour: a combined epidemiological and observational approach. In P. J. Graham (Ed.), *Epidemiological approaches in child psychiatry.* New York: Academic Press, 1977.

Yarrow, L. J., Goodwin, M. S., Manheimer, H., & Milow, I. D. Infant experiences and cognitive and personality development at ten years. In L. J. Stone, H. T. Smith, & L. B. Murphy, (Eds.), *The competent infant.* Tavistock Pub. Ltd., 1974.

PART II

INFANTS AT RISK
FOR DEVELOPMENT OF
AUTISTIC DISTURBANCES

CHAPTER 5

HENRY N. MASSIE

Pathological Interactions in Infancy

We are presently at an important historical moment in the field of child psychiatry and child development research when we can begin to describe specific pathological interactions that occur between a mother and infant in relatively precise, behavioral terms. In the past, deviant parenting has been understood in a more holistic fashion. That is, traditionally we have known that there are profoundly detrimental consequences for a child's psychological growth if any of several kinds of things befall it in infancy. These are as follows:

1. The child loses its mother permanently or for an extended period of time through death of the mother, abandonment, or illness.
2. The child's primary caregiver is often absent, inattentive, or uninterested in the baby, as occurs sometimes in situations with depressed, physically absent, or self-involved parents.
3. The parents are physically abusive to the infant.
4. The child has no one primary caregiver but a shifting kaleidoscope of caregivers as with institutionalized or foster children.
5. The parents overcontrol their infants—out of their need for a symbiotic union with their offspring or out of other anxieties related to giving children freedom—and refuse to allow them the steps toward separation and individuation.

79

HIGH-RISK INFANTS AND CHILDREN:
Adult and Peer Interactions

ISBN 0-12-255550-3

In the last few years research in child development and infant psychiatry has taken a closer look at some of the traumatic events in early childhood and described them more precisely. Such a precise description of the phenomenology of pathological Parent–Child interactions in infancy must pay attention to a group of core phenomena. These are the major modalities of mother–infant bonding: (a) eye gaze, (b) touching, (c) holding and clinging, (d) feeding, (e) vocalizing, and (f) affective reciprocity. Affective reciprocity is a phenomenon at a somewhat different level of abstraction than the other modalities. However, examination of mother-infant pairs suggests that mutual responsiveness to the displays of affect by the one to the other is an extremely critical developmental process. Such affective interaction may well come to be understood as a mode of bonding that is virtually as concrete as the other modalities. Each of the six modalities is comprised of eight behavioral components or parameters. These can be expressed as investigational questions:

1. What is the *timing* (rhythm of interaction) between mother and infant?
2. Who *initiates* an action; mother or child?
3. How is an interaction *maintained*?
4. How are interactions *terminated*?
5. What are the *spatial relationships* of the partners in an interaction?
6. What kind of *bodily shaping* or morphologic configuration exists during an interaction? For example, do parent and child mold awkwardly or smoothly to each other?
7. What is the *physical force* exerted by the participants? Is a partner aggressive, coercive, demanding, limp, or apathetic?
8. What is the affective *interchange* between partners? Does it seem reciprocal, synchronous, unconnected, or divergent? Simply stated, are the parent's affect and responses in general empathic with the child's?

In addition, comprehensive research cannot stop at just describing the components of bonding, for these are basically descriptions of surface or observable phenomena. There must also be consideration of an added dimension—that of the intrapsychic processes of mother and infant that underlie overt behaviors. Though more inscrutable to measurement, key intrapsychic processes are the child's development of self and object representation during the course of the basic individuation from the mother in the first 2 years of life.

Careful study of these components and the intrapsychic dimension goes beyond the more global—yet nonetheless profoundly productive—approaches to charting Parent–Infant pathological interactions which had largely characterized the field of child psychiatry until the last 15 years. However, along the path toward more precise delineations of deviance, there have been several contributions to our present level of understanding. René Spitz in his landmark book *The first year of life* (Spitz & Cobliner, 1965) described six pathological patterns of mothering that he had observed. He attempted to link the patterns of parenting to specific psychogenetically determined abnormalities in the infant. Over time, we have learned that Spitz's particular clinical characterizations do not necessarily lead to the predicted infantile pathology he described; nor do the particular psychogenic infantile disease states always have the pathologic pattern of mothering in their background. Nonetheless, Spitz's observations are very valuable because they advanced our sensitivity to aberrant Mother–Infant interaction, and sometimes are, in fact, connected with the developmental disturbances he outlined. The pathologic patterns of mothering observed by Spitz were (a) primary passive rejection of the child by the mother leading to coma in the newborn; (b) maternal, primary, anxious overpermissiveness leading to the syndrome of 3-month colic; (c) hostility in the guise of anxiety that was connected with infantile eczema; (e) maternal oscillation between pampering and hostility that led to infantile hypermotility (rocking); (d) cyclical mood swings in a mother that were connected with fecal play by the child; and (e) maternal hostility that was consciously compensated and linked to a young child's hyperaggressiveness.

Spitz's clinical descriptions go well beyond the more global categorizations such as child abandonment, abuse, or neglect. For example, a case of maternal, primary, passive rejection is described in the following way:

> During nursing the mother behaved as if her infant were completely alien to her and not a living being at all. Her behavior consisted in a withdrawing from the baby, her body, her hands, and face rigid and tense. The nipples, though not inverted, were not protruding and nursing did not appear to provoke turgor [Spitz & Cobliner, 1965, p. 2].

In a similar vein, Benjamin and Tennes (1958) described an unusual case of a mother and child with whom they had some longitudinal contact. The child at 6 months began to respond to the approach of strangers with a vigorous, abnormal, upward and downward head nodding that appeared very much like an autistic stereotypy. The authors felt that the behavior was traceable to an earlier pathological feeding situation. The child had a somewhat weak rooting reflex, and the mother appeared remote, holding the infant "low on her lap for feeding, sufficiently away from her body in such a way as to cause Sammy's head to bob up and down rhythmically, with each of her arm-wrist movements."

Another pioneering illustration of the movement toward more exact understanding of pathologic Mother–Infant interaction is provided in Justin Call's (1963) case study descriptively titled "Interlocking affective freeze between an autistic child and his 'as-if' mother." Call had first contact with Glen, the child in the case, when he was 2½-years old and suffering from autistic withdrawal, failure of speech development, and stereotypic mannerisms. One of Call's initial impressions was that physical contact between mother and child did not occur. However, the relationship between the two was not an indifferent one, for the "interaction between Glen and his mother was subtly regulated on both sides by unacknowledged safeguards against physical contact, spontaneity, surprise, enjoyment."[1] Extended and intensive psychoanalytically informed treatment of both mother and child led Call to conceptualize the case as a "failure of appropriate affective communication of the mother with her child and a resultant failure of the child to develop an appropriate affective life and object relations [p. 323]."

The mother's psychotherapy revealed some of the roots of her disturbed responses to the child. She recalled in therapy how when she tried to breast feed her newborn, she had

> The feeling of being deprived of her own body substance, and in one hour remembered the feeling of shriveling up and dying as she was breast feeding her infant. The fact that Glen was a male child was of great importance. She had not only been emptied out but she had lost a fantasied penis and now she must contend with one on the outside belonging to someone else, just as she earlier had been faced with such feelings of annihilistic rage toward her [sadistic and domineering] father . . . it has become clear to Mrs. L. that she had to put distance between her and the infant in order to prevent her from expressing impulses of cannibalism and castration [toward her child] [p. 332].

Ultimately, many years of treatment led both mother and child to make relatively normal noninstitutional adjustments to life.

These kinds of case studies make clear that it is very important to be knowledgeable about the particular manifestations and range of pathological Mother–Infant interactions. Such awareness on the part of child-care workers, pediatricians, nurses, and consulting psychiatrists and psychologists will make possible the earliest therapeutic interventions with parent–child dyads that are behaviorally aberrant. In addition, awareness of subtle interactional pathology also guides the therapeutic endeavor. That is, one way to determine the end point of an intervention with a mother and baby is to assess whether the core components of bonding previously outlined have approached a normal configuration.

My own research (Massie, 1975, 1977, 1978a,b) has uncovered several additional pathological Parent–Infant interactions. The remainder of this chapter will list and describe these. In effect, I am attempting to develop a lexicon with sharply defined descriptions of some of the most severe kinds of parenting disturbances. Data for such a lexicon have come from clinical work with parents and children—often augmented by close analysis of films of the mother and child employing slow motion and frame-by-frame projection—and from the Early Natural History of Childhood Psychosis Project.

[1] Extract from Call, J., Interlocking affective freeze between an autistic child and his "as-if" mother, *Journal of the American Academy of Child Psychiatry*, 1963, 2, 319–344. Reprinted by permission of International Universities Press, Inc.

In this project, I and my associates collected and studied 25 sets of home movies that parents had made of their infants between 1972-1977. What was unusual about these films was that the children had subsequently developed one of the forms of early childhood psychosis: autism, symbiotic psychosis of childhood, childhood psychosis, or childhood schizophrenia. We had obtained the films by approaching treatment centers, therapists, and parent groups of already diagnosed children suffering the profound symptoms of the different syndromes. Thus, the home movies functioned as a prospective-like data base to which we applied a variety of studies. These were a study of the Mother-Infant interaction in infancy prior to the onset of recognizable symptoms of psychosis; a delineation of the earliest signs and symptoms of psychotic disturbance in children; attention to signs of the constitutional qualities and signs of organically based motor developmental disturbance; and a delineation of mother-infant reciprocal attachment and ratings of the relative strength and/or avoidance of bonding in the first 6 months of life. The films were analyzed by three judges who were "blind" to whether the films were of index or control group (i.e., normal) children. There was also a Piagetian-based analysis of sensorimotor development as portrayed in the films of the psychotic and normal children.

The findings from these studies are reported in detail in the previously cited publications. I will focus on what the project, as well as other clinical research experience, have contributed to understanding pathological Parent-Infant interactions. To do this, I am going to enumerate on a series of paradigmatic aberrent Parent-Infant interactions that the investigations have identified. The cases appear paradigmatic because they embody deviance in a striking fashion in several of the core components of Mother-Infant interaction when compared to control films and to clinical experience in pediatric and child-care settings. As a group, the family that made home movies of "psychotic-to-be" children seemed to contain more of these disturbed interactions than appeared in normal families, but generally in not so striking a form as the cases I have selected as instructional models. Extremes of deviance help clarify critical developmental issues and communicate the quality of the less extreme disturbances that occur in many other families.

Most of the paradigmatic Parent-Infant interactions involve mothers and infants filmed by fathers as women were the primary caregivers of the infants—not that the mothers and their children exist in isolation from their families of origin, husbands, or partners. However, the mother's behavior with her child partially reflects the absence of support from her spouse. Therefore, a husband's criticism can severely impair a mother's capacity to parent. Furthermore, the mother's actions with her baby are critically determined by the positive and negative identification she has made in childhood with her parents, by her own internal self-representation, and by culturally advocated child-rearing customs to which she is exposed.

The first six of the nine illustrative cases following were selected because they highlight a pattern of pathology in one of the major modalities of bonding. The analyses of the cases attempt to look at how the components of bonding (e.g., rhythm, force) are disturbed. Case 7 is an illustration of parental interference with the autonomy of infant twin sisters, which functioned to impair their bonding across several modalities. It is included not because it is particularly instructive with regard to attachment phenomena, but because autism was the outcome for one sister, whereas the other sister was spared major psychiatric illness.

Additionally, in Case 7 we observed parents especially thwarting the infants' attempts at oral gratification. Traditional psychoanalytic theory has conceptualized orality as the primary libidinal impulse of infancy. Newer infancy research gives an added perspective on this and allows us to understand oral gratification as a central experience of the feeding modality of bonding while seeing it also as just one of the principal ways in which the baby bonds. Whenever any of the impulses toward bonding are consummated, it is likely that the baby experiences a pleasurable affect, as well as a transient establishment of physiologic homeostasis.

Case 8 addresses itself most particularly to the aforementioned dimension of the mother's intrapsychic experience. Here, the mother was present and went through the motions of parenting. However, due to her own self-involvement, she was unable to bring a sense of life to her interactions with her baby resulting in an experience of parental absence for the child. Case 9 is a discussion of the psychoanalytic treatment of an adult suffering from a narcissistic and obsessional character disorder. It does not contain direct observational data from infancy, but it is included because it provides a great deal of information that will assist us in hypothesizing how pathologic Parent–Infant interactions may be reflected in adult neurotic constellations.

In each of the case vignettes, there is a progression from the description of the parent–infant relational pathology to the *experiential outcome* of the child that may be linked with the disturbance in bonding, its components, and the allied internal affective states. For example, the experiential outcome for the baby may be a state of being over-controlled or of being alone or abandoned. Finally, there is the description of the subsequent psychopathology of the now older children and their diagnoses which reflect their emotional state and their overtly disturbed behavior.

This chapter's approach to conceptualizing data in this manner is exploratory. The linkages between pathologic bonding, outcome, and affective states is not precise and cannot be neatly followed through in each case because there is not sufficient information or understanding of these connections. Furthermore, there is an attempt in the examples to connect observationally derived infancy data with subsequent information about the child's or adult's fantasy life and symptomatology. This is an attempt to draw together some of the specific observations relating to pathologic bonding with existing psychodynamic and psychoanalytic theory. It is an important venture because these bodies of clinical knowledge represent our most potent therapeutic allies as well as our most complete understanding of the patient's experience of already established illness. However, the leap between seeing pathologic bonding interactions in infancy and integrating them into psychodynamic formulations of psychiatric illness is a difficult one that may be imperfectly made here.

As with Spitz's descriptions of disturbed mothering, we cannot say that the following descriptions of pathologic parent-infant behavior were the sole or most important determinants of the psychopathologic outcome in a given child. Our careful study of the cases suggest that there is a potential connection. However, the disturbed interactions are not a precise predictor of the same outcome in another mother–infant pair that may share a similar relationship in infancy. A different child, for example, would bring to the relationship a different spectrum of constitutional strengths and possible organic vulnerabilities. Furthermore, a different mother–child pair, although possibly interacting similarly to some of the cases in this report, would be exposed to other influences that might include stabilizing husbands and grandparents.

CASE 1: INTERFERENCE WITH EYE GAZE: MATERNAL AVOIDANCE

In the films of Joan, we observed an interaction between mother and infant at 4 months. The mother was holding the baby comfortably in her arms at shoulder level. Joan smiled and turned her head toward her mother's face and also shifted her eyes toward the mother. However, the mother blocked Joan's head from turning with the side of her own head. As Joan gave up the attempt to make eye contact with the mother, mother started to nuzzle Joan, which again elicited the baby's smile and turn toward the mother's face which mother again blocked. As the child lost its smile, an expression of perplexity appeared on the infant's face which just as quickly was erased in favor of a pleasurable affect when the mother patted Joan's head. This started the cycle over again, but after the third failure to make eye contact, Joan's expression lapsed into dejection and depression. The mother had remained smiling throughout. Each turn to the mother lasted about 3 sec, and the entire episode covered approximately 20 sec.

This Mother–Infant interaction—aberrant because it was not observed in any control films—was not an isolated instance. For example, prior to the birth of Joan, a film of the mother showed avoidance of eye contact with her father-in-law during a brief embrace, and there were no scenes of mother looking at the baby while holding her close to her chest, although the baby attempted to initiate eye contact. Finally, when the mother brought her child, then 4-years-old, for treatment, the mother did not make eye contact with the staff.

After 6 months of age, Joan was no longer looking at her mother, and by the second year of life, she had clear symptoms of profound autism (e.g., rituals, rocking, twirling, speech failure, and lack of interaction with people). This case is being emphasized, not because of a possible connection between the autistic symptom formation and earlier parenting, but because of the parental interference with the bonding modality of eye gaze. This was most prominent, but it also carried with it a failure on the mother's part to acknowledge and reciprocate the infant's affect that accompanied the baby's attempts to look at the mother's face.

If we consider the components of the social interaction, it is clear that the mother and child had established a markedly aberrant rhythm with each other. The mother did not know how to entrain with the child's social behavior so as to maintain it. Rather, the mother avoided it, leading to what must have been for the child an experience of maternal avoidance. Internally, the mother had struggled for many years with mistrust of people and anger at the overwhelming behavior of her own parents, which we know from her history. The intra-psychic experience of autism for Joan may well have been a withdrawal from a confusing and perplexing interpersonal world where inborn, biologically based rules of social behavior, as well as subsequent emotional impulses toward contact, were sublty thwarted.

CASE 2: INTERFERENCE WITH BODY CONTACT AND HOLDING: MATERNAL AVOIDANCE

Amy was a somewhat subdued infant with a very confused mother. The mother had always doubted herself, but her self-esteem was further depreciated by a hostile mother-in-law who lived in the same house and a husband who did not support her against the attacks of the mother-in-law. The films of Amy's infancy revealed a mother who held the infant in the first weeks of life facing outward, awkwardly strapped to her torso with her forearm. Amy was not supported from below, and could only hang limply over her mother's forearm with a view of the floor. There were no scenes of comfortable chest–chest contact.

Later scenes of Amy and her mother showed how the interference with holding reappeared, though somewhat altered and elaborated under different circumstances. For example at 6 months while seated in an infant seat, the baby arched her chest toward her mother who remained inflexible; there was no movement of her thorax toward Amy. Amy brought her hand to rest on her mother's blouse while the mother's hand touched the plastic infant seat. Nonetheless, mother and child did engage in fond smiling and gazing. Another example occurred at 9 months when the mother tried to walk Amy forward, supporting her from behind at the grandmother's instigation. Amy was too young to support herself and tried, in anguish, to grasp hold of the mother who did not notice or give body support, but continued to walk her forward. A final illustration of this form of pathological parent–child contact occurred at 18 months. Amy was distressed. The mother rather remotely placed her on her knees but established no further contact. It remained for Amy to throw herself against her mother's chest.

In this case, then, there were interferences across many parameters— timing, initiation, spatial relations, and configuration or bodily shaping of the mother's response to her child, which lacked molding. Amy must have experienced her mother as lacking warmth and not providing gratification of her impulses to closeness nor resolving her distress. Amy's illness was a form of early childhood psychosis most closely resembling symbiotic psychosis of childhood. She could not separate from her mother to go to nursery school, and subsequently voiced delusional fears of food being poisoned and fears that she could cause earthquakes and the destruction of people.

CASE 3: INTERFERENCE WITH AFFECTIVE RECIPROCITY, TOUCHING, GAZING, AND HOLDING: PARENTAL OVERSTIMULATION

In the case of Ken, we saw repeated scenes of overwhelming parental overstimulation of the boy in early childhood. Growing from their own deep-seated sense of inadequacy and resentment over earlier emotional deprivations in their lives, the parents needed their son to be an emblem for the world of their adequacy. We observed them doing this in repeated episodes as they coerced the boy to perform for them. In an informative scene at 2-years old, the mother placed the child on a hobby horse and with increasing rapidity bobbed the horse up and down to try to induce the child to do likewise on his own. Ken did not comply, and the mother did not acknowledge the growing tension on his face. In a moment of respite, Ken stumbled off the horse and sat on the floor. The father stepped in and tickled Ken, who looked anguished, with no sign on his face of the smile that the father seemed to be so compulsively seeking. Ken rolled away from his father and hid his face. A moment later the father threw the boy's cowboy hat at him.

The episodes from this child's early life demonstrate failures across several bonding modalities. Holding is absent or not gentle when it occurs. The parents are not involved and do not respond to the child's affect. There are no instances of eye gaze or gentle, playful, mutual touching, and the timing and force of the parental actions are too swift and aggressive so as to be severely controlling, if not painful. The parents are the initiators and maintainers of all interactions. Ken's only resource is to terminate an encounter through withdrawal. Furthermore, the parental bodily shaping with the child is jabbing and angular, rather than rounded, and molding.

Ken was an autistic child with some relatedness when brought for treatment at 3 years old. In the course of inpatient and day treatment, which lasted almost a decade, he revealed intense fears of being controlled and of disintegration and fragmentation. Ultimately, he was able to return to a regular high school, but remained unusually concrete in his perceptions and expressions.

CASE 4: INTERFERENCE WITH THE BABY'S ATTACHMENT TO ONE PARENT BY THE OTHER: MATERNAL OVERCONTROL AND STRUGGLE FOR POSSESSION OF THE CHILD

Edward was recognized as ill when he was unable to separate from his mother to enter school. He was diagnosed as suffering a symbiotic psychosis of childhood. The particular behavioral configuration in this case was that of a father who was unusually gentle and responsive to his child, and of a mother who was brusque and demanding. There were several episodes in the first year of life when Edward was looking at his mother, or attending to an object or another person. Unmindful of the tempo of her son's attention and his wish to maintain his attention on a person or object for a few seconds, the mother was observed to spin, push, and pull her son away from his activity, prematurely terminating it and pushing him toward something else.

Such an interaction also involved the father in a vivid sequence when Edward was 21-months old. First, the mother, in a shallow swimming pool, approached Edward who was seated on the edge of the pool. She strode up and brusquely pulled the boy off the edge of the pool and toward her chest; however, he twisted his face away. The mother returned him to the edge of the pool. After a moment the father approached and reached his hands out to his son seated on the side of the pool. After 3–4 sec, while the father had waited patiently, Edward extended his arms toward his father, leaned off the edge of the pool and into his father's waiting arms with a smile on his face. After another 3 sec, the mother interrupted and pulled Edward away from his father and into her arms. The boy's face showed a grimace, and his body twisted away from his mother toward his father.

This dramatic episode illustrated a core problem in the family, the mother's need to control her child. However, she did not control him by offering him a nurturing, well timed, and molding closeness, which seemed to be the father's inclination, but rather she controlled by directing him from person to person and object to object. Ultimately, it appeared that Edward was unable to achieve a self-differentiation, having never been allowed a normal and healthy symbiosis with his mother during the first 6 months of life, which is the precursor of individuation. Therefore, he was reduced to panic and the threat of fragmentation at the experience of going to school. The already established patterns of maternal over-control and paternal helplessness continued when Edward entered treatment at 4 years old. After a year of therapy, the boy began to improve and show signs of being able to function autonomously. At this juncture, the mother stepped in (as she had in the swimming pool sequence) and withdrew her son from treatment. Approximately 2 years later the father died of a stroke.

CASE 5: INTERFERENCE WITH ATTACHMENT THROUGH MATERNAL ABSENCE SECONDARY TO ILLNESS

In 1950 Erik Erikson in *Childhood and Society* reported the case of a young girl named Jean who developed a psychotic illness. Through a detailed reconstruction of the earliest events in her life, Erikson elegantly described the process of "early ego failure" in the little girl. We were able to obtain the family-made movies of the infancy of this child which Erikson had alluded to, and they graphically support his earlier understanding of the case.

In the first months of life, Jean was an alert, smiling, and responsive baby. The mother was gentle and well placed with her daughter, and held her comfortably and closely. However, nurses were photographed treating the baby roughly, in a way that did not allow her autonomy or oral self-gratification. In one scene at 7 months, the mother patiently tried to interest her daughter in looking at her, but the infant gazed instead at her own hands, seemingly unaware of the mother.

Thus, in the first 7 months there was problematic caretaking on the part of nurses and a suggestion of problematic responsiveness on the baby's part, while there was also evidence of adequate bonding behavior on the mother's part and good initial responsiveness by the infant. However, the critical interference with attachment (i.e., the normal outgrowth of adequate, preliminary reciprocal bonding) followed shortly when the mother developed tuberculosis. She was isolated from her infant in her bedroom and shielded from her by a screen in the doorway from Jean's ninth to thirteenth month. When the mother was reunited with Jean at 13 months, the movies resumed and the first clear signs of an autistic illness were apparent. Jean spent long periods of time rocking to and fro and making no response to the people about her. Additionally, her facial expression became fragmented, rather than expressing meaning and interpersonal communication, and stereotypic finger movements also appeared.

CASE 6: INTERFERENCE WITH ATTACHMENT DUE TO A FEEDING DISTURBANCE SECONDARY TO MATERNAL DEPRESSION AND A BABY'S AGGRESSIVENESS

Willa is a little girl whose case I have been familiar with since she was 6-months old. She came to the attention of pediatricians at that time because of a life-threatening refusal to eat when her mother bottle- or spoon-fed her. The baby would close her lips to the food, or take a little into her mouth and push it out with her tongue after a few seconds. A small amount of food was swallowed, and of this a portion was occasionally vomited. Organic causes for this infantile anorexia were ruled out during repeated hospitalizations. During hospitalizations Willa ate somewhat, but not remarkably better from nurses than from her mother, and slowly gained weight. But very importantly, the hospitalizations gave us an opportunity to observe and film, for close analysis, the mother, Helen, feeding her daughter.

Helen fed Willa with a stolid, if expressionless, look on her face with eyes largely cast down toward the floor. When Willa was in her first year of life she was propped in an infant seat and not held. There had never been any breast feeding. Interactionally, Willa periodically looked up at her mother's face with an initiatory spark of interest in her eyes, as if to start some interaction between her and her mother. However, the mother never responded to these 1–2 sec overtures. The mother never altered her expression or met Willa's eyes, and even occasionally shifted her own gaze further from her daughter—a termination of potential discourse. Willa's brief excursions of gaze toward her mother were followed by looking at the floor, walls, ceiling, and any other person or object but not at the food. Often, at these moments, Willa's expression seemed to reflect a quizzical interest, but equally often her face showed a stolidity that mirrored the mother's affect. If anything, Willa's expression contained more anger than the mother's.

Other dimensions of the interference with feeding were in the hands and vocalizations of the mother. Helen's behavior seemed to be organized toward negating pleasurable and playful interchanges during feeding. This stemmed from a compulsion Helen felt to treat feeding as a business-like proposition to be accomplished quickly and without fuss. This compulsion also grew from her severe and chronic depression that left little capacity for spontaneity and pleasure. Helen had been treated harshly by her mother and abandoned by her father as a child, and had likewise been abandoned by the man who was Willa's father. We observed that whenever Willa tried to play with a utensil or with food, Helen sharply restrained her hands. There was no drawing of these actions into play with her daughter. The mother said that to incorporate playfulness into feeding "would take too much time." Similarly, the only vocalizations Helen uttered to her daughter were "No," although Willa herself would occasionally babble as an infant or utter words as a toddler. In terms of general body shaping, the mother's chest remained stiffly unyielding to her daughter.

Apart from feeding, the mother could function no better and, in fact, left Willa alone most of the time. Feeding and other body ministrations, such as diapering, drew mother and daughter together, but the interaction was mechanical. The nurses who fed Willa were, of course, more flexible, playful, and spontaneous. Willa rewarded their activity with smiles and weight gain that was quickly lost as soon as the mother fed a series of the meals. But even with the nurses, Willa's eating was still recalcitrant, although in terms of timing she maintained eye contact with her nurse, interest in food, and mutual play with food and utensils for seconds at a time. However, these were much shorter periods than those that take place with normal parent–child dyads.

What seems to have occured is that the feeding situation became the focus of the mother's despair and Willa's aggression. It was as if Willa—who has given every indication of superior intelligence in her comprehension of her environment and its objects as she has grown—felt that she was going to elicit a response from her mother or else turn away in anger. The baby's anger—clearly on her face from 6 months on—had become displaced onto feeding, so that even when nurses were feeding Willa, the now internalized anger continued to characterize eating though less intensely than with the mother. A child with less constitutional vigor and less drive to bond with the mother may have been spared the anger and accepted the mother's apathy and rejection passively. This seemed to be the case with Willa's younger sister who at 9-months old was an apathetic, inactive, and obese child passively taking in all food offered her by her mother. The mother's behavior with this daughter was no more joyful or spontaneous, but there was less mutual anger in this dyad because this daugher made fewer demands or initiations of interactions.

At this writing Willa is now $2\frac{1}{2}$-years old. She is still far below the normal growth curve and delayed in speech and gross motor development. However, psychotherapy is for the first time showing fruits with Helen who has more capacity for relaxation of her body and for interaction with Willa. Consequently, for the first time we see episodes of mutual enjoyment occurring between the mother and child.

CASE 7: INTERFERENCE WITH AUTONOMY:
PARENTAL OVERCONTROL

Martha and her reportedly identical twin sister, Madge, appeared to be similarly overcontrolled by their parents. Though not subjected to the intense overstimulation that Ken experienced, there were repeated scenes in which the baby sisters sought to gratify oral impulses but were thwarted. For example, in one extended episode, Madge at about 8 months old tried to put her hand in her mouth, then a washcloth, and finally tried to put her mouth on the edge of the bathtub. At each attempt the mother forcefully restrained the child who momentarily looked dejected and then made her next attempt. There were no scenes of feeding, but it is likely that similar interferences with oral gratification extended to the feeding situation. Similar to Ken's case, there were major parental interferences across virtually all modalities of bonding.

By 1-year old Martha was in the throes of a crippling autistic illness that was characterized by a lack of speech development, disorganized flailing, repetitive motor activity, and labile affect that did not allow interpersonal contact. She did not make any significant steps toward recovery during childhood. On the other hand, Madge currently seems spared of a major psychiatric illness.

CASE 8: INTERFERENCE WITH BONDING THROUGH
MATERNAL ABSENCE OF INVOLVEMENT SECONDARY
TO EMOTIONAL UNAVAILABILITY

Still another form of interference observed is exemplified by Ethan, who came to psychiatric attention at 4 years old because of undeveloped speech and echolalia. In this case the infant films revealed a mother whose chest always remained planar with her infant; there was no curvature of the shoulders or chest to nestle the child. The mother's expression was largely constricted into a pensive, emotionally uncommunicative gaze at her child. She never showed a spark of excitement with the baby who in turn had an impassive, somber mien that mirrored the mother's. Furthermore, we did not observe the parents initiate interaction through touching, or with toys or vocalizations.

However, in contrast to several of the other pathological Parent-Infant interactions already described, this configuration was not characterized by elements of coerciveness or thwarting of infant behavior. Rather, the predominant feature was the absence of involvement with the child. Several years after Ethan's infancy and considerable therapy of the mother, she was able to speak of herself as "not a real person then" (i.e., during Ethan's first year of life). She had been narcissistically too self-involved and fearful of her own angry and loving impulses to reach out to her child.

CASE 9: A MOTHER'S ABERRANT RESPONSE TO HER BABY'S CRY RECONSTRUCTED FROM THE PSYCHOTHERAPY OF AN ADULT PATIENT

This case highlights an abnormality in a mother's response to her infant's vocalizations, although it is likely that disturbance existed across a range of Mother-Infant interactions. The case is included to show how the psychodynamic picture of an adult patient may accurately reflect specific mother-infant dyadic pathology. The material in this vignette comes from reconstructions from material gathered during psychoanalysis of an adult patient, Mr. P., as well as from historical information the patient sought about his earliest childhood during the course of his treatment.

P. was in his late thirties and had come for treatment for complaints of sexual impotence, a sense of isolation from people, and anxiety attacks in social situations. Diagnostically he had both an obsessional character disorder—he was an individual who required great orderliness and sameness in his life and avoided strong emotions while relying on intellectualizations—as well as a severe narcissistic personality disorder (Kernberg, 1975; Kohut, 1971). That is, Mr. P. had a markedly impaired sense of self-esteem so that he needed to feel admired, approved of, even loved by virtually all people including his supervisors at work and his psychoanalyst. He compensated for and defended against his underlying fragility by social withdrawal and a muted grandiosity. All of these defensive and pathologic elements were gradually understood and shared with the patient in the course of his treatment, eventually alleviating many of his symptoms.

However, during therapy a critical piece of information surprisingly came from P.'s aunt. In the course of a conversation with P., the aunt recalled how once she had been visiting with P. and his mother (the father was away on business as had been the case during most of the patient's infancy) when P. was about 6 months old. The infant P. started to cry and the mother said to the aunt, "The baby is crying; he must hate me," and continued her conversation. Although such historical information is a very incomplete picture of what went on most of the time between P. and his mother, it does dramatically illustrate a deviant maternal response and interpretation of a baby's cry. Normally, the baby's cry functions as an alerting signal and sign of the child's distress. The mother responds rapidly with a range of behaviors that include soothing vocalizations, touching, and holding to comfort and re-establish a state of homeostasis in the infant. A mother who responds to her child's cry as if it is a communication that she is hated is projecting onto the child her own conflicts over nurturing. In general terms, a mother who is inhibited in this fashion has difficulty providing loving behaviors to an infant unless she herself receives frequent and strong proof of being loved. It is difficult for a mother to find such proof in her baby's crying.

From P.'s adult clinical picture and from historical information such as this, we can hypothesize that P. did not experience the "mirroring" response, both vocally and across a range of other bonding modalities, which Kohut (1972) has speculated is absent in the early life of the group of narcissistic adults about whom he has written. Such a mirroring, alternatively described as a confirming response, is analogous to the process of pleasurable affective reciprocity between mother and child. It seems to be crucial in the process of basic identity formation and the establishment of an internal sense of self and self-worth.

DISCUSSION

These case examples demonstrate absence of parental response as well as pathological response. The cases, chosen because they have stood out among others in my clinical and research experience, do not by any means encompass the range of disturbances that may occur. They do, nonetheless, illustrate certain essential features that are likely to be operative in most instances of pathological Parent–Infant interaction.

Infants are born with the capacity to bond to their parents via a group of basic drives. These are the drives toward eye gaze, touching, clinging, feeding, and vocalizing. The primary caregiver heightens and sometimes makes successful the consummation of the drive by reciprocating it or eliciting it. Moreover, the process of reciprocation is not haphazard but requires a synchronization with the infant in the dimensions of timing, moment of initiation, maintenance, termination, bodily shaping, physical force, and emotional empathy or sensitivity to the infant's affective displays. In the situations of pathology, there is a failure on the parent's part that interferes with one or more of the bonding modalities. A modality may be totally absent or thwarted in the case of a given parent–child dyad, or the components of the parent's response may be so unusual as a consequence of parental intrapsychic disturbance that an aberrant, even perverse, social interaction occurs.

Basic developmental research by Stern (1971) and Tronick and his associates (Tronick, Als, Adamson, Wise, & Brazelton, 1978) documents the existence of rules and rhythms of behavior in normal relationships between mothers and their infants during the first weeks of life. More specifically, Stern has shown how a mother establishes a pattern of eye gaze initiation and termination with one child in a twinship that is relatively stable but different from the pattern with the other twin. Even more significant for our study of pathological Parent–Infant interactions is Tronick's experimental manipulation of parent–infant affective reciprocity. In his experiment, a mother is asked to briefly avoid smiling back at her infant's excitement when the baby smiles or brightens at the mother's face. This lack of response on the mother's part leads in the space of seconds to the baby becoming restless, irritable, confused, and dejected. It also leads to an internal dysphoria in the mother participating in the experiment. The parallel between Tronick's study and the findings in the paradigmatic cases with psychopathology is evident.

In some of the previously mentioned cases, it is not simply that bonding was interfered with (e.g., the case of Jean where the mother disappeared behind a screen for 4 months with tuberculosis) or that a rule of behavior was broken (e.g., the case of Willa where the mother stared blankly at her daughter even when the little girl brightened—a parallel to Tronick's experiment), but that paradoxical or contradictory messages were given to the infants. The most graphic example of this is the case of Joan where the mother first nuzzled the child in a way that elicited a smile and an impulse to seek out the mother's face. But the mother blocked Joan's attempt at eye contact. The mother's mixed message may be translated verbally, "Look at me, but don't really look at me." The contradiction produces confusion and depression on the child's face; the baby must feel the same affects internally as well.

Ontogenetically, the process of bonding in the first 6 months of life eventuates in an attachment occurring during the second 6 months of life. If bonding has been disturbed, the attachment will either be pathological or absent. The cases provided here demonstrate both outcomes. Out of the matrix of the attachment follows the separation and individuation process (Mahler, Pine, & Bergman, 1975) in the second year of life. Ultimately out of the matrix of attachment comes the particular quality of affiliation and object relations a given child has with its parents and other human beings.

The examples of Parent–Infant interactions presented here appeared pathological because they were markedly different from interactions seen in normal control populations. However, it is not possible to say with any certainty that the pathological interactions isolated from these films had a direct cause and effect relationship with the occurrence of the subsequent psychotic illnesses. There are a variety of possible mechanisms. In some cases, an organically mediated defect in the child may have caused the illness, or parental disruption of inborn social responses in the baby or failure to elicit these responses may have led to the psychosis. In still other cases, an organic vulnerability coupled with a pathological interaction may have caused the illness. The case of the twin sister supports this possibility because it appeared that both sisters were treated with similar coercion and brusqueness by their parents. The fact that only one developed serious mental illness suggests that there was also an organic factor operative in the illness of this girl.

Also, we have been concerned in this chapter with the parents' contribution to pathological dyadic interaction. Cases were chosen where there was sufficient evidence that the infants had at least a basic capacity to initiate an action toward the parents or make a response when the parents initiated a social behavior. However, it is possible that some of the children were unusually subdued and slow in response that may have disturbed a parent's capacity for normal interaction.

Finally, what may be an aberrant Parent–Infant interaction in Western culture may be normal in other societies and subcultures. Certainly in many non-Western societies there is more emphasis on bonding with children via holding and breast feeding than in America. As an example, in a Southeast Asian Hindu culture on the Island of Bali, I filmed (1978) a standardized situation of moderate stress for parents and infants and then compared these films to films of a similar situation in the United States. In Bali there was less Maternal–Infant interaction via vocalization and eye gaze than in the West as the parents managed the distress of their children. On the other hand, there was a great deal more holding of infants and offering of the breast for pacification. A society characterized by one pattern of Parent–Infant social interaction will raise an adult with a substantially different ego and style of object and group relatedness than a society marked by a different pattern of Parent–Infant interaction. Similarly, given families may be seen as a unit of their own that also establishes a unique developmental process with thir children. What concerns us most as researchers and clinicians are the questions concerning the child's basic inborn needs across the core bonding modalities and their components, and how they are perverted in some instances so that a child grows up unable to adapt in some fashion to his or her own culture.

ACKNOWLEDGMENTS

Research described in this chapter has been supported by a grant from the L. J. and Mary C. Skaggs Foundation, Oakland, California. I am also very indebted to Kay Campbell, Dan Beugelmans, Judith Rosenthal, Ken Wulff, Abbot Bronstein, Martha Harris, and Toni Heineman, colleagues who have assisted me in recent aspects of this work.

REFERENCES

Benjamin, J., & Tennes, K. *A case of pathological head nodding.* Paper read at the Los Angeles Society for Child Psychiatry, and at the American Psychoanalytic Association, Los Angeles, California, 1958.

Call, J. Interlocking affective freeze between an autistic child and his "as-if" mother. *Journal of the American Academy of Child Psychiatry*, 1963, *2*, 319-344.

Erikson, E. *Childhood and society*. New York: Norton, 1950.

Kernberg, O. *Borderline conditions and pathological narcissism*. New York: Jason Aronson, 1975.

Kohut, H. *The analysis of the self*. New York: International Univ. Press, 1971.

Kohut, H. Thoughts on narcissism and narcissistic rage. *Psychoanalytic Study of the Child*, 1972, *27*, 360-400.

Mahler, M., Pine, F., & Bergman, A. *The psychological birth of the child*. New York: Basic Books, 1975.

Massie, H. The early natural history of childhood psychosis. *Journal of the American Academy of Child Psychiatry*, 1975, *14*, 683-707.

Massie, H. Patterns of mother-infant behavior and subsequent childhood psychosis: a research and case report. *Child Psychiatry and Human Development*, 1977, *7*, 211-230.

Massie, H. The early natural history of childhood psychosis: 10 cases studied by analysis of family home movies of the infancies of the children. *Journal of the American Academy of Child Psychiatry*, 1978, *17*, 29-45. (a)

Massie, H. Blind ratings of mother-infant interaction in home movies of prepsychotic and normal infants. *American Journal of Psychiatry*, 1978, *135*, 1371-1374. (b)

Spitz, R. & Cobliner, W. G. *The first year of life*. New York: International Univ. Press, 1965.

Stern, D. A micro-analysis of mother-infant interaction. *Journal of the American Academy of Child Psychiatry*, 1971, *10*, 501-517.

Tronick, E., Als, H., Adamson, L., Wise, S., & Brazelton, T. B. The infant's response to entrapment between contradictory messages in face-to-face interaction. *Journal of the American Academy of Child Psychiatry*, 1978, *17*, 1-13.

CHAPTER 6

LORRAINE F. KUBICEK

Organization in Two Mother–Infant Interactions Involving a Normal Infant and His Fraternal Twin Brother Who Was Later Diagnosed as Autistic

INTRODUCTION

The normal human infant, through a varied repertoire of nonlanguage behaviors, actively engages in social interactions with his caregivers from the first months of life (see Ciba Foundation, 1975; Lewis & Rosenblum, 1974; Schaffer, 1977; Stern, 1977). In contrast, the autistic infant reportedly fails to establish a normal interaction even with his primary caregiver. Mothers report the absence of infant smiling, nonresponse to the human voice, and a general "noncuddliness" (Clancy & McBride, 1969; Rendle-Short, 1969). However, the diagnosis of autism is seldom made before 2 years of age, so most of the information concerning the earliest development of such children is anecdotal and retrospective. Because the impairment in social relationships is believed to be present very early in childhood (Kanner, 1943; Rutter & Schopler, 1978), face-to-face interactions between infant and mother would be an ideal focus for systematic study of this developmental disorder (DesLauriers & Carlson, 1969).

This study describes data taken from a filmed interaction between a mother and her 16-week-old son who was diagnosed as autistic approximately 2 years after the film was made. A comparable filmed interaction of his fraternal twin brother provided a normal control for comparison. Thus, these films provided not only a unique opportunity to observe an interaction of a young infant

99

HIGH-RISK INFANTS AND CHILDREN:
Adult and Peer Interactions

who was later diagnosed as autistic, but also provided an optimal, normal control (i.e., an infant of exactly the same age interacting with the same caregiver).

Because social relationships are by nature interactive, the methodology used for describing them must account for their interactive aspects. Accordingly, an analysis of the organization of each interaction was done that was based upon sequences of action involving both mother and infant. The data are detailed frame-by-frame transcriptions of a wide range of each participant's behaviors observable in their filmed interaction. The face-to-face interaction methodology is similar in its behavioral comprehensiveness and in its emphasis on the organization of sequences of action to that presented by Duncan and Fiske (1977).

The research of Stern (1971, 1974) and Brazelton, Koslowski, and Main (1974) is most relevant to this study, as these authors have used detailed transcriptions in describing Mother–Infant interactions and have been concerned with the organization of sequences of mother–infant behaviors. Stern has focused on sequences of maternal and infant visual behaviors involved in initiating and terminating periods of mutual gaze and avoidance. Brazelton and his colleagues used a transcription system, which included behaviors such as smiling, crying, and reaching, to describe, in a general way, the sequential relationships between various clusters of maternal and infant behaviors for particular cycles of looking and nonlooking within the overall Mother–Infant interaction.

The present study builds on this earlier research by including a wider range of behaviors in the transcription system and by providing more detailed physical descriptions of the observed behaviors. Furthermore, an attempt was made to describe the nature and extent of organization in the two interactions, based on regularities in the sequencing of mother–infant behaviors. This exploratory study represents part of an ongoing research project aimed at developing a more objective and systematic methodology by which to characterize both normal and abnormal Mother–Infant interactions.

METHOD

Source of Data

These male fraternal twins were delivered by Caesarean section to their 38-year-old primiparous mother. Twin B was first born and weighed 6 lbs.; Twin A weighed 7 lbs., 2 oz. Apgar ratings for the infants were 9–10. Both were assumed normal when the films were made. Twin A was diagnosed as autistic at approximately age $2\frac{1}{2}$ years old; Twin B has had a normal developmental history.

The films (16-mm black and white, without sound, and filmed at 24 frames per second) were part of a short term, longitudinal study conducted by D. G. Freedman in 1967. The purpose of that study was to investigate genetic influences on social development by comparing the behaviors of identical and fraternal twin pairs. Mother–infant pairs were filmed at weekly intervals when the infants were between the ages of 3 and 16 weeks.

The filmed segments included one face-to-face interaction between the mother and Twin A and another between her and Twin B. Each segment consisted of a continuous observation of approximately 20 sec. Filmed segments at 16 weeks were selected for transcription because the two interactive settings were similar and because the two segments were of comparable length and photographic quality. Furthermore, the interactions appeared to be characteristic for the two infants. It must be emphasized that this impression is based only on normal viewing of the other filmed segments, as detailed analysis of these segments is not complete.

Filming

For each filmed segment, the mother simply was instructed to "elicit a smile from her infant." The infant was in his crib, and she was standing at the side of the crib where she remained throughout the segment. Of her own accord, the mother lifted the infant up following the first few seconds of their interaction. She freely moved the infant (as she interacted with him) and these movements often necessitated changing the position of the camera so as to obtain a complete picture of her and the infant at all times. Both mother and infant were filmed from the waist up. Infants were photographed from the front and the mother was generally photographed from the side. No lighting in addition to normal room lighting was required for filming.

Transcription

Because a wide range of behaviors is believed to be involved in mother–infant communication, a behaviorally inclusive transcription of each participant's observable behaviors was carried out. Transcription was based on a comprehensive system designed specifically for this study. Categories of the system were derived from the infant and maternal behaviors observed in the two interactions. Repeated viewing of the filmed interaction between Twin A and his mother resulted in a preliminary list of actions and their descriptions. This system was applied to the interaction involving Twin B in order to test its comprehensiveness; categories were expanded to include any additional behaviors. For example, the category "neutral face" was adequate for describing Twin A's facial expressions, however, five additional categories were needed to describe Twin B's facial expressions. Finally, the entire system was revised to provide more explicit, low-level categories.

The basic categories of actions for the mother and twins included aspects of facial expression (e.g., neutral face, open-mouth smile), gaze (e.g., maintaining eye contact or looking away), positioning of the head and neck (e.g., head erect and turned 45° to the left), hand configuration (e.g., open hand or fist), the posture of each arm as well as its orientation to the body (e.g., arm extended and held in front of the body at shoulder level), postural shifts (e.g., seated upright or back arched), and transitional movements of a particular body part. Additional categories transcribed for the mother were manner of holding each infant, the mother's movements which increased or decreased her proximity to the infant, and her movements of the infant in space which altered their physical orientation to each other.[1]

A stop-frame projector was used for the frame-by-frame transcription. Each category in the system was transcribed separately, and individual actions within each category (i.e., movements as well as stationary positions) were recorded from onset to termination. The transcribing was done on large data sheets with vertical rulings for film frames and horizontal rulings for mother and infant actions. The transcriptions provided a presentation of the correspondence, in time, among mother and infant actions to the accuracy of 1/24 sec.

Analysis

The films and transcripts were reviewed to discover exchanges between the mother and each twin that were characteristic of their interaction and around which their behaviors might be organized. A general description of each interaction follows.

Twin B was attentive to his mother and his surroundings. His posture was normal, and he generally held his extended or slightly flexed arms comfortably at his sides. The mother picked him up at the beginning of their interaction and held him that same way for its entirety. She and Twin B spent much of their time mutually attending and in social play.

Twin A, on the other hand, did not establish eye contact with his mother during their interaction. His face was without expression. His head was either turned away from her or held back, his gaze directed upwards at the ceiling. For most of their interaction, his back was arched, his arms were rigidly flexed

[1]Operational definitions of these categories may be obtained from the author. They are not intended as a comprehensive listing of the behaviors which occur in all Mother–Infant interactions. Rather, they are restricted to those behaviors actually observed in the two interactions transcribed for this study. Several descriptions of facial expression are adapted, in part, from Brannigan & Humphries (1972).

or extended and held up and away from his body, and his hands were fisted. This rigid posturing was an indication of overall body tension. The interaction progressed with Twin A avoiding, in various ways, his mother's successive approaches. The mother continually changed how she was holding him and moved herself and/or the infant, always attempting to position herself within his line of vision.

On the basis of regularities in the sequencing of the transcribed actions, a number of behavioral elements was hypothesized for describing the organization of each interaction (i.e., behavioral elements for initiating, maintaining, ending, recapturing, and avoiding social contact were hypothesized [Stern, 1977]). Behavioral elements are higher order, multimodality units of behavior composed of certain actions that actually cooccurred or were commonly grouped for the purpose of description. Next, flow models illustrating the hypothesized organization of each interaction were constructed according to regularities in the sequencing of these behavioral elements. To facilitate later discussion of the flow models, a description of each of the hypothesized behavioral elements follows.

BEHAVIORAL ELEMENTS HYPOTHESIZED FOR THE INTERACTION
BETWEEN THE MOTHER AND TWIN B

Mother

Play. Play consists of several social games that, as described by Stern (1974), are repetitive sets of behaviors done over and over again with slight variation (e.g., rocking, turning, and nodding). The mother smiled during play. She used these behaviors either to maintain contact with Twin B or to recapture his attention after he withdrew gaze.

Exaggerate Play. The mother exaggerated the play behaviors that preceded Twin B's positive response. Exaggeration of the "turning" game, for example, consisted of more extreme turns, raising the infant higher and lowering him more, as well as the mother tilting her head to correspond with the direction of his turns. In the "nodding" game, she raised her head higher and nodded down further, adding a head turn to the right as she nodded forward. Exaggerated play was used for maintaining social contact.

Intrude. If one round of play did not recapture the infant's attention (i.e., he continued to look away), the mother turned him somewhat abruptly, alternating right, then left, several times. This always resulted in the infant turning his head toward his mother. If he did not immediately establish eye contact with her, she repeated this behavior, but with less intensity.

Twin B

Positive Response. This was primarily a smile, accompanied by specific body movements. For example, Twin B's arms were flexed or were extended and raised up and out to his sides. The hands were fisted, indicating some degree of body tension. A positive response, when it occurred, followed a round of play and maintained social contact with the mother.

Withdraw Gaze. These behaviors varied, depending upon whether or not Twin B withdrew following a smile. If he were merely attending, withdrawal was a matter of simply looking away, turning away, or both. Additionally, his expression may have changed to something other than that of his normal face. If, on the other hand, he withdrew his gaze following a smile, his eyelids may have closed slightly and his smile may have either remained or faded before he looked away and turned his head away. After the infant broke eye contact, his arms tended to return to the neutral, relaxed position and his fisted hands opened. In this way, he slowly terminated the exchange with his mother.

Attend. Essentially, the infant was oriented toward his mother. He accommodated his head and eyes to maintain eye contact and his face was neutral or showing minimal expression (e.g., mouth corners down). His arms were generally relaxed at his side or small indiscriminant movements of his hands and arms were noticeable. Twin B passively maintained contact with his mother in this way.

Look. The infant turned back toward the mother following an intrude or a repeat play. This turning back was accompanied by slight closure of the eyelids and a change in facial expression.

Look Away. Twin B was not looking at his mother, and his head may have been turned away from her. His body was relaxed, his arms extended, and his hands were in the neutral position. There was no expression on his face, and he appeared to be attending to something else in his environment (e.g., staring at the camera).

BEHAVIORAL ELEMENTS HYPOTHESIZED FOR THE INTERACTION
BETWEEN THE MOTHER AND TWIN A

Mother

Approach. These are actions by the mother used to maintain a full face positioning between her and Twin A. Included here are the mother's head and body movements, as well as her movements of Twin A. These movements occurred either separately or in various combinations, e.g., mother moving forward while turning the infant toward herself. The mother's actions included "lean toward," "move forward," and "nose to face." The mother's movements of the infant included turning him toward herself, moving the infant toward her, tilting him forward into her face, moving him up to her eye level, looking directly down into the infant's face, and moving the infant up while bending over into his face.

Reposition. These are changes in how the mother was holding Twin A, including the movements involved in changing him from one of these positions to another. Included here are how the mother supported the infant, whether she held him face front or on an angle to herself, whether or not the infant's body was perpendicular to the floor, or if he was tilted in a particular direction.

Back Off. These are movements back, away from the infant, which coincided with Twin A's abrupt arm movement.

Twin A

Abrupt Arm Movement. This was an abrupt movement of Twin A's right arm and fist, moving either from a frontal position to the side or the reverse. This movement always stopped the mother's approach.

Cut-Off Behaviors. Included here are a number of actions which tended to limit social input from the mother. For example, Twin A would close his eyes and evidence muscle tension, open his eyes but look away, turn his head away or tilt it back, or arch his back with his arms strained back beyond his sides.

SEQUENCES OF BEHAVIORAL ELEMENTS HYPOTHESIZED FOR
EACH INTERACTION

Flow models illustrating the hypothesized organization of each interaction, based on regularities in the sequencing of the behavioral elements, are represented in Figure 6.1 and Figure 6.2. Each model accounted for all of the transcribed actions occurring within its respective interaction. A description of the different sequences in each model follows.

Mother and Twin B

As indicated by Figure 6.1, once the mother and Twin B had established eye contact, she proceeded with one of the three games she played with him.

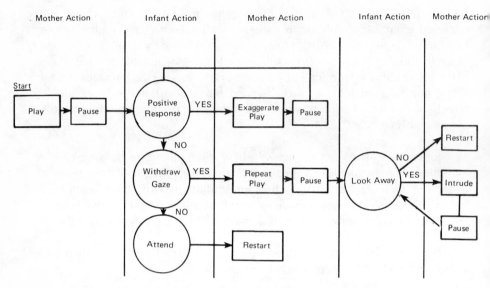

FIGURE 6.1. The diagram represents a flow model of the interaction between the mother and Twin B.

He, in turn, responded to her play either by smiling, withdrawing his gaze, or merely continuing to attend. The mother's response related to Twin B's behavior.

Twin B was attending to his mother as she lifted him from the crib. As she straightened into an upright posture, the mother initiated play by raising her head and nodding forward. She then paused to watch Twin B, who continued to look at her. The mother repeated this play cycle twice. As she paused to watch him, Twin B responded positively by smiling and moving both arms up and out to his sides. Following this pause, the mother exaggerated play and again paused to watch him. Still smiling, Twin B slowly withdrew his gaze. There were two sequences of mutual attending in this interaction during which Twin B eventually smiled.

At this point in the interaction, the mother attempted to recapture Twin B's attention by repeating play and pausing. However, Twin B continued to look away. To recapture his attention, the mother intruded by turning him right, then left, several times in succession. Twin B responded by turning in his mother's direction without looking at her. She made a second, but milder, attempt to attract him, that resulted in Twin B and his mother re-establishing eye contact, whereupon the mother initiated a round of the "turning" game. There were two sequences of this type in their interaction.

There were three sequences in which, after withdrawing gaze and turning away, the infant re-established eye contact following the mother's repeat play.

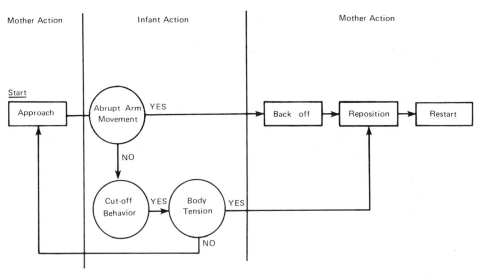

FIGURE 6.2.   The diagram represents a flow model of the interaction between the mother and Twin A.

Here, in contrast to the kind of sequence described in the preceding paragraph, the infant resumed the social exchange on his own, i.e., without mother intruding. For example, after one round of the turn game, Twin B withdrew gaze and turned away. His mother then repeated a round of the turn game and Twin B attended to her once again. This sequence proceeded with Twin B smiling for the second time during their interaction.

Mother and Twin A

As was mentioned previously, the give and take of attending and not attending characterizing the interaction between the mother and Twin B was absent in her interaction with Twin A—they never established eye contact. Rather, there were three typical sequences that preceded the mother's repositionings of Twin A.

During the opening sequence of their interaction, Twin A was seated in his crib with his mother's hand supporting his neck and back. The mother made successive approaches toward him, to which he responded by looking away and then turning his head away. His mother continued to approach him and Twin A's head turns were accompanied by signs of increasing body tension. Finally, he abruptly moved his right arm out to the side. At this point his mother's approach stopped. This was the only sequence during which an abrupt arm movement followed successive attempts to avoid his mother.

After this initial exchange, the mother moved Twin A closer to her and began to rub her nose on his face. This ended with Twin A posturing himself in a full arch, his head held back, and his gaze directed upward at the ceiling. The arching of his back was accompanied by an abrupt arm movement. He maintained this posture during the next two sequences, each of which involved a single approach by the mother, followed immediately by an abrupt arm movement. For example, the mother turned Twin A while simultaneously moving toward him. He responded to this approach by moving his right arm directly forward; she backed off and then repositioned him. Thus, there was a total of three sequences during which a single approach by the mother was followed by an abrupt arm movement. This always terminated her approach and lead to a repositioning.

There was a third type of sequence that occurred three times during their interaction. In this third type, the mother's successive approaches were followed by signs of increasing body tension in Twin A; she eventually stopped her approach and repositioned him.

DISCUSSION

A comparison of the individual actions transcribed for the twins revealed at least two ways in which Twin A's behavioral repertoire differed from his brother's: (a) within a modality, Twin A characteristically used a more restricted subset of possible behaviors (i.e., primarily those behaviors which effectively limit social contact), and (b) he did not vary the intensity of the few behaviors he used. For example, Twin A maintained a neutral expression throughout the entire interaction with his mother. In contrast, Twin B's facial expressions included smiles, frowns, and neutral face. Furthermore, Twin B varied his intensity (e.g., his smiles ranged from a slight retraction of the lips to a wide-open grin).

Differences between the interactions in organizational complexity were revealed by comparing the sequences of behavioral elements in Figure 6.1 with those in Figure 6.2. A number of distinguishable sequences make up each interaction model. However, all of the sequences in Figure 6.2 involve the same kind of exchange (i.e., some form of approach by the mother and some form of avoidance by Twin A). In contrast, sequences in Figure 6.1 each represent a different kind of exchange between the mother and Twin B. As Figure 6.1 illustrates, once eye contact was established, the mother proceeded with one of the "games" she played with Twin B. He, in turn, responded by either smiling, withdrawing his gaze, or merely continuing to attend. How the mother responded varied depending upon his behavior. This interaction was characterized by a give and take of action and reaction that involved active and passive responses on both parts (Spitz, 1964). Through their mutual attending, the mother and Twin B effectively moderated their behaviors in relating to each other and thereby facilitated a positive exchange.

This system of mutual exchange, based on subtle differences in facial expression and body movement, never occurred in the interaction between the mother and Twin A. Twin A failed to provide his mother with positive feedback, which is considered essential for establishing a "normal" Mother–Infant interaction (Prechtl, 1963; Thoman, 1975). Furthermore, he did not respond differentially to subtle changes in maternal behaviors, making it difficult for her to respond appropriately (Thoman, 1975). The mother, in effect, ignored the same cues for limiting social input that she attended to in Twin B (e.g., withdrawal of gaze and turning the head away). Instead, she appeared to moderate her behavior only in response to increases in Twin A's overall body tension. Throughout their interaction she moved herself and the infant so that she was within his line of vision. Twin A's responses to these persistent physical approaches were either active or passive avoidance.

Despite these differences, the analysis revealed two notable similarities. First, although his repertoire was restricted in comparison to his brother's behavior, Twin A, like his brother, used a variety of behavioral modalities in communicating. For example, the behavioral element "cut-off behavior" involves a number of actions that limit social input (e.g., eyes closed with accompanying muscle tension or eyes open but looking away; head back, head turned away, or tilted away, from his mother; arms strained back beyond Twin A's sides and a noticeable arching of the back).

Second, although the system of positive exchange between Twin B and his mother was absent in the interaction between her and Twin A, their behavior was not random with respect to each other. The lack of positive exchange resulted in a change in organization of the Mother–Infant interaction, not an absence of organization.

In conclusion, the frame-by-frame analysis of relatively short sequences of Mother-Infant interaction revealed a consistent organization, sugggesting that similar patterns may be found as more data are analyzed. Therefore, it appears that this method may be potentially useful, both in diagnosing problems in Mother–Infant interactions that may arise with high-risk infants and in describing more normal interactions.

ACKNOWLEDGMENTS

I am grateful to Starkey Duncań, Jr., Susan Goldin-Meadow, and Janellen Huttenlocher for their comments and guidance throughout this project, and to Alan Stepneski for figure design, comments, and as always, his understanding and encouragement. Special thanks are due to Daniel G. Freedman for his generosity. This research was supported by a U.S. Public Health Service

Training Grant (HD 00419-04) and pre-doctoral National Research Service individual fellowship award (MH 07523-01), both from the Department of Health, Education, and Welfare.

REFERENCES

Brannigan, C. R., & Humphries, D. A. Human non-verbal behavior. In N. Blurton Jones (Ed.), *Ethological studies in child behavior.* New York: Cambridge Univ. Press, 1972.

Brazelton, T. B., Koslowski, B., & Main, M. Origins of reciprocity. In M. Lewis & L. Rosenblum (Eds.), *Origins of behavior* (Vol. 1). New York: Wiley, 1974.

Ciba Foundation. *Parent infant interaction.* New York: American Elsevier, 1975.

Clancy, H., & McBride, G. The autistic process and its treatment. *Journal of Child Psychology and Psychiatry,* 1969, *10,* 233-244.

DesLauriers, A. M., & Carlson, C. F. *Your child is asleep.* Homewood, Illinois: Dorsey Press, 1969.

Duncan, S. D., Jr., & Fiske, D. W. *Face-to-face interaction: Research, methods and theory.* Hillsdale, New Jersey: Lawrence Erlbaum, 1977.

Kanner, L. Autistic disturbances of affective contact. *Nervous Child,* 1943, 3, 217-250.

Lewis, M., & Rosenblum, L. A. *The effect of the infant on its caregiver.* New York: Wiley, 1974.

Prechtl, H. F. R. The Mother-Child interaction in babies with minimal brain damage (a follow-up study). In B. M. Foss (Ed.), *Determinants of infant behavior II.* New York: Wiley, 1963.

Rendle-Short, J. Infantile autism in Australia. *The Medical Journal of Australia,* 1969, 2, 245-249.

Rutter, M., & Schopler, E. (Eds.). *Autism: A reappraisal of concepts and treatment.* New York: Plenum, 1978.

Schaffer, M. R. (Ed.). *Studies in Mother-Infant interaction.* New York: Academic Press, 1977.

Spitz, R. The derailment of dialogue. *Journal of the American Psychoanalytic Association,* 1964, *12,* 752-775.

Stern, D. N. A microanalysis of Mother-Infant interaction. *American Academy of Child Psychiatry,* 1971, *10,* 501-517.

Stern, D. N. Infant and mother at play. In M. H. Klaus & M. A. Trause (Eds.), *Maternal attachment and mothering disorders: A round table.* Sausalito, California, 1974.

Stern, D. N. *The first relationship.* Cambridge, Massachusetts: Harvard Univ. Press, 1977.

Thoman, E. B. How a rejecting baby affects mother-infant synchrony. In Ciba Foundation, *Parent-Infant Interaction,* New York: American Elsevier, 1975.

PART III

INFANTS AND CHILDREN AT
RISK FOR DEVELOPMENTAL DELAYS

CHAPTER 7

TIFFANY M. FIELD

Interactions of Preterm and Term Infants with their Lower- and Middle-Class Teenage and Adult Mothers

INTRODUCTION

A teenage lower-class mother and her preterm infant might be at consider-able risk for early interaction disturbances due to the cumulative effects of adolescent parenting, lower-class conditions, and developmental delays associated with prematurity. Singly or in various combinations, these factors have been noted to contribute to early interaction disturbances among preterm Infant–Mother, lower-class Mother–Infant, and teenage Mother–Infant dyads. Although interaction studies have typically investigated only one of these variables and used different measures of interactions, they combine to suggest that adolescence, lower socioeconomic status, and prematurity might contribute to early interaction disturbances.

Teenage mothering is a fairly recent subject of investigation. To date, studies in this area have suggested that teenage mothers have less realistic expectations and more punitive childrearing attitudes (DeLissovoy, 1973), and their offspring are at greater risk for child abuse (Sudia, 1978). Thus far, only one study has analyzed the dynamics of early interactions between teenage mothers and their offspring (Sandler, & Vietze, 1979). Their analysis of lower-class Neonatal–Mother feeding interactions suggested that maternal age did not contribute to the differences noted except for a tendency of teenage mothers to be less verbal during interactions with their infants.

113

HIGH-RISK INFANTS AND CHILDREN:
Adult and Peer Interactions

Comparisons of early interactions across socioeconomic status groups have frequently revealed that both lower-class infants and their mothers are less active, particularly verbally, than their middle-class counterparts. As early as the first month of life, lower-class infants received significantly less verbal stimulation from their mothers in both a lulling and chatting fashion during interaction and care-giving activities (Kilbride, Johnson, & Streissguth, 1977). Studies of 4-month-old infants, for example, by Lewis and Wilson (1972) report less smiling and vocalizing among the lower-class infants and less contingent responsivity among their mothers, although no class differences were reported for the frequency of mother vocalizations.

A cross-cultural study comparing British working and middle-class mothers to American lower- and middle-class mothers suggested that both in England and the United States the lower-class mothers engaged in less verbal and imitative behavior and less game playing during early face-to-face interactions (Field & Pawlby, 1980). Their 4-month-old infants were simultaneously less verbal, smiled less frequently, and engaged in less eye contact. Interactions of slightly older infants (10-month-old infants) and their lower-class mothers also featured less verbal activity and fewer reciprocal vocalizations (Bee, Van-Egeren, Streissguth, Nyman, & Lockie, 1969: Tulkin & Kagan, 1972). Similarly, lesser educated mothers talked less frequently, used less positive language, responded with less contingent vocalizations, and gave less specific communications when engaging in face-to-face talk with both their one and 8-month-old infants (Cohen & Beckwith, 1976).

These maternal age and social-class comparisons have focused primarily on the less responsive mother's contribution to interaction differences. Studies on preterm Infant–Mother interactions have focused primarily on the contribution of the less responsive infant to interaction differences. Comparisons between term and preterm infants suggest that the preterm infant–mother dyad experiences more difficulty interacting. For example, analyses of early feedings of preterm and term infants revealed that the preterm infants were more distracted during feeding and their mothers were less sensitive to infant feeding-behaviors and rhythms (Field, 1977a). The mothers of preterm infants, unlike those of term infants, stimulated their infants continuously, failing to reserve their stimulation for the nonsucking periods when the infant was otherwise unoccupied and free to interact. Although some have suggested that sensitive mothers reserve stimulation for these periods (Kaye & Brazelton, 1971), the mothers of preterm infants may provide constant stimulation in order to organize their distracted infants and encourage milk ingestion. Their infants appeared to be less responsive and less organized in their feeding behavior, and they elicited more coaxing or "stimulation-to-feed" behavior from their mothers. The increase in maternal stimluation in response to infant unresponsiveness, however, seemed to enhance rather than diminish the infant's unresponsiveness.

Another study of feeding interactions of both term and preterm infants reported that infants who were "more difficult-to-rouse" or unresponsive to auditory stimulation received more auditory and tactile stimulation during feedings (DiVitto & Goldberg, 1979). Mothers of the preterm infants were more active and invested more effort when interacting with their infants (albeit with less success) than parents of term infants.

Brown and Bakeman (1979) report similar findings. Unlike the middle-class White mother samples of the Field and Goldberg studies, the Brown and Bakeman sample was comprised of lower-class Black mothers and their preterm infants. During early feeding interactions, preterm infants were less active and were viewed as less responsive than term infants. Mothers of the preterm infants generally were more active, and in particular they were more persistent and more likely to initiate and continue behavioral episodes. When compared to mothers of term infants, they exerted more effort, and their interactions were more stereotyped. Thus, the burden of maintaining the interactions fell disproportionately on the mothers of the *preterm* infants (Brown & Bakeman, 1979).

The face-to-face interactions of preterm infants during the first few months of life (similar to their feeding interactions) have also been characterized by hypoactive, hyporesponsive infants and hyperactive mothers (Field, 1977b; Field, 1979a). In our studies of face-to-face interactions, the preterm infants were less responsive and showed more aversive behaviors (gaze aversion, squirming, and fussing). Their mothers were more stimulating in all modes (visual, tactile, auditory, and vestibular) during both the infant's eye contact and gaze aversion periods. A follow-up of these infants at 2 years (Field, 1979a) suggested that the mothers who were overactive during early face-to-face interactions were overprotective and overcontrolling later on. At 2-years old, the infants who had been visually inattentive during the early interactions were verbally less responsive and showed language delays.

Floor-play interactions of 8-month-old and 1-year-old preterm infants and their parents also featured less playing and smiling and more fretting by the infants (Goldberg, Brachfeld, & DiVitto, Chapter 8 of this volume). The parents of the preterm infants spent more time being close to, touching, and demonstrating toys than the parents of term infants.

The picture emerging from these analyses of different types of interactions (feeding, face to face, and floor play) at different stages during the first 2 years of life among preterm infants and their parents is one of a vicious cycle of the infant being relatively inactive and unresponsive, the parent trying to engage the infant by being more and more active or stimulating which, in turn, leads to more inactivity and unresponsivity on the part of the infant. Although the parent's activity appears to be directed at encouraging more activity or responsivity in the infant, that strategy is, in fact, counterproductive.

From the existing literature, it is difficult to determine how the factors of teenage mothering, lower-class status, or prematurity may combine to affect early interactions. The present study attempted to address this question. The approach to studying the interactions of these mother–infant dyads was as follows: (a) infant's interaction skills were assessed at birth and at 4 months; (b) mothers assessed their infants' interaction skills at birth and temperament at 4 months; and (c) mother and infant behaviors during feeding and face-to-face interactions were measured at 4 months by rating videotapes. Based on these studies, we hypothesized that the prematurity of the infant, teenage mothering, and lower-class status would have cumulative effects on early interactions— with the preterm infant–lower-class, teenage mother dyad experiencing the most difficult interactions.

METHOD

Sample

One hundred and sixty infant–mother dyads were assigned to eight groups according to the following criteria: (a) term–preterm infant; (b) age of mother (teenage–adult); and (c) socioeconomic status (lower or middle class). Twenty teenage–adult and lower middle-class mothers as well as preterm–term infants were recruited for each cell. Ethnicity was confounded with socioeconomic status because the available lower-class dyads were Black and the available middle-class dyads were White.

The criteria for term infants were 40-weeks gestation and a birthweight exceeding 2500 gm, and the criteria for preterm infants were less than 37-weeks gestation and a birthweight of less than 2500 gm. The teenage mothers were under 19-years old and the adult mothers were 20–29-years old. (The means for these measures appear in Table 7.1.)

Procedure

NEONATAL PERIOD

The infants were assessed at birth by examiners using the Brazelton Neonatal Behavioral Assessment Scale (BNBAS) (Brazelton, 1973) and by their mothers using the Mother's Assessment of the Behavior of her Infant Scale (MABI) (Field, Dempsey, Hallock, & Shuman, 1978a). The Brazelton performance was summarized according to the four a priori scoring dimensions

ABLE 7.1
Means for Neonatal and 4-month Measures

	Lower class				Middle class			
	Teen		Adult		Teen		Adult	
Measures	Preterm	Term	Preterm	Term	Preterm	Term	Preterm	Term
	Neonatal							
irth measurements								
Gestational age (days)	249	278	247	280	243	277	239	277
Birthweight (gm)	2347	3113	2370	3287	2235	3477	2116	3570
Ponderal index	2.13	2.17	2.28	2.45	2.31	2.37	2.48	2.52
razelton[a]								
Interactive	2.6	2.5	2.6	2.4	2.0	1.4	2.2	1.4
Motoric	2.7	2.2	2.6	2.2	2.6	2.1	2.6	1.9
State regulation	2.5	1.8	2.4	2.0	2.1	1.9	2.3	1.8
Response to stress	1.7	1.7	1.6	1.7	1.8	1.6	1.7	1.6
MABI[a]								
Interactive	2.2	2.1	2.2	2.1	2.2	1.5	2.3	1.6
Motoric	1.8	1.9	1.8	1.9	2.5	2.2	2.8	2.0
State regulation	2.2	2.0	2.2	2.0	2.0	1.9	2.2	1.8
Response to stress	2.0	1.9	2.0	1.9	1.7	1.8	1.7	1.7
	4 month							
Denver Motor	13	16	12	14	9	12	9	14
Carey Infant Temperament Questionnaire	4	4	4	3	3	2	3	2

[a] Lower ratings are optimal.

labeled interactive processes, motoric processes, state control, and response to stress (Als, Tronick, Lester, & Brazelton, 1978). The Brazelton assessments of the preterm infants were made just prior to their discharge (i.e., when the infants approximated term age, 37–40 weeks, as Brazelton and his colleagues have questioned the validity of their instrument for use with preterm infants. Differences relating to this broad age-range might still be expected. Nonetheless, we wanted to assess the newborn as he might present himself to his mother, and we considered the Brazelton Scale the most adequate measure of the newborn's interaction skills.

The MABI is an adaptation of the Brazelton Neonatal Behavioral Assessment Scale (Brazelton, 1973) and was designed to tap the mother's assessment of her infant's behaviors, including alertness and responsivity (Field *et al.*, 1978a). This scale was used to determine the degree of mother objectivity in assessing her infant as evaluated by a comparison of the mother's ratings on the MABI and the tester's independent ratings on the Brazelton Scale. Each of these two sets of ratings are summarized by four a priori scores (interactive, motor, state control, and response to stress). The MABI also provided a measure of how the mother viewed her infant's interactive abilities prior to her interactions with her infant (during the neonatal period) and following 1 month of interactions. In addition, this scale was used because a recent study suggested that mothers' assessments are highly correlated with those of the more objective testers (Field et al., 1978a).

4 MONTHS

At four-months old, infants were given the Denver Developmental Screening Test (Frankenburg & Dodds, 1967), and mothers assessed their infants' temperament on the Carey Infant Temperament Questionnaire (Carey, 1970). The Carey Infant Temperament Questionnaire was used because recent studies have reported relationships between Brazelton and Carey measures (Field et al., 1978b; Sostek & Anders, 1977). The Carey questionnaire is a mother's assessment of her infant's temperament, including questions relating to the infant's rhythmicity, intensity, adaptability, mood, distractability, and threshold to stimulation. A summary score that categorizes the infant as having a "difficult" or "easy" temperament is derived from these measures (Carey, 1970). Also at the 4-month evaluation, Mother–Infant feeding and face-to-face interactions were videotaped, eye contact and verbal activity were coded, and the interactions were rated on a number of behaviors summarized by our Interaction Rating Scales (IRS) (see Appendix).

Mother–Infant feeding and face-to-face interactions were assessed because previous studies by our group suggested some disturbed interactions among preterm infant–mother dyads (Field, 1977a,b). These interactions were coded on a number of variables, including the amount of infant gaze aversion, fussiness, maternal attentiveness, and stimulation. In addition, ratings were made according to the criteria outlined in our Interaction Rating Scales.

Feeding interactions were assessed as there are a number of studies suggesting differential sensitivity and different feeding attitudes of mothers. Studies by Kaye and Brazelton (1971) and by our group (Field, 1977a) suggest that the sensitive mother who views the feeding interaction as an opportunity for social interaction takes her cues from the infant and sensitively reserves her stimulation for pauses from feeding activity when the infant is otherwise unoccupied. Some mothers focus mainly on the feeding aspects of the situation and do not attend to the infant's sucking rhythms or feeding signals. They may be primarily interested in milk ingestion because their babies are small or difficult to feed. The differences may also relate to the temperament of the mother, infant, or both, but will invariably contribute to a peaceful or disturbed feeding interaction. The mother who is not sensitive to her infant's feeding rhythms may unwittingly contribute to infant colic or atypical amounts of milk ingestion, which could create further problems. For these reasons, feeding interactions were filmed and coded for maternal sensitivity to feeding rhythms (Field, 1977a), and a rating was made of both infant and mother feeding behaviors according to our feeding IRS. This scale includes feeding position, eye contact, contingent responsivity, and a number of other feeding behaviors.

Face-to-face interactions were assessed by taking into account the varied factors shown to be critical to harmonious interaction patterns. These include eye contact, variability of stimulation, infantized stimulation (i.e., a slowing down and exaggeration of maternal behaviors), imitative behavior on the part of the mother, contingent responsivity, and sensitive pacing and timing of behavior (e.g., respecting the infant's pauses or need to take breaks from the conversation) (Brazelton, Koslowski, & Main, 1974; Field, 1977b, 1978, 1979a,b; Stern, 1974; Tronick, Als, Adamson, Wise, & Brazelton, 1978). When the infant is either "difficult" (unresponsive or shows excessive gaze averting or fussiness) and/or the mother is hypoactive or hyperactive, the interaction is characteristically disturbed (Field, 1979c).

Data Analyses

Prior to data analyses, log transformations were made on those variables that were not normally distributed. Multivariate and univariate analyses of variance and subsequent multiple comparisons were performed for each assessment period to determine differences between the groups. As several ANOVAs were performed to determine the specific variables on which the groups differed, an error rate or p level per comparison was set at .001 in order to maintain an experimentwise error rate of .05.

RESULTS

Neonatal Measures (See Table 7.1 for Means)

BIRTH MEASUREMENTS

Analysis of birth measurements including gestational age, birthweight, and Ponderal Index (an assessment of appropriate weight for date) revealed the following: (a) birthweight was lower for preterm, for lower-class, and for the infants of lower-class teenage mothers; and (b) ponderal index data suggested that the lower-class, the teenage, and particularly the lower-class teenage mothers gave birth to small-for-date infants.

BRAZELTON NEONATAL BEHAVIORAL ASSESSMENT
SCALE PROCESS SCORES

Analyses of these data revealed the following: (a) preterm infants performed less optimally on all dimensions except for their response to stress; (b) lower class infants performed less optimally on the interactive process dimension; and (c) an interaction effect suggested that middle-class term infants performed more optimally than all other groups.

MOTHER'S ASSESSMENT OF THE BEHAVIOR OF HER INFANT

Analyses of these data suggested that (a) lower-class mothers rated their infants more optimally on the motoric process dimension; and (b) an interaction effect suggested that middle-class mothers rated their preterm infants less optimally on the motoric process dimension.

4-Month Measures

DENVER DEVELOPMENTAL SCREENING TEST

On the motor score of the Denver test the infants of lower-class mothers received higher ratings and the preterm infants received lower ratings.

CAREY INFANT TEMPERAMENT QUESTIONNAIRE

The mothers of the preterm infants and lower-class mothers rated their infants as more difficult on this temperament scale.

Interaction Ratings

As a number of significant main and interaction effects resulted from the analyses of feeding and face-to-face interactions by sex and birth status of the infant and by socioeconomic status and age of mother, they will be presented first, followed by interactions of these factors. The means for these measures appear in Tables 7.2 and 7.3.

MAIN EFFECTS FOR SEX OF INFANT

These were limited to only two effects: (a) males were held in a less optimal position during feeding; and (b) mothers were less persistent in feeding their female infants when they rejected the bottle.

TABLE 7.2
Means for Face-To-Face Interaction Ratings

	Lower class				Middle class			
	Teen		Adult		Teen		Adult	
Face-to-face interaction measures	Preterm	Term	Preterm	Term	Preterm	Term	Preterm	Term
Mother measures								
Time mother vocalizing (sec)	19.5	33.3	27.8	28.5	48.9	42.5	65.3	44.7
Ratings								
State	2.5	2.5	2.4	2.8	3.0	2.7	2.7	2.9
Physical activity	1.9	2.0	2.1	1.9	2.1	2.2	2.2	2.6
Head orientation	2.6	2.9	2.8	2.9	3.0	3.0	2.8	2.9
Gaze behavior	2.4	2.8	2.7	2.8	2.8	3.0	2.8	2.9
Silence during I gaze aversion	2.5	1.9	2.3	2.2	1.9	1.8	1.6	1.9
Facial expressions	2.2	2.6	2.7	2.6	2.7	2.6	2.6	2.8
Vocalizations	1.5	1.8	1.9	2.0	2.6	2.5	2.8	2.4
Infantized behavior	1.6	1.9	1.7	2.0	1.6	1.9	2.1	2.3
Contingent response	1.1	1.3	1.2	1.7	1.8	2.3	2.1	2.4
Game playing	1.1	1.4	1.2	1.4	1.4	1.9	1.5	2.5
Summary (mother face)	1.9	2.1	2.1	2.2	2.3	2.4	2.3	2.6
Infant measures								
Time infant gaze averted (sec)	69.0	66.6	65.9	52.5	49.5	26.7	43.0	33.1
Ratings								
State	2.8	2.9	2.9	2.9	2.6	2.7	2.8	3.0
Physical activity	2.8	2.9	2.8	2.6	2.5	2.5	2.2	2.7
Head orientation	2.1	2.4	1.9	2.2	2.4	2.5	2.5	2.6
Gaze behavior	2.0	2.3	2.1	2.4	2.4	2.6	2.3	2.5
Facial expressions	2.6	2.8	2.5	2.6	2.8	2.9	2.9	2.9
Fussiness	2.2	2.5	2.0	3.0	2.6	2.8	2.8	3.0
Vocalizations	2.3	2.4	2.2	2.2	2.4	2.7	2.6	2.9
Summary (infant face)	2.4	2.6	2.3	2.6	2.5	2.7	2.6	2.8

MAIN EFFECTS FOR BIRTH STATUS OF INFANT

Analyses of face-to-face interactions suggested that (a) preterm infants engaged in more head and gaze aversion and were less vocal, and (b) mothers of preterm infants were more verbal, less contingently responsive, and engaged in less infantized behavior and gameplaying.

During feeding interactions preterm infants were less persistent in feeding and mothers of preterm infants received less optimal summary ratings which

TABLE 7.3
Means for Feeding-Interaction Ratings

Feeding interaction measures	Lower class				Middle class			
	Teen		Adult		Teen		Adult	
	Preterm	Term	Preterm	Term	Preterm	Term	Preterm	Term
Mother measures								
Feeding position	1.3	1.8	1.5	1.9	1.8	2.0	2.0	2.2
State	1.9	1.9	2.0	1.9	2.1	1.9	2.3	2.7
Physical activity	1.4	2.1	2.1	2.6	1.6	2.3	1.8	2.4
Head orientation	1.9	2.3	1.8	1.8	2.0	2.4	2.0	2.8
Gaze behavior	2.1	2.3	2.1	2.5	2.1	2.3	2.1	2.7
Contingent response	2.8	2.8	2.7	2.8	2.4	2.8	2.5	2.9
Timing bottle removal	2.7	3.0	2.7	3.0	2.3	2.6	2.6	3.0
Burping	2.7	3.0	2.7	2.8	2.6	3.0	2.8	3.0
Persistence	2.1	2.2	2.0	2.3	2.1	2.5	2.2	2.6
Summary	2.1	2.4	2.2	2.4	2.1	2.4	2.3	2.7
Infant measures								
State	2.2	2.5	2.4	2.8	2.4	2.5	2.3	2.5
Physical activity	2.2	2.7	2.2	2.3	2.3	2.5	2.6	2.8
Head orientation	2.5	2.8	2.3	2.5	2.5	2.6	2.7	2.9
Gaze behavior	1.4	1.6	1.4	1.6	1.6	1.9	1.7	2.3
Persistence	1.8	2.3	2.1	2.4	2.1	2.7	2.0	2.2
Summary	2.0	2.4	2.1	2.3	2.2	2.4	2.3	2.5

related to their holding their infants in a less optimal position and engaging in less eye contact but more physical activity and more burping.

Main Effects for Socioeconomic Status of the Mother

Analyses of the Mother, face-to-face interaction measures revealed that (a) lower-class mothers vocalized for lesser proportions of the time, and (b) lower-class mothers received more optimal ratings on silence during gaze aversion but less optimal ratings on the physical activity, vocalizations, infantized behavior, contingent responsivity, gameplaying, and summary measures that derived from their showing lesser amounts of these behaviors. Analyses of the ratings on infants during face-to-face interactions suggested that (a) infants of lower-class mothers used gaze aversion for a greater proportion of the time, and (b) infants of lower-class mothers received less optimal ratings on head orientation, gaze behavior, facial expressions, vocalizations, and animation.

Analyses of feeding interactions revealed that lower-class mothers held their infants in a less optimal feeding position and showed more head aversion during feedings.

Main Effects for Age of Mother

Analyses of face-to-face interactions suggested that (a) teenage mothers were less vocal, less contingently responsive, and engaged in less game playing during face-to-face interactions, and (b) during feeding interactions, they held their infants in a less optimal position and gazed less often at their infants.

Second and Higher Order Interaction Effects

Interaction effects for face-to-face interactions suggested the following: (a) lower-class teenage mothers received less optimal ratings on facial expressions (particularly with females); (b) teenage mothers of preterm infants engaged in less game playing and (c) lower-class teenage mothers of preterm infants received less optimal ratings on vocalizations, facial expressions, and gameplaying and engaged in more head and gaze aversion with preterm infants.

Interaction effects for feeding interactions suggested that (a) lower-class mothers of preterm infants received less optimal, feeding summary ratings related to their engaging in more head and gaze aversions, and (b) lower-class teenage mothers held their preterm infants in a less optimal feeding position.

DISCUSSION

Analyses of these data in general suggested that mothers of preterm infants, lower-class mothers, and teenage mothers experienced some difficulties in relating to their infants. Being born to a lower-class mother or being born preterm appeared to pose some problems for the infants, but being born to a teenage mother, despite her interaction difficulties, did not seem to add significantly to the problems of the lower-class preterm infants during these first months of infancy.

The picture that emerged on the preterm infant–mother dyad was similar to that described in previous studies. The preterm infant received less optimal Brazelton ratings except for the physiological response to stress (Brown & Bakeman, 1979; DiVitto & Goldberg, 1979; Field, 1977b). They also received less optimal ratings on the MABI, at least in the middle-class sample (Field, Dempsey, Hallock, & Shuman, 1978a). At age 4 months, the preterm infants received less optimal Denver motor ratings and temperament ratings (Field, Hallock, Ting, Dempsey, Dabiri, & Shuman, 1978c). During face-to-face interactions, they showed more head and gaze aversion and were less vocal (Field, 1977b). Their mothers, however, were more verbal (Cohen & Beckwith,

1976; DiVitto & Goldberg, 1979; Field, 1977b). Although the data of Brown and Bakeman (1979) suggest that this finding generalizes to lower-class Black mothers, the lower-class Black mothers of preterm infants in this sample were the least verbal of the mothers. Perhaps the film methodology we employed inhibited these mothers more than a silent observer would have. Although mothers of preterm infants generally were more verbal, they engaged in less infantized, contingently responsive, and game playing behaviors (Field, 1979d).

The less persistent feeding of the preterm infant is consistent with previous findings (Field, 1977a). The less optimal, noncradling position used by the mothers of preterm infants is similar to the feeding position differences reported by DiVitto & Goldberg (1979). The greater amount of physical activity and burping during feedings might be explained by their infants' relative lack of persistence in feeding.

Infants born to lower-class as opposed to middle-class mothers were lower in birthweight and received lower Ponderal indexes, suggesting that they were small for date. Because some have suggested even poorer developmental outcomes for small-for-date than for preterm infants, the lower-class infants may be at a particular risk (Neligan, Kolvin, Scott & Garside, 1976). Less optimal Brazelton interactive process scores have been previously noted for small-for-date infants by Als and her colleagues (Als, Tronick, Adamson, & Brazelton, 1976). Unlike the middle-class mothers, the lower-class mothers assigned their infants more optimal MABI scores (particularly motor scores), which were different from the examiners' ratings on the Brazelton. This finding plus the lower-class mothers' failure to differentiate the performance of term and preterm infants raises questions concerning the validity of the MABI ratings of lower-class mothers. In contrast, middle-class mothers have been noted to be in fairly close agreement with Brazelton examiners on the MABI scale (Field et al., 1978a, 1978b), and lower-class mothers are reportedly in close agreement with independent ratings on the Caldwell Home Scale and on the Denver (Frankenburg, 1978). The lack of agreement in this study suggests that either lower-class mothers experienced more difficulty with the task, possibly due to reduced literacy, or that they were biased about their newborn's behavior (particularly in the motoric dimension) regardless of the infants' gestational age.

At 4 months, the lower-class mothers rated their infants as having more difficult temperaments. Again, the lower-class mothers, unlike the middle-class mothers, did not differentiate between term and preterm infants. This effect was particularly notable in the teenage lower-class group. The lower-class infants, however, performed more optimally on the motor items of the Denver Scale. Perhaps the lower-class mothers' more optimal view of their infants' motor abilities at birth (on the MABI) contributed to better motor performance of their infants at 4 months via a practice or expectancy effect. Because the lower-class sample was Black, racial differences may also account for their motoric advantage at 4 months. Black infants have previously been noted to perform more optimally on the Bayley Motor Scale at 8 months.

In the same way that the lower-class mothers' higher ratings of their neonates' motor performance may have contributed to their better motor performance at 4 months, the infants' lesser interaction skills at birth may have contributed to their lesser interaction skills at 4 months (Field, 1977b). Like the lower-class infants of Lewis and Wilson (1972) who smiled and vocalized less, the lower-class infants of this sample were less vocal, less expressive, and less animated. Similarly, the lower-class mothers engaged in less verbal activity (Bee et al., 1969; Kilbride et al., 1977; Tulkin & Kagan, 1972) contingent responsivity (Lewis & Wilson, 1972), physical activity, infantized behavior, and gameplaying (Field & Pawlby, 1980). Their infants, in turn, showed more head and gaze aversion. Overall, the lower-class infants in this study showed less optimal interactive skills at birth (not unlike the preterm infants as a group) and in both preterm and lower-class infants there appeared to be a continuity in these deficits across the first 4 months. The mother's activity levels differed, with the lower-class mother being hypoactive and the middle-class mother of the preterm being hyperactive. Both the hypoactivity of the lower-class mothers and the hyperactivity of the middle-class mothers may be their means of coping with less responsive infants. In any case, both levels of maternal activity may be arousing and may contribute to gaze aversion in the infant in accordance with an inverted "U" shape function. Either extremely high or extremely low levels of stimulation may be arousing (Fiske & Maddi, 1961) and produce differences in early interactions (Field, 1979c). It should be noted, however, that the significance attached to maternal stimulation and eye contact may vary with cultures, as lower levels of maternal stimulation and eye contact have been noted in other cultures such as Britain (Field & Pawlby, 1980), Africa (Keefer, 1977), Japan (Caudill, 1972), and the South Pacific islands (Martini, 1979; Zaslow, Sostek, Vietze, Kreiss, & Rubenstein, 1979). Similarly, the noncradling position and the less frequent alignments of the lower-class mother's head with that of the baby during feeding may relate to a cultural or ethnic difference in feeding-interaction patterns. Unfortunately, socioeconomic status and ethnic or cultural differences are confounded in this study.

The teenage offspring, who were the initial focus of this study, have taken on less significance as a topic of discussion because fewer maternal-age effects than effects of birth status and socioeconomic status were noted for the infants in this sample. The teenage offspring showed a lower mean Ponderal index, but in other ways were not differentiated from adult offspring. The teenage mothers, however, differed from adult mothers in a number of their interaction behaviors. For example, they were less verbal during face-to-face interactions (Sandler & Vietze, 1979), less contingently responsive, and engaged in game playing less often. During feedings, the teenage mothers held their infants in a noncradled position and gazed less frequently at their infants.

Higher-order interactions of the factors of maternal age, socioeconomic status, and infant birth status suggested that the lower-class teenage mothers of preterm infants in particular were the least vocal, the least expressive facially, played infant games the least frequently, and held their infants in a noncradling feeding position most often. Thus, although the preterm infants of lower-class teenage mothers were characteristically similar to the preterm offspring of adult lower-class mothers, the teenage mothers were less active during interactions. The smallness for date of their infants may have contributed to their lesser responsivity. Or, they may have been less responsive because of their reputedly less realistic developmental milestones and less desireable childrearing attitudes (DeLissovoy, 1973). In any case, the lesser responsivity of the lower-class teenage mothers of preterm infants may not have any differential effects on the offspring until later in development. Similar to the transactional model of Sameroff and Chandler (1975), the smallness for date at birth may contribute to differences in maternal interaction patterns, which, in turn, may contribute to differences in infant developmental patterns at a later age. Alternatively, social class, teenage mothering, and preterm delivery may combine in various other ways as more important risk factors than the particular combination reflected in the title of this chapter. In any case, the first 4 months of infancy may be "too soon to tell."

ACKNOWLEDGEMENTS

I thank the mothers and infants who participated in this study. Further thanks are owed to Sue Widmayer who was instrumental in data collection, coding, and analyses, and to the graduate students who assisted in data collection. This research was supported by Office of Human Development grants #OHD 0090CI764-01 and OHD 90-C-1358 to Tiffany M. Field.

APPENDIX: INTERACTION RATING SCALES (IRS)[1]

Face-to-Face Ratings

INFANT RATINGS

A. State rating (.91)[2]
   1. predominantly drowsy
   2. somewhat drowsy
   3. predominantly alert

[1] The ratings of these scales derive from those measures which differentiated middle- and lower-class high-risk and normal 4-month-old infant-mother dyads in microanalyses of 120 videotaped feeding and face-to-face interactions.
[2] Numbers in parentheses are interobserver reliabilities.

B. Physical activity (.82)
    1. frequent squirming or arching of back
    2. occasional squirming or arching of back
    3. relaxed body with cycling of limbs toward mother

C. Head orientation (.96)
    1. frequent head aversion
    2. occasional head aversion
    3. rare head aversion

D. Gaze behavior (.85)
    1. seldom looks at mother
    2. sometimes looks at mother
    3. frequently looks at mother

E. Facial expressions (.84)
    1. frequent pouting or cry face
    2. bland expression
    3. occasional smiling or "contented" expression

F. Fussiness (.96)
    1. frequent fussing or crying
    2. occasional fussing
    3. no fussing

G. Vocalizations (.82)
    1. no vocalizations
    2. a few vocalizations
    3. several vocalizations

Infant Face-to-Face Rating = Total/7_____

MOTHER RATINGS

A. State rating (.83)
    1. predominantly depressed or anxious looking
    2. somewhat depressed or anxious looking
    3. alert and attentive

B. Physical activity (.83)
    1. minimal activity or overly active
    2. moderate activity
    3. some activity

C. Head orientation (.96)
    1. frequent head aversion
    2. occasional head aversion
    3. infrequent head aversion

D. Gaze behavior (.92)
    1. seldom looks at infant
    2. sometimes looks at infant
    3. constantly looks at infant

E. Silence during infant gaze aversion (.82)

    1. rarely quiet when infant looking away
    2. sometimes quiet when infant looking away
    3. usually quiet when infant looking away

F. Facial expressions (.83)

    1. flat or tense expression
    2. alternatively flat or tense and contented
    3. frequent smiling or "contented" expression

G. Vocalizations (.92)

    1. constant, noncontingent talking or no talking
    2. moderate amount of talking and somewhat contingent
    3. contingent talking and sensitive pacing of vocalizations

H. Infantized behaviors (.91)

    1. never imitative of infant or no simplified behaviors
    2. sometimes imitative and some simplified behaviors
    3. frequent imitative and simplified behaviors

 I. Contingent responsivity (.82)

    1. rarely responds in kind or with short latency to infant behaviors
    2. sometimes responds in kind or with short latency to infant behaviors
    3. often responds in kind or with short latency to infant behaviors

 J. Game playing (.98)

    1. rarely plays infant, age-appropriate games
    2. sometimes plays infant, age-appropriate games
    3. often plays infant, age-appropriate games

Mother Face-to-Face Rating = Total/10_____

Feeding Ratings

INFANT RATINGS

A. State Rating (.94)

    1. predominantly drowsy
    2. somewhat drowsy
    3. predominantly alert

B. Physical activity (.87)

    1. frequent squirming
    2. occasional squirming
    3. relaxed body, molding to mother

C. Head orientation (.92)

    1. frequent head aversion
    2. occasional head aversion
    3. rare head aversion

D. Gaze behavior (.89)

    1. seldom looks at mother
    2. sometimes looks at mother
    3. frequently looks at mother

E. Persistence in feeding (.91)

    1. frequent rejection of nipple
    2. occasional rejection of nipple
    3. rare rejection of nipple

Infant Feeding Rating = Total/5_____

MOTHER RATINGS

A. Feeding position (.98)

    (note whether baby is held on right (1) or left (2) side)
    1. holds baby in lap position
    2. holds baby with head cradled
    3. holds baby with head and legs cradled

B. State rating (.83)

    1. predominantly depressed or anxious looking
    2. somewhat depressed or anxious looking
    3. alert and attentive

C. Physical activity (.81)

    1. overly active
    2. moderate activity
    3. minimal activity

D. Head orientation (.95)

    1. frequent head aversion
    2. occasional head aversion
    3. infrequent head aversion

E. Gaze behavior (.92)

    1. seldom looks at infant
    2. sometimes looks at infant
    3. constantly looks at infant

F. Contingent vocalization (.84)

    1. frequent vocalization during sucking
    2. occasional vocalization during sucking
    3. rare vocalization during sucking

G. Timing of bottle removal (.82)

    1. frequently initiated by mother
    2. occasionally initiated by mother
    3. rarely initiated by mother

H. Burping (.97)

1. frequent burping
2. occasional burping
3. rare burping

I. Persistence of feeding by mother (.84)

1. persistence in feeding as infant rejects bottle
2. some persistence in feeding as infant rejects bottle
3. little persistence in feeding as infant rejects bottle

Mother Feeding Rating = Total/9 _____

REFERENCES

Als, H., Tronick, E., Adamson, L., & Brazelton, T. B. The behavior of the full-term yet underweight newborn infant. *Developmental medicine and child nurology,* 1976, *18,* 590–594.

Als, H., Tronick, E., Lester, B. M., & Brazelton, T. B. The Brazelton Neonatal Behavioral Assessment Scale (BNBAS). *Journal of Abnormal Child Psychology,* 1977, *5,* 215–231.

Bee, H. L., VanEgeren, L. F., Streissguth, A. P., Nyman, B. A., & Lockie, M. S. Social class differences in maternal teaching styles and speech patterns. *Developmental Psychology,* 1969, *1,* 726–734.

Brazelton, T. B. *Neonatal behavioral assessment scale.* London: Heineman (National Spastics Society Monograph), 1973.

Brazelton, T. B., Koslowski, B., & Main, M. The origins of reciprocity: The early mother–infant interaction. In M. Lewis & L. Rosenblum (Eds.), *The effect of the infant on its caregiver.* New York: Wiley, 1974.

Brown, J. V., & Bakeman, R. Relationships of human mothers with their infants during the first year of life: Effect of prematurity. In R. W. Bell & W. P. Smotherman (Eds.), *Maternal influences and early behavior.* New York: Spectrum, 1979.

Carey, W. B. A simplified method of measuring infant temperament. *Journal of Pediatrics,* 1970, *77,* 188–194.

Caudill, W. Tiny dramas: Vocal communication between mother and infant in Japanese and American families. In W. P. Lebra (Ed.), *Transcultural research in mental health.* Honolulu, Hawaii: East–West Center Press, 1972.

Cohen, E. S., & Beckwith, L. Maternal language in infancy. *Developmental Psychology,* 1976, *12,* 371–372.

DeLissovoy, V. Child care by adolescent parents. *Children Today,* 1973, *2,* 22–25.

DiVitto, B., & Goldberg, S. The effects of newborn medical status on early parent–infant interaction. In T. Field, A. Sostek, S. Goldberg, & Shuman, H. H. (Eds.), *Infants born at risk.* New York: Spectrum, 1979.

Field, T. Maternal stimulation during infant feeding. *Developmental Psychology,* 1977, *13,* 539–540. (a)

Field, T. Effects of early separation, interactive deficits, and experimental manipulations on infant–mother face-to-face interaction. *Child Development,* 1977, *48,* 763–771. (b)

Field, T. The three Rs of infant-adult interactions: Rhythms, repertoires, and responsivity. *Journal of Pediatric Psychology,* 1978, *3,* 131–136.

Field, T. Interaction patterns of high-risk and normal infants. In T. Field, A. Sostek, S. Goldberg, & Shuman, H. H. (Eds.), *Infants born at risk.* New York: Spectrum, 1979. (a)

Field, T. Visual and cardiac responses to animate and inanimate faces by young term and preterm infants. *Child Development,* 1979, *50,* 188–195.

Field, T. Interactions of high risk infants: Quantitative and qualitative differences. In D. B. Sawin, R. C. Hawkins, L. O. Walker, & J. H. Penticuff (Eds.), *Current perspectives on psychosocial risks during pregnancy and early infancy.* New York: Brunner-Mazel, 1979. (c)

Field, T. Games parents play with normal and high-risk infants. *Child Psychiatry and Human Development,* 1979, *10,* 41–48. (d)

Field, T., Dempsey, J., Hallock, N., & Shuman, H. H. Mothers' assessments of the behavior of their infants. *Infant behavior and development,* 1978, *1,* 156–167. (a)

Field, T., Dempsey, J., & Shuman, H. H. Developmental follow-up of preterm infants surviving the respiratory distress syndrome. In T. Field, A. Sostek, S. Goldberg, & H. H. Shuman (Eds.), *Infants born at risk.* New York: Spectrum, 1979.

Field, T., Hallock, N., Dempsey, J., Dabiri, C., & Shuman, H. H. A first year follow-up of high-risk infants: Formulating a cumulative risk index. *Child Development,* 1978, *49,* 119–131. (c)

Field, T., Hallock, N., Dempsey, J., & Shuman, H. H. Mothers' assessment of term infants and preterm infants with respiratory distress syndrome: Reliability and predictive validity. *Child Psychiatry and Human Development,* 1978, *1,* 156–167. (b)

Field, T., & Pawlby, S. Early face-to-face interactions of British and American working and middle class mother-infant dyads. *Child Development,* 1980, *51.*

Fiske, D. W., & Maddi, S. R. *Functions of Varied Experience.* Springfield, Illinois: Dorsey Press, 1961.

Frankenberg, W. K. Personal communication, 1978.

Frankenberg, W. K., & Dodds, J. B. The Denver Developmental Screening Test. *Journal of Pediatrics,* 1967, *71,* 181–185.

Kaye, K., & Brazelton, T. B. *Mother–infant interaction in the organization of sucking.* Paper presented at meeting of the Society for Research in Child Development, Minneapolis, Minnesota, April, 1971.

Keefer, C. *A cross-cultural study of face-to-face interaction and its developmental functions.* Paper presented at the biennial meeting of the Society For Research in Child Development, New Orleans, 1977.

Kilbride, H. W., Johnson, D. L., & Streissguth, A. P. Social class, birth order, and newborn experience. *Child Development,* 1977, *48,* 1686–1688.

Lewis, M., & Wilson, C. D. Infant development in lower class American families. *Human Development,* 1972, *15,* 112–127.

Martini, M. Interactions between caretakers and infants on the Marquesan Island of Ua Pou. In T. Field, A. Sostek, & P. Vietze (Eds.), *Culture and early interactions.* Hillsdale, New Jersey: Lawrence Erlbaum, 1979.

Neligan, E. A., Kolvin, I., Scott, D. McL., & Garside, R. F. *Born too soon or born too small.* Philadelphia: Lippincott, 1976.

Sameroff, A. J., & Chandler, M. J. Reproductive risk & the continuum of caretaking casualty. In F. D. Horowitz, M. Hetherington, S. Scarr-Salapatek, & G. Siegel (Eds.), *Review of child development research* (Vol. 4). Chicago, Illinois: Univ. Chicago Press, 1975.

Sandler, H. M., & Vietze, P. M. Obstetric and neonatal outcomes following intervention. In K. Scott, T. Field & E. Robertson (Eds.), *Teenage parents and their offspring.* New York: Grune & Stratton, 1979.

Sostek, A. M., & Anders, T. F. Relationships among the Brazelton Neonatal Scale, Bayley Infant Scales, and early temperament. *Child Development,* 1977, *48,* 320–323.

Stern, D. N. Mother and infant at play: The dyadic interaction involving facial, vocal, and gaze behaviors. In M. Lewis & L. A. Rosenblum (Eds.), *The effect of the infant on its caregiver.* New York: Wiley, 1974.

Sudia, C. Personal communication, 1978.

Tronick, E., Als, H., Adamson, L., Wise, S., & Brazelton, T. B. The infant's response to entrapment between contradictory messages in face-to-face interaction. *Journal of Child Psychiatry,* 1978, *17,* 1-13.

Tulkin, S., & Kagan, J. Mother-child interaction in the first few years of life. *Child Development,* 1972, *43,* 31-41.

Zaslow, M., Sostek, A., Vietze, P., Kreiss, L., & Rubinstein, D. Contribution of context to interactions with infants in Fais and the U.S.A. In T. Field, A. Sostek, & P. Vietze (Eds.), *Culture and early interactions.* Hillsdale, New Jersey: Lawrence Erlbaum Associates, 1979.

CHAPTER **8**

SUSAN GOLDBERG
SHEILA BRACHFELD
BARBARA DIVITTO

Feeding, Fussing, and Play: Parent-Infant Interaction in the First Year as a Function of Prematurity and Perinatal Medical Problems

INTRODUCTION

In early studies of the development of infants born prematurely, it was assumed that the sequelae of prematurity were confined to the infant alone. Thus, follow-up assessments were directed toward evaluation of the physical and cognitive development of the child and sometimes his or her emotional adjustment. Furthermore, it was assumed that, like most other children, the preterm infant was likely to develop optimally in a supportive environment and poorly in an inadequate one. Hence, follow-up assessments often included relatively global assessments of the environment as potential influences on the infant's development. The infant and the environment (including caregivers) were envisioned as independent entities with the environment having important influences on the infant.

More recently, the significance of the care-giving environment as a predictor of subsequent development in the preterm infant has been underscored. In a 1975 review, Sameroff and Chandler concluded that the caregiving environment was a more potent predictor of developmental outcomes than early medical events or assessments. A recent comprehensive study of a large sample of preterm infants (Sigman & Parmelee, 1979) indicated that measures of the infant–caregiver relationship were essential for differentiating infants continuing at risk from those developing normally. Consequently, one important rea-

133

HIGH-RISK INFANTS AND CHILDREN:
Adult and Peer Interactions

son for studying patterns of interaction in families with preterm infants is that they hold vital clues to understanding the sequelae of prematurity and making long-term predictions about development.

Those studies that have made systematic comparisons between patterns of interaction in full-term and preterm dyads have reported consistent group differences in the developing parent–infant relationship (see Goldberg, 1978 for a review of these studies). At hospital discharge, preterm infants were found to be less alert and responsive than their full-term counterparts (DiVitto & Goldberg, 1979; Field, 1977). In addition, they were more poorly organized in their motor coordination and in their modulation of states of arousal. Initially, parents of preterm infants appeared to be less actively involved with their infants than parents of full-term babies. They made less body contact with their infants (DiVitto & Goldberg, 1979; Leifer, Leiderman, Barnett, & Williams, 1972; Kalus, Kennell, Plumb, & Zuelke, 1970) spent less time face-to-face (Klaus *et al.*, 1970), smiled at their infants less (Leifer *et al.*, 1972), touched them less (DiVitto & Goldberg, 1979; Klaus *et al.*, 1970; Leifer *et al.*, 1972), and talked to them less (DiVitto & Goldberg, 1979). Observations of older infants and their parents report that parents were more actively involved with those infants who had more medical problems (Beckwith & Cohen, 1978). Furthermore, while parents exerted more effort in interacting with their preterm infants, their babies engaged less readily and actively in the task at hand (Brown & Bakeman, 1979; Field, 1977). These studies seem to indicate that the parent–infant relationship in preterm dyads may follow a different course of development from full-term dyads.

Under normal conditions, the behavioral repertoires of young infants and their parents appear to be well adapted for the development of harmonious reciprocal interactions (Goldberg, 1977; Stern, 1974, 1977). In contrast, the preterm infant, being less well-adapted (as evidenced by immaturity associated with poorer organization and lowered responsiveness) makes unusual demands on caregiving abilities. Parents of such infants may need to make unusual adaptations or require more time to establish a satisfactory relationship. Therefore, it is not only the baby who is affected by the event of premature birth. There are important consequences for the care-giving environment as well. The infant and the environment constitute a system with reciprocally influential components. A disturbance or inadequacy in one part stresses the system, and unless unusual resources are available to cope with such stress, it is likely that disturbance or inadequacy in other components will surface. Within this framework, it is not surprising to find that preterm infants are overrepresented in reported cases of child abuse and failure to thrive (Elmer & Gregg, 1967; Goldson, Fitch, Wendell, & Knapp, 1978; Klein & Stern, 1971; Shaheen, Alexander, Truskovsky, & Barbero, 1968). Although the vast majority of parents and their preterm infants do make successful adjustments, the risk of interactive difficulties in this group is relatively high. Therefore, it is likely that descriptions of the ways in which preterm and full-term dyads differ can provide clues to the etiology of interactive disturbances.

With this in mind, we began a longitudinal study of Parent–Infant interaction during the first year in families presumed to differ in risk for interactive difficulty as a consequence of prematurity and associated, neonatal medical problems. We reasoned that as infant medical problems increased, infants would be behaviorally more limited in social experience and skills at the time of hospital discharge, and parents would be more worried and anxious. Furthermore, severity of medical complications would be correlated with the length of hospitalization and the extent to which normal parent–infant relations would be disrupted by hospital procedures. Thus, we expected to find systematic variations in interactive behavior correlated with these presumed stresses on the parent–infant dyad. Therefore, in contrast with prior studies comparing full-term and preterm dyads (e.g., Brown & Bakeman, 1979; Leifer et al., 1972), we divided preterm infants into groups according to their medical problems, thus selecting groups from points along a presumed continuum of interactive risk rather than setting up a dichotomy.

Furthermore, our sample was predominantly a White middle-class sample with good medical care in a hospital with extensive supports for early Parent–Infant interaction. Hence, they represent a relatively advantaged portion of the preterm population. Many of the confounding factors usually associated with prematurity are absent in this group and cannot account for observed group differences. Subsequent administration of the Home Observation for Measurement of the Environment (HOME) inventory (Caldwell, B., Heider, J., & Kaplan, B., 1966), for example, revealed no group differences in this respect.

Finally, we did not correct infant ages for prematurity in scheduling appointments. The preterm infants were therefore developmentally younger than their full-term counterparts at each assessment. We reasoned that developmental immaturity was part of the preterm infant–parent relationship, and that it would be inappropriate to omit it from the design. Where it appeared that infant immaturity might explain group differences, we later added a cross-sectional group of age-matched, full-term infants as additional controls.

Each dyad was observed eight times in the course of the infant's first year, thus providing extensive longitudinal interaction data. Four of these assessments were scheduled in the second half of the first year where data from prior studies are especially sparse (Goldberg, 1978). Detailed presentation of the data for each age period appear elsewhere (Brachfeld, Goldberg, & Sloman, 1979; DiVitto & Goldberg, 1979). In this chapter we will present an overview of the group comparisons made in the first year of life, indicating at what ages and in what situations we did and did not find group differences.

In the study of infant cognitive development, the data suggest that preterm infants develop at the same rate as their full-term counterparts with a lag attributable to prematurity. Because the extent of prematurity becomes a relatively smaller proportion of the life span with increasing age, the initial differences between groups gradually diminish (Hunt & Rhodes, 1977). It is possible that a similar pattern characterizes the development of Parent–Infant interaction. Part of this chapter will, therefore, examine the data to ascertain whether differences between preterm and full-term dyads are (like cognitive developmental phenomena) primarily attributable to immaturity differences or there exist qualitative differences acting instead of, or in addition to, developmental lags. Finally, to provide some perspective on the infant's behavioral contribution to the interaction, we present data on behavior ratings of the infant arising from interactions with the project staff.

PROCEDURES AND FINDINGS

Four groups of infants were selected for study. The criteria for making this selection were based on the assumption that the more severe the infant's medical problems at birth, the more stressful the initial experiences of both infant and parents would be, therefore, more interactive difficulties would be expected. Thus, the continuum along which the groups were selected was one of increasing medical complications, and increasing risks for subsequent developmental problems.

Ten first-born infants from intact families were selected in each of four groups: healthy full-term infants (FT), healthy preterm infants (HP), sick (respiratory distress) preterm infants (SP) and preterm infants born to diabetic mothers (IDM). The IDM group was selected as being highly vulnerable to complications of prematurity and subsequent problems. In addition, nurses had described these babies as behaviorally unresponsive. They were expected, therefore, to be similar to the sick preterm group but with some additional developmental risk (Lubchenco, 1976). Table 8.1 summarizes some characteristics of these four groups. It can be seen that they differed systematically on most indicators of medical status. (For a detailed description of the sample and selection criteria, see DiVitto & Goldberg, 1979).

Families were enrolled in the study before the infant was discharged from the hospital. Insofar as possible, we tried to ensure that the groups had similar distributions with respect to gender, initial feeding method, and socioeconomic status. In every case where the duration of the infant's hospital stay exceeded that of the mother, the infant had been visited daily by one or both parents. Early studies of Parent–Infant interaction with preterm infants reported an average frequency of parent visiting of once every 6 days or less (Fanaroff, Kennell, & Klaus, 1972; Leifer et al., 1972). In a more recent study, Minde and his

TABLE 8.1
Sample Characteristics[a]

Group	Sex	Initial feeding method	X̄ Birth						
			X̄ Gestational age (in weeks)	Weight (gms)	X̄ 1-min Apgar	X̄ 5-min Apgar	X̄ days in hospital	Morbidity index
Full-term normal (FT)	5 M	4 Breast	39.5	3260	8.6	9.3	3.5	9.8
	5 F	6 Bottle	(38–41)[b]	(2920–3685)	(8–9)	(9–10)	(3–5)	
Healthy prematures (HP)	6 M	5 Breast	34.8	1928	7.1	8.7	13.2	42.2
	4 F	5 Bottle	(31–37)	(1531–2147)	(4–9)	(7–10)	(6–28)	
Sick premature (SP)	5 M	4 Breast	30.3	1531	6.4	7.6	34.6	60.3
	5 F	6 Bottle	(26–33)	(879–2438)	(4–8)	(6–9)	(9–69)	
Infants of diabetic mothers (IDM)	2 M	3 Breast	36.6	3232	6.1	8.2	11.7	64.3
	8 F	7 Bottle	(31–39)	(1417–3941)	(1–8)	(5–9)	(4–40)	

[a] Adapted from DiVito, B., & Goldberg, S. Effects of neonatal status on early parent-infant interaction. In T. Field, A. Sostek, S. Goldberg, & H.H. Shuman (Eds.), *Infants born at risk: Behavior and development.* New York: Spectrum, 1979.
[b] Figures in parentheses are ranges for each measure

137

colleagues (Minde, Trehub, Carter, Boukydis, Celhoffer, & Marton, 1978) suggest that two visits per week was a high visiting frequency in their sample. Consequently, although our preterm infants were initially separated from their parents more often and for longer periods of time than the full-term group, they had more frequent early contacts than the preterm infants in previous research projects.

Assessments on the Bayley scales over the course of the first year indicated that the development of all infants was within normal range with correction for prematurity. However, from the parents' point of view, it is clear that those with preterm infants had to wait longer for the achievement of developmental milestones and felt that their babies were "slower" or "behind." During the pediatric interview at each laboratory visit, parents were asked about the new skills their infant's had acquired. Table 8.2 shows the average postnatal age of achieving developmental milestones as reported by parents. With the limitations of parental reports in mind, one can see that parents in the preterm groups did have to wait longer than their full-term counterparts to see positive signs of growth and development in their children. For example, in the sick preterm and IDM groups, some infants were still not sleeping through the night at 1-year old. Therefore, although we can consider all three of our preterm groups as developing within normal expectations, parents in these groups had to "put up with" immature and sometimes frustrating behavior for a longer period of time than did parents of full-term infants.

Parent-Infant Interaction

Parent–Infant interactions were assessed in two different situations. Each was chosen to represent a salient aspect of the parent–infant relationship at particular ages. In the early months (neonatal and 4-month assessments), feeding was chosen for its ubiquity as the context in which most early Parent–Infant interaction takes place in our culture. Home and laboratory visits were scheduled so that they would include a routine feeding. Parents determined when the infant needed to be fed and when feeding was to be terminated. Except for adjustments necessitated by the relatively strange situation of the laboratory, parents were instructed to follow their usual feeding routine.

For the 8- and 12-month observations, we chose floor play as more representative of the time parents spend with older infants. Whether in the home or the laboratory, we provided four age-appropriate toys and instructed the parents to behave in the way they would normally behave when the infant was playing. Unlike the feeding session which varied in length according to the parent's judgment, the play sessions were each 15 min in duration. In some cases where the infant became distressed and could not be comforted, play sessions were terminated before the 15 min had elapsed.

TABLE 8.2

Mean Age of Achieving Developmental Milestones Reported by Parents

Behavior	FT $\overline{X}$	FT Range	HP $\overline{X}$	HP Range	SP $\overline{X}$	SP Range	IDM $\overline{X}$	IDM Range
Smile (weeks)	5.0	3–8	8.2	0–13[a]	13.8	0–20[a]	6.9	1–12
Sleep all night (weeks)	8.2	4–10	11.5	3–18	13.7	8–?[b]	11.7	1½–?[b]
Turn front to back (months)	4.0	2–7½	3.6	½–8½	5.7	3–8	4.1	3–7
Turn back to front (months)	4.2	2½–7½	5.3	3½–7½	6.6	3–9	4.5	½–7½
Transfer objects hand to hand (months)	4.8	3½–6	6.3	5–7½	7.4	5½–10	5.7	3½–9½
Sit (months)	6.5	4–8	8.1	6–9	8.4	7–10	7.6	5–10
Pincer grasp (months)	7.9	7–10	10.4	7½–?[c]	9.8	8–?[c]	9.2	8–?[c]
Walk	11.5	10–13	—[d]		—[d]		—[d]	

[a]One mother in HP group and one in SP reported smiling from birth. These mothers probably treated reflex smiles as social smiles.

[b]There were 2 SP infants and 1 IDM infant not sleeping all night by 12 months. The means are based on the remaining infants.

[c]One HP infant, 2 SP, and 1 IDM infant were not showing pincer grasp ability at 1 year. The means are based on the remaining infants.

[d]No HP or SP infants were walking at 1 year. However, four IDM infants were walking.

Where both mothers and fathers were present, we allowed them to choose who was to interact with the baby. Fathers participated in 7 feeding observations and 13 play observations. Although fathers were more likely to participate in the preterm groups, there was some father participation in all groups (Goldberg, 1979). Preliminary comparisons indicated that, within each group, there were no significant differences in mother and father behavior for the variables we analysed.

At each observation session two observers coded preselected parent and infant behaviors on a time-marked code sheet in 10-sec blocks.[1] For the feedings, the behaviors coded included whether the infant's eyes were open, whether the infant was sucking, and motor and vocal behaviors. For the parent, the observers coded the care-giving activity (e.g., feeding, burping, cleaning, play), the position in which the infant was held, and motor, vocal, and gaze behaviors. Reliabilities for behaviors that occurred relatively infrequently (e.g., parent smiles) ranged from .75–.88; those for more frequently coded behaviors (e.g., holding and looking at the infant) ranged from .94–1.00.

During the play observation, the observers coded infant manipulation of toys, the location and proximity of parent and infant, infant locomotion and vocalizing, and touching and gaze behaviors for both parent and infant. The

[1]A manual for the coding of interactive behaviors is available from the authors.

reliabilities for these ranged from .83 –.98. Regardless of the reliabilities, coding sheets for the two observers were reconciled and the reconciled data were used in all analyses. The primary data to be discussed here are measures of the frequency of different parent and infant behaviors during an observation session. As the feeding sessions varied in length, all frequencies were converted to proportions of the total session time. The play sessions were intended to be of uniform length, and we were therefore able to use the raw frequency measures. In cases where the session was terminated prematurely, the data for the remaining minutes were prorated.

The analyses and findings are presented in detail in previous papers (Brachfeld & Goldberg, 1978; DiVitto & Goldberg, 1979). The following summary is designed to highlight the changing patterns of group differences from age to age. Our initial expectation was that the full-term group would experience the lowest level of interactive stress, followed by the HP group, the SP group, and then the IDM group. This was based upon the assumption that medical complications and risks for developmental problems would increase in that order.

Because this summary often combines several analyses, the following conventions have been adopted in reporting statistics. Where p levels are reported alone, they refer to t tests following a significant overall F test. Where correlations are summarized, the text reports the range of the correlations as well as the range of p levels. We report F levels only where overall age or group differences are discussed without further reference to differences between particular groups.

FEEDINGS

We predicted that during feedings the preterm groups would show less body and eye contact as well as more infant distress than the full-term group, and that the differences between the full-term and preterm groups would increase as the assumed risk for interactive difficulties increased. That is, on each measure the groups would order themselves FT, HP, SP, IDM. The primary analyses were univariate analyses of variance with Groups (4), Age (2), or Location (2) as factors.

1. Parents in all four groups spent virtually all their time (88–100%) looking at the baby. Mutual regard was therefore controlled by the baby, and there were no group differences in infant looking behavior.

2. The most striking difference concerned the way in which infants were held during feedings. The position of the baby was coded in three categories during actual feeding: *Arms* (i.e., cuddled close with the infant's entire body

supported in the parent's arms), Lap (i.e., held at arm's length with the infant's body resting in the parent's lap and the head supported with a hand), and Lap and Arms (an intermediate position in which the infant's body rested on the parent's lap and the head and shoulders were cradled in the parent's arm). At the first observed feeding, FT infants spent 25% of the time in the Arms compared to 21% for the IDM group, 8% for the HP, and 3% for the SP group. At the other extreme, the sick preterm infants spent the most time in the Lap position (61%), followed by the IDM group (41%), the healthy preterm group (37%), and then the full-term group (24%) (all t tests significant at $p < .05$).

3. Over the four observed feedings, the time in the Arms and time on the Lap decreased so that babies were held more and more in the intermediate position regardless of group (F arms $= 4.26$, $p < .01$; F lap $= 6.17$, $p < .01$). However, the full-term infants continued to spend the least time on the lap. Furthermore, although both the HP and SP infants experience an increase in time-cuddled in the arms from the first to the second feeding, they never approached the amount of cuddling the full-term infants experienced at the initial feeding.

4. At the first two feedings, the full-term infants were touched and talked to more than infants in any of the preterm groups ($p < .05$ each comparison).

5. There were no group differences in fussing or crying except at the 4-month laboratory feeding (IDM $>$ HP $=$ SP $>$ FT, $p < .05$ for each pair of groups separated by the symbol for "greater than").

6. From the newborn to the 4-month observations, the group differences diminished. Although the same pattern of differences in holding, talking, and touching were evident in the data for each observation, they did not diverge enough to yield statistically significant differences in the 4-month period.

7. In addition, interactive behaviors during neonatal and 4-month feedings were systematically correlated with scores on the Brazelton Neonatal Behavior Assessment Scales (BNBAS). Infants who had received optimal scores on items in the interactive cluster were more likely to be alert ($.29 < r < .33$, all $p < .05$), to look at their parents ($.25 < r < .35$, $p < .05$), and to be cuddled in the arms ($.28 < r < .40$, $.05 > p \geq .01$). Infants who had been in predominantly drowsy states and showed little state change during the neonatal assessment were likely to receive a high level of functional stimulation during feedings ($.32 < r < .38$, $p < .01$), whereas those who were unresponsive to auditory stimulation received more auditory and tactile stimulation during feedings than more responsive babies ($.31 < r < .46$, $.05 > p \geq .01$).

The group differences observed during the feedings were generally consistent with our predictions. With the exception of the IDM group, whose ordering was inconsistent, the relative position of the groups on each measure was consistent with the hypothesized continuum. Furthermore, the observed changes over the first 4 months were consistent with the notion that group differences would gradually diminish over time.

FLOOR PLAY

The only prior comparison of preterm and full-term infants and their parents during play was that of Field (1977) who worked with younger infants in a face-to-face, social-play setting. On the basis of Field's report, we expected to find that the infants in the preterm groups would be less attentive to both toy and social play and that their parents would be more active than those in the full-term group. Group by Age by Session analyses of variance were applied to measures of behavior frequency.

1. The most striking feature of these sessions was that although no play sessions for FT or HP infants had to be terminated for infant distress, seven such sessions occurred in the remaining two groups. At the 8-month observations, six laboratory sessions (four in the SP group, two in the IDM group) and one home session (in the IDM group) had to be terminated early. At the 12-month observations, the early termination occurred for a SP infant at a home visit.

2. All behaviors for which there were significant group differences showed a consistent pattern of group differences at 8 months that diminished and were no longer significant at 12 months. Furthermore, the full-term group showed little change from the 8- to the 12-month sessions, whereas the remaining groups changed in ways that made their behavior more similar to that of the full-term group. Behaviors showing this pattern were infant play, infant fret or cry, infant smile, and parent proximity, parent–infant contact, parent touch, and parent demonstration of a toy. At 8 months, the SP infants spent the least time in play ($p < .01$) and smiling ($p < .05$) and the most time fretting ($p < .01$), whereas their parents spent the most time being close ($p < .01$), touching ($p < .05$), and demonstrating toys ($p < .01$). In contrast, the full-term infants spent the most time in play and smiling and the least time fretting of all four groups. Their parents were also least active of all four groups.

3. Because it seemed possible that the irritability and distress of the SP infants may have been related to an inability to manipulate objects as a consequence of their developmental immaturity, a second FT control group was included in the 8-month assessments. This group was constituted by matching each SP infant with a FT infant of the same sex and postconceptional age. No infant in this group was irritable or distressed to a point requiring termination of either home or laboratory sessions. Correlated t tests that compared each SP with a paired control infant indicated that the SP group fussed more ($p < .01$) and smiled less ($p < .05$) than the controls, though there were no

differences in total play. Their parents touched SP infants ($p < .05$) and demonstrated toys more frequently ($p < .001$) than the parents of the control babies. Thus, immaturity alone did not account for the differences between SP and FT dyads.

4. The play sessions for the HP infants were most like those of the FT infants, whereas those of the IDM group most resembled those of the SP group. The HP infants spent less time playing with toys than the FT group ($p < .05$), but did not show significantly more distress. Their parents did not differ from those in the FT group in proximity, touching, or demonstrating toys. The IDM infants also played with toys significantly less than FT infants ($p < .01$), but did not differ in amount of distress. Their parents spent more time in their proximity ($p < .05$), touching them ($p < .05$), and demonstrating toys ($p < .01$) than parents in the FT group.

5. There were no significant group differences at the 12-month sessions.

Thus, our predictions concerning group differences in play behavior were generally confirmed. Again, the groups generally ordered themselves as predicted, except that the IDM group occupied a less extreme position than the SP group. Over time, the early differences diminished, lending support to the notion that such differences decrease over time and cease by the end of the first year. However, when we examine the overall pattern of group differences, this view is not unequivocally supported. Although initial differences in feeding interactions have diminished by 4 months of age, assessments at 8-months old in the floor play situation again indicate highly significant differences. These group differences seem also to diminish by 12 months of age. Thus, we have observed group differences in Parent-Infant interaction in the neonatal period and at 8-months but not at 4 and 12 months.

Infant Behavior Ratings

At each age, in addition to the interaction observations, we included a separate behavioral assessment of the infant. In the neonatal period, we used the Brazelton Neonatal Behavioral Assessment Scales (Brazelton, 1973) because they appeared to include behaviors relevant to parent concerns. At 4-, 8-, and 12-months old we did not have a comparable instrument for evaluating infants' potential interactive skills. At these ages, we used the Bayley Scales of Infant Development (Bayley, 1969) to assess more general aspects of infant development. Although both of these assessments are generally considered to assess the infant, each depends upon interactions with the examiner (with or without objects). For the Brazelton examination, many scores depend upon the examiner's judgment of how easy or difficult it was to engage the baby in a task and how socially responsive the baby was. The Bayley Infant Behavior Record also involves ratings that evaluate the ease or difficulty of administering the assessment and the characteristics of the infant contributing to these judgments. In this way, we can consider both of these instruments as assessments of the baby, and we can also view them as indications of the infant's behavior with a relative stranger. Therefore, an examination of group differences on the Brazelton Scales and the Bayley Behavior Record can provide some indication of whether the findings for Parent-Infant interaction reflect group interaction differences that are restricted exclusively to parents or whether they are more generally applicable to social relationships with adules.

The Brazelton Neonatal Behavioral Assessment Scales were administered in the hospital prior to discharge and again at the 10-day home visit. The procedures followed those of the manual and the examiners had been trained to .95 reliability. The Bayley Scales were administered at each laboratory visit. Two members of the research staff were present at each assessment. The first interacted with the infant and parent(s), whereas the second scored and made sure all relevant items were administered. The Behavior Record was scored immediately after the assessment with the two observers reaching a consensus for each rating.

NEONATAL PERIOD

Because the preterm infants were less mature and had been physiologically stressed, we expected that they would be more dififcult for us to interact with than full-term infants. Again we predicted that the full-term group would obtain optimal scores followed by the HP, SP, and IDM groups in that order. Infants were scored on four *a priori* clusters recommended by Brazelton and his colleagues (Als, Tronick, Lester, & Brazelton, 1977). Individual items within clusters were examined for group differences only if the cluster showed group differences. In addition, because both parents and experimenters spontaneously commented about the absence of crying among SP infants, all items involving crying were examined regardless of their cluster location. Individual items were subjected to a Group by Session (hospital versus home) analysis of variance. The findings can be summarized, as follows:

1. Items which differentiated the groups (at hospital discharge) included three items from the interactive cluster (orienting response to ball [$F = 7.23$, $p < .01$], rattle [$F = 4.63$, $p < .05$], and alertness [$F = 3.18$, $p < .05$]), two motor items (hand-to-mouth behavior [$F = 3.33$, $p < .05$] and pull to sit [$F = 3.34$, $p < .05$]), and four items which potentially involve crying (peak excitement [$F - 6.99$, $p < .01$], rapidity of buildup [$F = 3.90$, $p < .05$], irritability [$F = 6.19$, $p < .05$], and state lability [$F = 3.67$, $p < .05$]).

2. On interactive and motor items, the FT infants consistently obtained the best scores, whereas the SP group obtained the poorest scores (with the exception of pull to sit, where the IDM group was poorest).

3. At the hospital assessment, the FT infants reached higher states of arousal ($p < .05$, all comparisons), reached their peak states more rapidly ($p < .05$), cried more often ($p < .05$), and had more state changes ($p < .05$) than the remaining groups, whereas the SP group consistently scored at the opposite extreme (had the lowest peak arousal states, took longer to reach these peak states, cried least of all groups, and had the fewest state changes).

4. From the first to the second assessment, FT and IDM babies became more alert ($p < .05$ each group), whereas the HP and SP babies showed no change. In addition, the FT infants were significantly less irritable at the second session ($p < .05$), whereas all other groups became more irritable ($p < .05$ in each case).

In general, with the exception of the IDM group showing generally better performance than expected, the ordering of groups was as predicted. We had the most difficulty getting and keeping the SP group alert and responsive and the least difficulty with the FT group. In evaluating the data for items involving crying, it is important to note that although most parents think they would like a baby who doesn't cry, crying is an important attention-getting signal for the neonate. The SP infants' scores on peak excitement, rapidity of buildup, irritability, and state lability reflects not only that they cried very little but that they also spent little time with us in alert waking. They were difficult to rouse and tolerated a great deal of mildly aversive stimulation without signaling distress or discomfort.

LATER DEVELOPMENTAL ASSESSMENTS

As with other interactive assessments, we expected that those groups considered to be at greater risk for interactive difficulty would in fact be more difficult to work with in the testing situation. Thus, it was predicted that the FT group would receive optimal ratings followed by the HP, SP, and IDM groups. It is important to note that although all of the prior data may have been influenced by the expectations of the experimenter, the ratings on the behavior record may be most subject to this bias. We had not originally planned to use these for analysis, but mainly to evaluate the adequacy of the assessment. However, we did have different expectations concerning performance on the assessment for infants in different groups and may have behaved accordingly.

The Bayley behavior record also yields a large number of ratings. In order to reduce the likelihood of accidental chance findings, we chose three types of items: those that seemed to be most clearly social (e.g., cooperativeness, response to examiner), those reflecting responses to test materials (e.g., attention span, persistence), and those reflecting temperament and emotional expression (e.g., emotional tone, endurance). Scores for each of these were subjected to a Group by Age analysis of variance.

The findings can be summarized as follows:

1. Items which showed a significant main effect for groups were responsivity to objects ($F = 20.38$, $p < .01$), goal directedness ($F = 5.10$, $p < .01$), attention span ($F = 7.00$, $p < .01$), reactivity ($F = 3.94$, $p < .05$), and manipulation of objects ($F = 13.99$, $p < .01$). Follow-up comparisons indicated that these differences were most often accounted for by FT infants obtaining the best scores with the SP group obtaining the poorest scores.

2. Most of these items showed significant changes over age with the preterm groups showing significant improvement in scores with increasing maturity, whereas the FT group showed little change over time. On two items, attention span and reactivity, there were no age changes or Group–Age interactions indicating that, regardless of the age of testing, the ordering of groups remained the same (i.e., FT infants obtaining the best scores, SP groups obtaining the poorest scores, and the remaining groups occupying an intermediate position.

3. Preliminary comparison of the age-matched controls and the SP group at 8 months suggested that the preterm group spent more time in visual exploration and less time manipulating objects than the controls. Thus, differences between the SP group and their postnatal age mates on most of the rating scales appear to be a function of immaturity. However, in comparison with the age-matched controls, we spent more time in administering the Bayley scales to the SP group.

4. Correlations between neonatal assessment scores and ratings on the behavior record suggest that the same infants were consistently rated as difficult to work with. Those infants who received poor interactive scores on the neonatal assessment were later rated less cooperative ($.29 < r < .45$, $.05 > p \geq .01$), more negative in emotional tone ($.29 < < .36$, $p < .05$), poorer in endurance ($.29 < r .38$, $.05 > p \geq .01$), and less responsive to tasks ($.29 < r < .38$, $.05 > p \geq .01$) during the Bayley assessment.

DISCUSSION

The primary purpose of this study was to examine differences among four groups. The groups were expected to differ as a consequence of interactive stress arising from newborn medical problems. Our sample, from a teaching hospital in a major medical center, consisted primarily of White middle-class families receiving good medical care. For this reason, many of the problems ordinarily present as correlates of prematurity were absent in this sample and can be ruled out as confounding stresses on the parent–child relationship. In addition, hospital support for parent–infant attachment was more comprehensive and parent–infant contact was more extensive than in studies reported earlier. All of these factors could be expected to minimize the predicted group differences.

Nevertheless, many of the predicted differences were observed and our findings are consistent with those of preterms in vastly different, less advantaged samples (e.g., Brown & Bakeman, 1979; see also Field, Chapter 7, this volume). Furthermore, the groups were generally ordered as predicted, with the FT and SP groups occupying the extreme positions and the HP group in an intermediate position.

Our initial expectation that the IDM group would experience the greatest interactive stress was not borne out for several reasons. First, because this group was small and the refusal rate high, we did not impose any criteria concerning the infant's birth condition on our selection process. As a consequence, we had a more heterogeneous group of infants than originally expected. In general, the physical condition of the infants was better than that of the SP group and more like that of the HP group. The data suggest that on the behaviors we recorded, their position relative to the other groups corresponded to their position with respect to their initial physical condition. Therefore, our data indicate some support for a dimension of interactive stress related to the severity of medical problems.

At the early feedings, parents of FT infants touched, cuddled, and talked to their babies more than parents of preterm infants. Although physical contact with the preterm infants showed some increase over time, it remained below that initially given to FT infants. In other words, initial contacts were not only delayed but depressed. Although these group differences were similar in pattern at 4-months old, they were no longer large enough to be statistically significant. On the basis of these feeding observations, it would seem that the group differences were diminishing with time. Indeed, this is what the few existing prior studies report (Brown & Bakeman, 1979; Leifer, Leiderman, Barnett, & Williams, 1972). However, at 8-months old, in the free-play situation, even more striking differences were observed. Sick preterm infants played less, fussed more, and received more parental attention than the FT group. Comparison with an age-matched cross-sectional control group indicated that immaturity alone did not account for the excessive irritability. These differences are similar in quality to those noted by Field (1977) for similar groups in face-to-face social play, and by Brown and Bakeman (1979) during early feedings. In all of these situations, parents of preterm infants were more active and invested more effort interacting with their infants with notably less success than parents of FT babies.

Similarly, in our own ratings of developmental assessments, we found the preterm infants were less responsive to the materials and tasks and were more difficult to test. Thus, the extra effort required to engage these babies in a task seems to extend across a variety of situations and occurred with experienced professional "baby handlers" as well as parents. At 12-months, differences in the free-play situation were no longer evident, again suggesting that the groups become more similar over time. In behavior ratings taken from the developmental assessments, many of the group differences did decrease with time. However, the preterm infants continued to be rated less attentive and responsive than the FT group at 12-months old. Comparison with the age-matched controls at 8-months old indicates that relative immaturity accounts for some but not all of the observed group differences. In general, the 12-month data show fewer group differences than the 8-month data, and one is again tempted to conclude that the group differences diminish with age and will eventually disappear.

The fact remains that the most dramatic differences in our study appeared at 8 months. Were it not for these differences, the conclusion that the groups consistently become more similar in their interactions with time, would be warranted. It is therefore necessary to seek explanations for the "see-saw" pattern of increasing and decreasing group differences that have been observed. The remainder of this chapter discusses alternative interpretations of this phenomenon.

1. The 8-month differences may represent a temporary perturbation in a pattern of decreasing differences. One reason for this perturbation may be developmental. Developmental data from several studies of preterm infants (Field, Hallock, Ting, Dempsey, Dabiri, & Shuman, 1978; Hunt, 1975), including our own, indicate that at 8-month assessments, preterm infants appear to lag further behind their FT counterparts than they do at earlier or later ages. Our observations suggested to us that this may be an artifact of the number of items on standardized infant tests that require sensorimotor skills in this age range. Few of our SP infants were able to sit well and manipulate objects at their 8-month assessments. This is not surprising considering their developmental immaturity. However, their motor scores on the Bayley scales were significantly lower than those of their age-matched controls. These conditions limited the number of appropriate items that could be administered.

It is also apparent that, from the parent's standpoint, their babies are not doing the things they expect of them or that they see other babies doing. Although, they may be prepared for some delay related to prematurity, they may also become particularly anxious about the infant's development during this period of maximal lag. If this is so, they may, in fact, be pressing the infant to "perform" during play at a level beyond his or her capacity, producing the unhappy play sessions we observed. By 12 months, when the SP group seems to have "caught-up" developmentally, particularly in motor skills, some of this anxiety may have abated, allowing for more relaxed play.

2. The 8-month differences may be an artifact of introducing a new observation situation. Our reason for choosing two different interactive situations was that we wished to observe Parent-Infant interactions under conditions that were representative and salient for each age period. However, it may be that with each new situation, the stress of being observed is activated or reactivated. It may be that underlying group differences become more evident under stress. At both 4 and 8 months, the laboratory (second) session was characterized by more signs of stress, including fretting, than the home (first) session. Therefore such an explanation would have to be qualified by home versus laboratory differences.

3. The major differences between groups may be the ease with which they adapt to new developmental stages. Although most preterm dyads eventually establish a harmonious relationship, they may take longer to make a successful adaptation. Thus, group differences are maximal when initial adaptations are being made (in feeding or floor play) and will be less evident in these same activities at a later time. Although the situations we chose were salient for the newborn and 8-month periods, other situations may have been more appropriate at ages 4 and 12 months. For example, Field's (1977) data on face-to-face play at 3½-4 (considered to be a peak period for such play) suggest that it might be more revealing of group differences at this age than a feeding observation.

Data on the cognitive development of preterm infants suggests that their rate of development is similar to that of FT infants with a delay equal to the extent of their prematurity (Hunt & Rhodes, 1977). The apparent "catch-up," whereby the differences between preterm and FT infants of the same postnatal age seem to diminish and eventually disappear, is explained as an artifact reflecting two phenomena. First, the number of weeks that an infant was premature becomes a relatively smaller proportion of his lifetime as he gets older. A lag of 8 weeks is relatively large at 4 months of age but barely measureable at age 6. Second, the rate of development does slow down and approach an asymptote. Preterm infant development approaches the same asymptote even though this occurs at a later postnatal age.

It is of interest to ask whether a similar process occurs in the domain of social interaction. We do not have norms for the development of Parent-Infant interaction that allow us to plot a growth curve as we do for cognitive or motor development. Because a dyad involves two participants and is a complex system, it seems unlikely that its development could be described by a simple growth curve. We might ask then, whether the skills of each participant and particularly the infant could be plotted in this way. Although we do have some developmental milestones for infant social development, we do not have the same kind of normative data that are available for cognitive and motor skills. However, we can examine our own data and ask to what extent the relative immaturity of the preterm infant accounts for the group differences observed.

In this respect, the pattern of differences we observed (newborn and 8-month differences, but no 4-month or 12-month differences) argues against a simple developmental lag as an explanation for the group differences. If this were the case, differences at 4 months would be expected to be at least as great as (if not greater than) those at 8 months. We have discussed some reasons why this might have happened, however, the nature of the differences that we originally observed at 8 months suggested that infant immaturity and parent reactions to it might be making a large contribution. Therefore, as a follow-up of the longitudinal study, we did a small cross-sectional study in which we replicated the 8-month procedures with a group of infants pair-matched by postconceptional age to each of the infants in our youngest group, the SP group. Comparisons between the SP group and their age-matched controls indicated that there was more negative affect, less positive affect, and more parent activity in the preterm group than in the control group. Therefore, these differences are not explained by the immaturity of the preterm infants.

SUMMARY: DIFFICULTIES OF CARING FOR THE PRETERM INFANT

It has often been suggested that separation of parent and infant in the newborn period deprives parents of opportunities for interaction during a sensitive period for maternal attachment (Klaus & Kennell, 1976). Subsequent interactive difficulties are interpreted as consequences of separation. Although the effects of separation may contribute to interactive difficulties, the data presented earlier indicate that the preterm infant may also be more difficult to care for than the FT infant.

First, at hospital discharge, the behavior of the preterm infant is not as well adapted to normal caregiving as that of the FT infant. The infant is not alert and responsive to caregivers and is unable to provide clear distress signals by crying when attention is needed. Although the pediatrician or psychologist may explain these differences in terms of underlying differences in maturity, parents must cope with the behavior that confronts them regardless of the "cause".

Similarly, parents of preterm infants are denied the gratifications of signs of growth and development for a relatively long period of time, even where development of their infant is normal. Although parents may understand the reasons for such delays in terms of the baby's postconceptional age, their early rewards are quite meager.

It appears that preterm infants continue throughout the first few months to present somewhat problematic interactive behavior both to parents and others. Whether in feedings, face-to-face play, or object play, the adult partner appears to put more effort into the endeavor than is the case with a full-term infant. Although it is not clear how long such differences exist, the findings from most available studies are consistent on the nature of these differences.

The infant–caregiver relationship can be viewed as an adaptive species-specific system of interlocking behaviors. The initial repertoires of infant and caregiver are preadapted to facilitate social interaction and any limitations or handicaps in the behaviors of one member of the dyad requires compensatory efforts on the part of the partner if the system is to be maintained. The birth of a premature infant appears to confront the caregiver with a poorly adapted social partner. Therefore it is not surprising that the development of social interactions in this group should follow a different course than that of FT infants. The available data suggest that the differences cannot be explained as a simple developmental lag in the preterm group as some qualitative differences (particularly in infant affective expression and parent activity level) are observed even when maturity is held constant.

ACKNOWLEDGMENTS

This research was supported by OCD Grant No. 90-C-388, National Institutes of Health Biomedical Research Support Grant No. RR-07044-12, and a Radcliffe Institute Fellowship to Susan Goldberg. It was carried out with the cooperation of Boston Hospital for Women. Project staff members who contributed in various phases of the research included Elaine Jacowitz, Elizabeth Judd, Janet Leshne, Martha McKay (consulting pediatrician), Robert Muller, Nancy Sheiman, and Jone Sloman.

REFERENCES

Als, H., Tronick, E., Lester, B. M., & Brazelton, T. B. The Brazelton Neonatal Behavioral Assessment Scale (BNBAS). *Journal of Abnormal Child Psychology, 1977, 5,* 215–231.

Bayley, N. *Manual of Bayley Scales of Infant Development.* New York: Psychological Corporation, 1969.

Beckwith, L. & Cohen, S. E. Preterm birth: Hazardous obstetric and postnatal events as related to caregiver–infant behavior. *Infant Behavior and Development, 1978, 1,* 403–412.

Brachfeld, S. & Goldberg, S. *Parent-infant interaction: Effects of newborn medical status on free play at 8- and 12-months.* Paper presented at the Southeastern Conference on Human Development, Atlanta, Georgia, April, 1978.

Brachfeld, S., Goldberg, S., & Sloman, J. *Parent–Infant interaction in free play at 8 and 12 months: Effects of prematurity and immaturity.* Manuscript submitted for publication, 1979.

Brazelton, T. B. Neonatal behavioral assessment scale. In *Clinics in Developmental Medicine (No. 50)*. London: Spastics International Medical Publications/Heineman, 1973.

Brown, J. V., & Bakeman, R. Relationships of human mothers with thier infants during the first year of life. In R. W. Bell & W. P. Smotherman (Eds.), *Maternal influences and early behavior*. Holliswood, New York: Spectrum, 1979.

Caldwell, B., Heider, J., & Kaplan, B. *Home observation for measurement of the environment*. Little Rock, Arkansas: Center for Early Development and Education, University of Arkansas, 1966.

DiVitto, B., & Goldberg, S. The development of early Parent-Infant interaction as a function of newborn medical status. In T. Field, A. Sostek, S. Goldberg, & H. H. Shuman (Eds.), *Infants born at risk*. Holliswood, New York: Spectrum, 1979.

Elmer, E., & Gregg, G. S. Developmental characteristics of abused children. *Pediatrics*, 1967, *40*, 596-602.

Fanaroff, A. A., Kennell, J. H., & Klaus, M. H. Followup of low birthweight infants—the predictive value of maternal visiting patterns. *Pediatrics*, 1972, *49*, 288-290.

Field, T. Effects of early separation, interactive deficits, and experimental manipulations on Mother-Infant interaction. *Child Development*, 1977, *48*, 763-771.

Field, T., Hallock, N., Ting, G., Dempsey, J., Dabiri, C., & Shuman, H. H. A first year followup of high risk infants: Formulating a cumulative risk index. *Child Development*, 1978, *49*, 119-131.

Goldberg, S. Social competence in infancy: A model of Parent-Infant interaction. *Merrill-Palmer Quarterly*, 1977, *23*, 163-177.

Goldberg, S. Prematurity: Effects on Parent-Infant interaction. *Journal of Pediatric Psychology*, 1978, *3*, 137-144.

Goldberg, S. Pragmatics and problems of longitudinal research with high risk infants. In T. Field, A. Sostek, S. Goldberg, & H. H. Shuman (Eds.), *Infants born at risk*. Holliswood, New York: Spectrum, 1979.

Goldson, E., Fitch, N. J., Wendell, T. A., & Knapp, G. Child abuse: Its relationship to birthweight, Apgar score, and developmental testing. *American Journal of Diseases of Childhood*, 1978, *132*, 790-793.

Hunt, J. V. *Mental and motor development of preterm infants during the first year*. Paper presented at Society for Research in Child Development, Denver, Colorado, April, 1975.

Hunt, J. V., & Rhodes, L. Mental development of preterm infants during the first year. *Child Development*, 1977, *48*, 204-210.

Klaus, M. H., & Kennell, J. H. *Maternal-infant bonding*. St. Louis, Missouri: Mosby, 1976.

Klaus, M. H., Kennell, J. H., Plumb, N., & Zuelke, S. Human maternal behavior at first contact with her young. *Pediatrics*, 1970, *46*, 187-192.

Klein, M., & Stern, L. Low birth weight and the battered child syndrome. *American Journal of Diseases of Childhood*, 1971, *122*, 15-18.

Leifer, A. D., Leiderman, P. H., Barnett, C. R., & Williams, J. A. Effects of mother-infant separation on maternal attachment behavior. *Child Development*, 1972, *43*, 1203-1218.

Lubchenco, L. O. *The high risk infant*. Philadelphia: W. B. Saunders, 1976.

Minde, K., Trehub, S., Corter, C., Boukydis, C., Celhoffer, L., & Marton, P. Mother-child relationships in the premature nursery: An observational study. *Pediatrics*, 1978, *61*, 373-379.

Sameroff, A. J., & Chandler, M. J. Reproductive risk and the continuum of caretaking casualty. In F. D. Horowitz, M. Hetherington, S. Scarr-Salapatek, & G. M. Siegel (Eds.), *Review of child development research* (Vol. 4). Chicago: Univ. Chicago Press, 1975.

Shaheen, E., Alexander, D., Truskowsky, M., & Barbero, G. Failure to thrive—a retrospective profile. *Clinical Pediatrics*, 1968, *7*, 255-261.

Sigman, M., & Parmelee, A. H. Longitudinal evaluation of the high risk infant. In T. Field, A. Sostek,

S. Goldberg, & H. H. Shuman (Eds.), *Infants born at risk*. Holliswood, New York: Spectrum, 1979.

Stern, D. Mother and infant at play: The dyadic interaction involving facial, vocal, and gaze behaviors. In M. Lewis & L. A. Rosenblum (Eds.), *The effect of the infant on its caregiver*. New York: Wiley, 1974.

Stern, D. *The first relationship: Infant and mother*. Cambridge, Massachusetts: Harvard Univ. Press, 1977.

CHAPTER **9**

LEILA BECKWITH
SARALE E. COHEN

Interactions of Preterm Infants with Their Caregivers and Test Performance at Age 2

INTRODUCTION

The importance of social interaction in organizing and promoting an infant's development has major theoretical implications. It supports the basic proposition that an infant's development is a complex interaction of genetic, maturational, and experiential factors. It links affective, social, and cognitive systems. It offers one focus for understanding individual differences in development.

Investigators have examined the relationship between early social interactions and competence in full-term infants, and have found Caregiver–Infant interaction to be significantly associated with cognitive-motivational behavior, including curiosity, exploration, language acquisition, and mental test performance assessed concurrently and at later ages (Ainsworth & Bell, 1973; Bradley & Caldwell, 1976; Clarke-Stewart, 1973; Elardo, Bradley, & Caldwell, 1975; Nelson, 1973; Yarrow, Rubenstein, & Pedersen, 1975).

We have proposed that a similar research strategy be used with preterm infants to make professional intervention more meaningful and to increase the predictive validity of risk designation (Beckwith, 1976). Preterm infants, as a class, have been found to be at increased statistical risk for deficits in cognitive functioning (Caputo & Mandell, 1970). But the fact of prematurity, alone, is insufficient to allow prediction of developmental disturbance. Preterm infants

155

are a heterogeneous group with multiple causes of prematurity and attendant perinatal complications. Furthermore, they grow up in a wide variety of care-giving environments. Within the preterm group, therefore, a wide range of outcomes can be anticipated. Although severe disability may result, it is a relatively infrequent outcome. With present, neonatal, intensive care procedures, the percentage of infants within the normal range of development has increased significantly (Fitzhardinge & Ramsay, 1973; Hunt, 1976). The range of competence among preterm infants is now as great as that within a normal full-term group. Some preterm infants, even those who were quite ill in the newborn period, or who showed an early delay in development, appear to make a successful recovery. Other preterm infants may appear less at risk as neonates but later show disabilities. If Caregiver–Infant interaction can attenuate—or increase—the adverse consequences of early biologic hazards, then intervention may be possible even after the insult has occurred.

There is evidence that the preterm infant is probably a less active, less capable social partner (Brown & Bakeman, in press; Field, 1977a). Its parents have experienced multiple stresses, which may include grief, anxiety, guilt, lowered self-esteem, increased isolation, and lessened emotional support as the infant's survival and psychological outcome remain in jeopardy. Furthermore, the parents of a preterm infant have been separated from their infant and have experienced a long delay in care giving. The research described in this chapter was a part of a larger prospective study of preterm development from birth to 2 years aimed at investigating whether there are identifiable consequences of the altered care-giving experience. The aim of the study was to improve assessment of risk factors and to identify ameliorative processes by including detailed, multiple measurements of medical, social, and developmental variables. A strategy was used based on short-term predictions in which multiple factors were considered as cumulative in determining the degree of risk. The goals, procedures, and sample have been described in several publications (Parmelee, Kopp, & Sigman, 1976; Parmelee, Sigman, Kopp, & Haber, 1975; Parmelee, Sigman, Kopp, & Haber, 1976; Sigman & Parmelee, in press). In this chapter, we shall focus on the contribution of social factors, particularly Caregiver–Infant interaction, to 2-year test performance.

METHODS

Subjects

Our study population consisted of 126 preterm infants, born in the UCLA nursery from 1972 to 1974, who had completed most of the project tests through 2 years of age. A small sample of normal full-term infants was also followed. Their data are not included here, as our interest was in identifying factors within the preterm group associated with developmental delay or later competence, rather than in comparing preterm to full-term infants. The sample covered a diverse group and included a variety of racial and ethnic backgrounds. There were 76 boys and 50 girls. The group had 67 infants who were firstborn and 59 laterborn infants. The average gestational age of the infants was 33.1 weeks (range 25–37); birthweight, 1911 gm (range 800–2495); and length of hospitalization was 22.7 days (range 2–88). Maternal education ranged from 3 years to 17 years with a mean of 11.0 years.

Caregiver–Infant Interaction Assessments

Interaction between the primary caregiver and the infant was assessed repeatedly through naturalistic observations in the home during everyday routines. These observations have been detailed and reported in a number of previous publications (Beckwith & Cohen, 1978; Beckwith, Cohen, Kopp, Parmelee, & Marcy, 1976; Cohen & Beckwith, 1979). A complete description of the first year's procedure, including its reliability, the variables, and the factors derived from the observations, is contained in the first report (Beckwith et al., 1976). Briefly, the observations were made in the subject's home as the family proceeded with usual activities. The behaviors of the infant and caregiver were time sampled every 15 sec using a precoded check list. Observations were made at 1 and 8 months after the expected date of birth and a subsample of families was also seen when their infants were 3-months-old. For the 1 and 3 month visit, the infant was observed through a cycle that consisted of waking from sleep, being fed, and all other activities that occurred until the infant was asleep again for more than one-half hr. For the 8-month visit, $1\frac{1}{2}$ hr of awake play time, plus a feeding, were observed.

At each visit, frequencies of specific, objective behaviors directed to the baby, or shown by the baby, were noted. These included (a) ways of talking to the baby, (b) measures of touching and holding, (c) ways of mediating the environment, (d) social play, (e) behaviors dependent on simultaneous eye-to-eye contact of the infant and the caregiver, (f) a measure of the caregiver's contingent responses to the fussing or crying of the infant, (g) the infant behaviors of fuss or cry, and (h) social approaches to the caregiver and observer made by the infant. All measures, with one exception, were ratio scores derived from frequency counts of the number of 15-sec units in which a given behavioral category occurred, adjusted to the length of the awake time of the infant during the observation. The caregiver's contingency to the infant's distress was defined as a percentage of the total number of fuss or cry episodes to which the caregiver responded within 45 sec.

In order to reduce the data to more global dimensions, these behaviors were used to derive factors at each age level by a principal component factor analysis with varimax rotation to orthogonal structure. The factors were derived from the first 50 babies in our sample from English-speaking homes. Surviving twins and infants with serious sensory and neurological handicaps were excluded. Both first- and later-born infants were included. Half the babies were born to mothers who had more than 12 years of education, and half the babies were born to mothers having 12 or less years of education. Weights derived on this sample were then used to generate factor scores for the entire sample.

The factors were as follows:

1 month

Factor 1: *Social* (defined by high loadings of the variables of affectionate touches, social play, contingent response to vocalization, and mutual gazing)

Factor 2: *Responsive holding* (attentiveness, long holds, soothing touches, contingent response to distress)

Factor 3: *Verbal* (total talk, comments, commands, criticism)

Factor 4: *Mutual gazing* (three categories of mutual gazing)

Factor 5: *Stressful holding* (stress musculature, interfering touches, short holds)

3 months

Factor 1: *Responsive social* (total talk, comments, contingent response to vocalization)

Factor 2: *Mutual gazing* (three categories of mutual gazing)

Factor 3: *Physical contact* (soothing touches, long holds, affectionate touches)

Factor 4: *Control* (commands, criticism)

Factor 5: *Interference* (interfering touches)

8 months

Factor 1: *Mutual social* (mutual gazing, attentiveness, face-to-face talks)

Factor 2: *Intellectual stimulation* (object presentation, comments)

Factor 3: *Control* (criticism, commands, interfering touches)

Factor 4: *Floor freedom* (floor freedom, short holds)

The factors accounted for a substantial amount of the variance in interaction at each age: at 1 month, 68% was accounted for; at 3 months, 71%; and at 8 months, 68%. In addition to the factors, the following single behaviors were analyzed separately: infant fuss cry, infant smiling at the caregiver during mutual gazing, infant smiling at the observer, and, at 8-months, vocalizing to the observer.

Home observations of 50 min of play time at age 2 (Cohen & Beckwith, 1979) were also made. The behaviors at this home visit were event sampled. Verbal and nonverbal behaviors were recorded by event sampling on a pre-coded check list. For purposes of this study, the behaviors included: positive attentiveness, object presentation, reciprocal play, negative attentiveness, mandatory bids, number of utterances, questions, commands, criticism, and contingent response to child's vocalizations. The major caregiver behaviors measured at 2 years were reduced to more global dimensions by a principal component factor analysis with varimax rotation to orthogonal structure just as was done for the earlier home observations. The following two factors were obtained and explained 77% of the variance:

24 months

Factor 1: *Positive caregiver attentiveness* (defined by positive reciprocal interaction, positive attentiveness, number of questions and ut-terances directed at the child by the primary caregiver, and the caregiver's responsivness to child's vocalizations)

Factor 2: *Negative caregiver attentiveness* (number of mandatory bids directed to the child, criticism of the child, interferences, and rejections of the child's bids to the caregiver)

We assume that the patterns of interaction, as we measured them, resulted from forces within the infant, the caregiver, and the effect of each on the other. In previous research, we had attempted to infer the direction of influence by coding each behavior as to whether the caregiver or infant was the initiator or the responder (Beckwith, 1972). We found the Caregiver–Infant social interac-tion to be a homeostatic system such that the caregiver who made more initia-tions had an infant who ignored her more, whereas the caregiver who made fewer initiations had a more responsive infant. A similar difficulty in assessing direction of effects, and in differentiating mother and infant measures indepen-dent of the course of interaction between them, was noted by Dunn (1976) and others. For the present study, we decided that the fact of a social exchange, and the frequency of such an occurrence, would be more predictive to later infant performance than would the understanding of the process by which it came about.

Perinatal Assessments

Two scales were used to measure perinatal complications: The Obstetrical Complications Scale and the Postnatal Complications Scale (Littman & Parmelee, 1978). The Obstetrical Complications Scale covered 41 events which could be defined as optimal or nonoptimal. It included maternal health history; pregnancy events including infection, bleeding, hypertension, toxemia, and diabetes; and birth events, including gestational age and 1-min Apgar score. The Postnatal Complications Scale assessed hazardous conditions that occurred in the first month of life, after the infant's initial adaptation to extrauterine life, including respiratory distress, hyperbilirubinemia, and metabolic and temperature disturbances. High scores on both reflected fewer complications.

Developmental Assessments

The infants were tested on a variety of developmental measures at several time periods during the first and second years. Those reported in this chapter are standard infant tests and include the Gesell Developmental Schedules, given at 4, 9, and 24 months, and the Bayley Mental Scale, given at 25 months.

Testing was done by independent examiners who were naive about the results of the home observations and the earlier or concurrent competence data, as well as the medical data. The observers of the home interactions were also naive regarding the infant's medical history and the results of the developmental assessments.

RESULTS

Perinatal Complications and Outcome

Prediction to 2-year developmental outcome could not be made on the basis of perinatal medical complications. Neither the obstetric nor the postnatal scale was significantly correlated with a 2-year outcome. In order to assess further possible differences associated with medical complications, the sample was divided into two groups on the basis of the median combined scores on the two measures of medical problems. The groups then represented those who had multiple obstetrical and postnatal complications and those with fewer medical problems in early life. The two groups did not differ in terms of their performance on the 2-year measures (Sigman and Parmelee, 1979). Thus, 2-year performance is not influenced by the number of hazardous perinatal events in preterm infants. An examination of what happens to sick infants in terms of caregiving may help clarify this apparent paradox.

Perinatal Complications and Caregiver–Infant Interaction

We have previously documented a relationship between hazardous perinatal events and caregiving at 1 month (Beckwith & Cohen, 1978). We found that preterm infants who had suffered more hazardous events received increased caregiving from their primary caregivers. Aspects of caregiving were correlated with both the Obstetrical Complications Scale and the Postnatal Complications Scale so that the caregiver, rather than withdrawing from the sicker preterm infant, appeared to be making increased effort. The association was modest, but of particular interest as it suggested compensation within the caregiver-infant dyad for the deficits of the sicker infant. Although the impact of the hazardous events on care giving was most noticeable in very early social interactions, the general effect persisted at 3 months. At 3 months, Factor 1 (responsive social) was related to the Obstetrical Complications Scale ($r = -.27$, $p < .01$) such that the sicker infant, according to the obstetrical history, received more attentiveness. At 8 months, the association of perinatal complications and care giving was such that the sicker infant, with the less optimal obstetrical history, received more control (Factor 3: commands, criticism, interfering touches) from the caregiver ($r = -.21$, $p < .05$). The effect was no longer present at 2 years.

Caregiver-Infant Interaction and 2-Year Outcome

Caregiver-Infant interaction variables, from the earliest months of life through age 2, were related to mental test performance at 2 years. Table 9.1 shows the simple and multiple correlations from stepwise multiple regression analyses for each home observation and the Bayley Mental Scale as well as the Gesell test. For comparison purposes, the table notes results from similar analyses of a special subsample, children from English-speaking families (Cohen & Beckwith, 1979).

BAYLEY MENTAL SCALE

At 1 month of age, Factor 1 (social) and Factor 3 (verbal) were significantly associated with the 2-year Bayley Mental Scale. At 3 months, infant affective expression, including smiling at the caregiver during mutual gazing and increased fussiness, was significantly related to 2-year competence. At 8 months, Factor 2 (intellectual stimulation) and Factor 3 (control) significantly predicted 2-year Bayley scores. Concurrent associations were also evident between the Caregiver-Infant interactional Factor 1 (positive attentiveness) at 24-months and Bayley performance. The amount of variance, however, that Caregiver-Infant interaction explained was modest, and varied from 11% for interactions at 1 month to 18% for interactions at 24 months.

GESELL TEST

Two-year performance on the Gesell test was predicted at 1 month by the infant's smiling at the caregiver during mutual gazing. No interactional be-

TABLE 9.1
Simple and Multiple Correlations between Caregiver–Infant Interaction and 2-Year Tests

Interaction variables	Gesell test	Bayley Mental Scale
	1 month	
F1: Social	.24[a]	.24[a] step 1
F2: Responsive holding	.08	.09
F3: Verbal	.15	.23* step 2
F4: Mutual gazing	.07	.16
F5: Stressful holding	−.03	−.01
Fuss cry	−.19*	−.12
Smiling during mutual gazing	.29*,[a] step 1	.24*,[a]
Smiling at the observer	.00	−.06
Multiple correlation	.29**	.33**
	$F = 11.44\,(1,121);\ p < .01$	$F = 7.00(2,114);\ p < .01$
	3 months	
F1: Responsive social	.19	.13
F2: Mutual gazing	.02[a]	.18[a]
F3: Physical contact	−.17	.08
F4: Control	.19	.02
F5: Interference	.12	.00
Fuss cry	.05	.18 step 2
Smiling during mutual gazing	.20[a]	.23[a] step 1
Smiling at the observer	.02	.06
Multiple correlation	N.S.	.33**
		$F = 4.95(2,82);\ p < .01$
	8 months	
F1: Mutual social	.25* step 2	.17
F2: Intellectual stimulation	.29* step 1	.33* step 1
F3: Control	.10	.19 step 2
F4: Floor freedom	.03	.02
Fuss cry	.00	.01
Smiling during mutual gazing	.10	.06
Smiling at the observer	.05[a]	.04
Vocalizing at the observer	−.09	−.12
Multiple correlation	.34**	.38**
	$F = 7.91(2,119);\ p < .01$	$F = 9.17(2,113);\ p < .01$
F1: Positive attentiveness	.47*,[a] step 1	.43*,[a] step 1
F2: Negative attentiveness	−.24 step 2	−.17
Multiple correlation	.53**	.43**
	$F = 14.46(2,74);\ p < .01$	$F = 15.91(1,72);\ p < .01$

[a]Significant correlation in English subsample (Cohen & Beckwith, 1979).
*$p < .05$
**$p < .01$

havior at 3 months was significant. At 8 months, Factor 1 (mutual social) and Factor 2 (intellectual stimulation) combined in a significant multiple correlation with the results of the 2-year Gesell test. At 24 months, Factor 1 (positive attentiveness) combined with a negative weighting for Factor 2 (negative attentiveness) for a significant multiple correlation with Gesell test performance. Variance explained by Caregiver–Infant interaction, however, was small and ranged from 8% for interactions at 1 month to 28% for 24-month interactions.

Caregiver–Infant Interaction and 4- and 9-Month Performance

Stepwise multiple regression analyses were conducted between Caregiver–Infant interactional variables at 1 and 3 months and 4-month Gesell scores. Similar analyses were conducted between 1-, 3-, and 8-month home visit variables and 9-month Gesell scores. (See Table 9.2, which also notes results from similar analyses of the English-speaking subsample [Also see Beckwith et al., 1976]).

GESELL TEST AT 4 MONTHS

The 1-month caregiver–infant Factor 5 (stressful holding) and the infant behavior of smiling at the observer were correlated with higher Gesell scores and explained 10% of the variance of the 4-month test performance. No behavior at 3 months was associated with 4-month Gesell scores.

GESELL TEST AT 9 MONTHS

At 1 month, Factor 1 (social) predicted 9-month competence, but explained only 6% of the variance. No variable at 3 months did. At 8 months, Factor 3 (control) and the infant behavior of smiling at the observer were significantly related to Gesell performance and explained 14% of the variance.

The Caregiver–Infant interactional patterns associated with competence at 24 months were quite different from those that were important for 4- and 9-month competence. The complexities of the association between Caregiver–Infant interaction and test performance become even more evident when social class, ordinal position, and sex-related differences are considered.

Social Status and 2-Year Outcome

Social status was not related to the developmental measures in the first year of life but was significantly related to 2-year performance. The relationship of social status, considered by itself, can be seen in Table 9.3, which presents

TABLE 9.2
Stepwise Multiple Regressions of Caregiver–Infant Interaction to 4- and 9-Month Tests

Interaction variables	4-month Gesell Test Multiple R	9-month Gesell Test Multiple R
	1 month	
F1: Social		.24
F5: Stressful holding	.25	
Smiling at the observer	.31	
	$(F = 4.2, p < .05)$	$(F = 7.4, p < .05)$
	3 months	
F4: Control[a]	N.S.	N.S.
	8 months	
F3: Control		.30
F4: Floor freedom[a]		
Smiling at the observer		.37
Vocalizing to the observer[a]		
		$(F = 7.6, p < .05)$

NOTE: Based on an F ratio to enter of 4.0.
[a] Significant correlation in English-speaking subsample (Beckwith *et al.*, 1976).

the relationship between competence and care giving after first forcing social class into the regression equation. Social status enters the equation at a significant level yet additional variance is explained when care-giving factors and behaviors enter after social class. Although social class appears to overlap with care-giving factors, by itself it cannot predict as reliably as do the care-giving factors and behaviors (compare Table 9.3 and Table 9.1). Therefore, the information for prediction that is relevant in social class is adequately measured by the care-giving factors and behaviors.

Additional evidence that social class by itself is not a variable that works in a simple way across groups can be seen in Table 9.4, which presents the means and indicates significant group differences for the competence measures for analyses of variance of the eight groups (sex × ordinal position × social class). Social class differences in 2-year outcomes were found as main effects for the Gesell and the Bayley measures. However, the Gesell measure showed a significant interaction of social class with other demographic variables, making a simple interpretation of social class insufficient. Analyses presented in the following section on sex-related differences further indicate that social class functions differently for girls than for boys. Briefly, social class is not associated with competence for boys whereas it is for girls.

TABLE 9.3
Stepwise Multiple Regressions of Caregiver–Infant Interaction Variables to 2-Year Tests (with Social Class as Variable)

Interaction variables	Gesell Test Multiple R	Bayley Mental Scale Multiple R
	1 month	
Social class	.25	.22
Smiling during mutual gazing	.38	.32
	$(F = 10.2, p < .01)$	$(F = 6.5, p < .01)$
	3 months	
	N.S.	N.S.
	8 months	
Social class	.25	.22
F2: Intellectual stimulation	.35	.36
F3: Control		.41
	$(F = 11.5, p < .01)$	$(F = 7.4, p < .01)$
	24 months	
Social class	.25	.22
F1: Positive attentiveness	.48	.44
F2: Negative attentiveness	.54	
	$(F = 10.1, p < .01)$	$(F = 8.5, p < .01)$

NOTE: Social class was forced in as the first independent variable, and other variables were free to enter if their contribution was based on an F ratio greater than 4.0.

The complexities of the relationships presented indicate that social class by itself does not optimize prediction. In a diverse group, such as that used in this study, however, it can explain a significant amount of the variance in 2-year competence and by itself may cautiously be used as a quick index.

Sex-Related Differences in 2-Year Outcome

Analyses of variance (sex × ordinal position × social class) indicated that at 2 years girls scored significantly higher than boys on the Gesell Developmental Schedules. Table 9.4 presents the means and indicates significant group differences. The sex-related differences were not simple main effects, however. There was a triple-order interaction on these measures such that first-born girls from higher social-class backgrounds did the best, whereas later-born males from the higher social-class backgrounds did best. The Bayley Mental Scale at 25 months indicated a Sex by Ordinal Position interaction in that for

TABLE 9.4
Means Scores of Developmental Measures Related to Sex, Ordinal Position, and Social Class

Test	Male first born (High SES)	Male first born (Low SES)	Male later born (High SES)	Male later born (Low SES)	Female first born (High SES)	Female first born (Low SES)	Female later born (High SES)	Female later born (Low SES)	Significant differences[a,b]
Gesell (4 months)	104.6	107.4	107.4	101.4	109.4	107.2	107.6	101.9	
Gesell (9 months)	101.9	101.4	96.2	96.0	107.1	101.7	99.4	96.0	O***
Gesell (24 months)	94.9	94.0	98.5	92.6	114.5	98.5	95.0	90.3	S*, O**, SES*** SXOXSES*
Bayley MDI (25 months)	94.8	92.5	103.2	92.4	118.3	105.1	100.5	85.8	O*, SES**, SXO**

[a] ANOVA comparison.
[b] S = Sex; O = Ordinal position; SES = Social class of family.
$*p < .05$
$**p < .01$
$***p < .001$

girls it was the first borns that performed better and for boys it was the later borns that performed better on the Bayley Scale. There were no sex-related differences in the developmental measures during the first year of life.

Demographic Differences in Care Giving

In order to assess differences in Caregiver–Infant interactional behaviors associated with social class, ordinal position, and infant gender, a series of ANOVAs were done. The design was 2 (sex) × 2 (ordinal position) × 2 (social class). The means for the caregiver and infant behaviors at 1, 3, 8, and 24 months showed significant group differences and are presented in Table 9.5.

SEX-RELATED DIFFERENCES

Sex-related differences in the mean frequency of behaviors were found as main effects at the 1-month visit only. At the 1-month visit, boys received higher scores on the factor labeled "stressful holding" (i.e., holding that required them to support their own weight and interfering touches) than did girls. The tendency to handle boys more roughly than girls (Maccoby & Jacklin, 1974) was not negated by the vulnerability of the preterm male. Additionally, boys were more irritable than girls—a finding consistent with results reported by Moss (1967). Sex-related differences in irritability bear further investigation. Differences in irritability at other ages were found to be an interaction of sex with demographic variables. There was a Sex × Ordinal Position interaction in irritability at 3 months in which first-born girls and later-born boys were more irritable. At 8 months there was a significant Sex × Social Class interaction in which the lower social-class boys and higher social-class girls cried more.

Although sex-related differences were not found as main effects in terms of the frequency of behaviors after the 1-month visit, sex-related differences were found in the association between maternal education and caregiving (Table 9.6). An examination of the intercorrelation matrices suggests that maternal education affects care giving very differently for the two sexes. The relationship between the number of years of maternal education and the home observation factors and behaviors is not related for boys with the exception of verbal interaction at 1 month. For girls at each age period, care-giving behaviors are related to years of maternal education. That is, a mother with a college education interacted with her girl—but not her boy—in markedly different ways than did a less educated mother. Sex-related differences were also found in the relationship of care-giving to competence (Table 9.7). The ability of care-giving behavior patterns to predict competence at age 2 was significantly better for girls than for boys.

TABLE 9.5
Mean Scores of Interaction Variables Significantly Different by Sex, Ordinal Position, and Social Class

Interaction variables	Male first born (High SES)	Male first born (Low SES)	Male later born (High SES)	Male later born (Low SES)	Female first born (High SES)	Female first born (Low SES)	Female later born (High SES)	Female later born (Low SES)	Significant differences [a,b]
				1 month					
F2: Responsive holding	.17	.27	−.34	−.46	−.08	.05	−.08	−1.07	O***, OXSES*
F3: Verbal	−.01	−.59	.13	−.21	.77	−.45	.15	.02	SES**
F5: Stressful holding	.66	.61	−.33	.14	−.23	.15	−.47	−.08	S*, O*
Fuss cry[c]	.17	.19	.19	.19	.13	.13	.14	.15	S*
Smiling during mutual gazing	.003	.007	.004	.003	.012	.008	.004	.002	O*
				3 months					
F1: Responsive social	.51	.05	−.27	−.74	1.02	−.27	−.71	−.55	O***, SES**
Fuss cry	.09	.10	.14	.12	.16	.18	.12	.08	SXO**
				8 months					
F1: Mutual social	.37	.10	.13	−.48	.92	−.12	.42	−.40	O*, SES***
F2: Intellectual stimulation	.52	.27	−.19	−.50	.74	.10	−.30	−.76	O***, SES*
Fuss cry	.06	.08	.06	.06	.09	.05	.07	.06	SXSES*
Smiling during mutual gazing	.02	.01	.02	.01	.02	.01	.02	.01	SES***
Smiling at the observer	.02	.03	.02	.02	.03	.03	.02	.02	O*
				24 months					
F1: Positive attentiveness	.22	−.37	−.30	−.47	.78	−.07	−.14	−.47	O*, SES*

[a] ANOVA comparison.
[b] S = Sex; O = Ordinal position; SES = Social class of family.
[c] Caregiver–Infant variables, which are not factor scores, are expressed as percentage of observed awake time.
*p < .05
**p < .01
***p < .001

TABLE 9.6
Comparison of Males and Females: Significant Correlation
Coefficients of Interaction Variables with Maternal Education

Interaction variables	Males	Females
1 month		
F1: Social	−.18[a]	.35[a]
F2: Responsive holding	.06	.37*
F3: Verbal	.31*	.34*
3 months		
F1: Responsive social	.21	.39*
8 months		
F1: Mutual social	.12	.44**
F2: Intellectual stimulation	.05[a]	.43[a],**
F4: Floor freedom	.05	.33*
Smiling during mutual gazing	.18	.39*
24 months		
F1: Positive attentiveness	.10	.41*

[a] Significant difference by z test between the correlation coefficients for females and for males.
*$p < .05$
**$p < .01$

We found, as have Yarrow *et al.* (1975), differences in the continuity and meaning of care giving. If a girl began early in life with intense, pleasurable social exchanges with her caregiver, she was more likely than a boy to continue to be exposed to, elicit, be responsive to, or be involved in such experiences later. For a boy, such social exchanges were more subject to discontinuity and associated with restrictive interaction.

SOCIAL CLASS

Social class differences in care giving, as main effects, were found at each home visit. Caregivers from the higher social class provided more verbal interaction at 1 month, responsive social behavior at 3 months, mutual social behavior and intellectual stimulation at 8 months, and positive attentiveness at 24 months. Infants of the higher social-class group engaged in more smiling with their caregivers at 8 months. The social experiences of infants from different social class groups diverge from the earliest period measured and continue to differ in quantity in a number of ways.

TABLE 9.7
Comparison of Males and Females: Correlation Coefficents of Caregiver–Infant Interaction Variables and Developmental Tests

Interaction variables	4-month Gesell Males	4-month Gesell Females	9-month Gesell Males	9-month Gesell Females	2-year Gesell Males	2-year Gesell Females	2-year Bayley Males	2-year Bayley Females
1 month								
F1: Social	.29*	.01	.38*	.13	.17	.30*	.18	.31*
F2: Responsive holding	-.23*	.06						
F3: Verbal			-.23[a],*	.27[a]	-.06[a]	.31[a],*	.11	.38*
F4: Mutual gazing							-.10[a]	.43[a],*
F5: Stressful holding	.43*	.13	.36*	.11				
Fuss cry					-.08	-.29*	.02	-.31*
Smiling during mutual gazing	.38[a],*	.02[a]			.02[a]	.43[a],*	.09	.33*
Smiling at the observer								
3 months								
					.01	.30*		

F1: Responsive social
F2: Mutual gazing
F3: Physical contact

Fuss cry
Smiling during mutual gazing
Smiling at the observer

Fuss cry						
Smiling during mutual gazing					.35*	
Smiling at the observer						.14

8 months

F1: Mutual social	.11	.30*	-.02[a]	.48[a],**	.00	.34*
F2: Intellectual stimulation	.32*	.23	.14[a]	.50[a],**	.18[a]	.52[a],**
F3: Control					.09	.31*
F4: Floor freedom						
Fuss cry	.04	.30*				
Smiling during mutual gazing			-.12[a]	.33[a],*		
Smiling at the observer						
Vocalizing to the observer						

24 months

F1: Positive attentiveness			.24[a]	.62[a],**	.22[a]	.59[a],**
F2: Negative attentiveness						

[a] Significant difference by z test between the correlation coefficients for males and for females.

*p < .05
**p < .01

ORDINAL POSITION

Ordinal position differences in care-giving behaviors were found at each home visit. We have previously reported differences in care giving that are related to birth order in an English-speaking subsample (Cohen & Beckwith, 1977). In considering the total group, there were more ordinal position differences found than in the subsample. Furthermore, differences between the first born (and the only child in the family) and children who were later born (and were raised with older siblings) were found at an earlier age in the total sample than in the English-speaking subsample. Of the demographic variables investigated, ordinal position provided the most differences. The following effects were found higher in first-born as compared to later-born infants: responsive holding, stressful holding, and smiling at the caregiver at 1 month; responsive social at 3 months; mutual social, intellectual stimulation, and smiling at the observer at 8 months; and positive attentiveness at 24 months. The infant raised without siblings in the family received significantly more care giving than infants whose caregivers had other children to care for.

DISCUSSION

Social experiences with the caregiver during the first months of life were significant predictors of a preterm infant's mental test performance at age 2. In an earlier report based on a subsample of English-speaking families (Beckwith et al., 1976), experiences with the caregiver were related to test performance at 9 months. Additionally, such early experiences with the caregiver continue to predict to competence at age 2. The findings are tantalizing but not clearcut. The degree of variance accounted for is small, the predictors differ from one age to another, they differ from test to test, and from sample to sample. Therefore, only limited predictability of behavior seems possible.

However, in general, a caregiver and infant's readiness to engage in positive social interactions with each other, as in mutual gazing, smiling during mutual gazing, social play, reciprocal play, and talking, were somewhat important to the infant's performance at 9-months old but appeared to be even more significant to his or her performance at 2 years. It appears that a mutually reinforcing social relationship between the caregiver and the infant, in part, mediates mental test performance, possibly because of the cognitive and motivational experiences it provides to the infant. This could also be explained by the infant's disposition, an eagerness to interact with others, including both the primary caregiver and the examiner (McCall, Hogarty, & Hurlburt, 1972). These infants will cooperate more readily with the examiner and will obtain higher test scores. These findings for a risk group resemble results with normal full-term infants (Clarke-Stewart, 1973; Yarrow, et al., 1975).

In contrast to the significance of early distal social interactions for competence at age 2, proximal interactions, that is, the degree to which the infant experienced kinesthetic or vestibular stimulation, and the kind received (holding or holding that stressed postural adjustment) were important to the infant's performance at 4 months but did not relate to competence at age 2. Other investigators have found that kinesthetic or vestibular stimulation enhances cognitive development in normal full-term infants (Ainsworth & Bell, 1973; Lewis, Goldberg, & Campbell, 1969; Yarrow et al., 1975). We had expected that vestibular stimulation would be a singularly important factor in preterm infant development (Korner, Kraemer, Haffner, & Cosper, 1975) and would have long-term effects. Yarrow, Goodwin, Manheimer, and Milowe (1973), who found such an association between a high level of physical contact in the first months of life and enhanced competence at age 10 in full-term infants, used rating scales rather than time sampling of objective behaviors. Perhaps, our negative findings were due to our measurement techniques. It is conceivable that the quality of the holding and the degree to which it marks other aspects of the interaction may have more lasting consequences and are more likely to be noted by rating scales than by time samples.

Denenberg (in press) has pointed out that the nature of the young organism and its rapid rate of change and growth dramatically increase the complexities inherent in any longitudinal research. The issue is one of identifying stabilities when both the predictor variables of social experience and the dependent variables of mental test performance change in form and meaning over time. That is, although the 4-month Gesell correlated with the 9-month Gesell, and it, in turn, with the 24-month Gesell and the 25-month Bayley Mental Scale, the correlations from 4 months to 24–25 months were low, indicating that many infants changed rank from high to low and vice versa. Lewis (1976) has emphasized that there is little consistency in competence across ages in tests designed to measure infant mental functioning. It is clear that mental functioning is a composite of changing skills which become more or less salient depending on the age and nature of the test (Bayley, 1970; McCall, 1976). It is, therefore, not surprising that social interactions linked to test performance at one age were not necessarily significant for performance at a later age. It is noteworthy, however, that social interactions between a caregiver and infant at 1 month were as related to 2-year competence as was the infant's own test performance at 4 months.

Our analyses have been essentially cross-sectional. They do not control or detail the sequences of experiences over time. Yet, the significance of relationships from one age to another age must, in part, reflect the continuity and discontinuity of care-giving patterns. Unraveling the consequences of differences in environmental encounters depends upon our ability to detail and understand the sequential nature of an infant's experience. Such detailing remains a major challenge.

Some beginnings have been made, which illustrate the adaptability, even under unfavorable circumstances, of the infant–caregiver system. Hazardous obstetrical and perinatal events acted to increase, rather than diminish, social interaction. Whether the sicker preterm infant was compared to the healthier preterm infant, as in our study, or the preterm was compared to a full-term infant (Brown & Bakeman, in press; Field, 1977b) the infant at greater risk evoked more social exchanges from the caregiver. Perhaps the attitude of the parents, their wish to compensate or to protect, or perhaps deficits in the behaviors of the infant itself (as suggested by the work of Berkson, 1974; Rosenblum & Youngstein, 1974) acted to heighten the caregiver's efforts. Those efforts, we believe, contributed to the unstable nature of the link between developmental outcome and perinatal complications.

Other characteristics of the infant at risk also affected later social relationships. Field (1977a) found that the infant at risk, who as a neonate was more ready to engage in social interaction, tended to capture more social interaction from the caregiver later. Similarly, we found that a baby who smiled early—and thereby rewarded the caregiver more—received more social interaction later. The importance of the social smile during mutual gazing is underlined by the fact that it occurred rarely.

Other factors, external to behaviors and attitudes of the infant and the caregiver, influence the nature of social experience. Social class and its closely linked correlate, parental education, have been found to be major determinants of the development of children with and without perinatal complications (Deutsch, 1973; Drillien, 1964; Werner, Bierman, & French, 1971). Our findings are similar to those of most studies in finding no relationship between social class and infant test performance at 4 months; at 9 months, only for females; and at 24 months for both males and females (Golden & Birns, 1976; McCall et al., 1972).

Social class is not a unitary variable (Deutsch, 1973). It is a variable that labels, among others, genetic factors, social experiences, and the amount and intensity of inanimate stimulation (Wachs, Uzgiris & Hunt, 1971). In our sample it was also confounded with language group. We used two strategies to understand its relationship to Caregiver–Infant interaction and to the development of preterm infants. One strategy attempted to statistically partial out the association of social class and developmental outcome and then see if the more specific Caregiver–Infant interaction variables added significant predictive power. Although social class entered the equations at significant levels, the interactional variables also contributed significantly. The power of the interactional variables in predicting to a 2-year developmental outcome, therefore, cannot be explained solely by their link with social class.

Our second strategy was to detail ways in which social class effects were mediated through the social experience of the infant. Caregivers from the higher social group talked more to their infant, and the increased talking was embedded in a pattern of increased social exchange and heightened infant affective behavior. Our findings with preterm infants and their caregivers complement studies of normal full-term infants (Golden & Birns, 1976; Tulkin, 1972). Performance on the 2-year outcome measures was affected not only by social class but also by a Sex and Ordinal Position interaction. The first-born girl of higher social class was most likely to show the skilled behaviors called for in mental test performance at age 2.

There are several possible explanations for first-born, higher social-class girls showing superior performance. First, boys have been found to be more vulnerable to a variety of noxious stimuli, including prenatal and perinatal complications (Caputo & Mandell, 1970; Garai & Scheinfeld, 1968). Second, boys experience differences in continuity and sequence of care giving. Third, more educated mothers interact with their girls in more intense, reciprocal social transactions that facilitate test performance at age 2. Fourth, if maternal education is assumed to partially reflect a genetic component in intellectual functioning, then genetic factors combine with experiential factors to facilitate test performance of girls of more educated mothers. The combined effect of genetic and experiential factors may act as a potent contributor to the earlier and more predictable nature of mental test performance for girls. Fifth, some investigators, among them Kagan (1971) and Yang and Moss (1978), have suggested that caregiver behavior more powerfully influences girls' behavior, whereas boys' behavior may be more a function of congenital characteristics. Our results from a large preterm sample with a diversity of social and ethnic backgrounds were consistent with this hypothesis. Our results from the more restricted sample of infants from English-speaking homes were not, however. The mystery of the effects of gender differences in care giving upon early competence clearly needs further investigation.

The study has some tentative implications for the timing, nature, and target group of intervention programs for preterm infants. It appears possible to identify those caregivers who engage in and are likely to continue low levels of social interaction with their preterm infants. As such low levels of social interaction are then predictive to lowered infant competence at age 2, identification and intervention might profitably be directed to such families. Furthermore, as low levels of social interaction were more predictive at an earlier age than were developmental assessments of the infant, intervention could proceed before deficits in infant behavior occur. Finally, it seems apparent that some aspects of the Caregiver–Infant interaction are more significant for later competence than are other aspects. Rather than the total amount of caregiver attentiveness, quantity of pleasureable and reciprocal social exchanges were emphasized. The goal of increasing such exchanges may be difficult to achieve, but may prove to be the most worthwhile (Bromwich, 1976).

ACKNOWLEDGMENTS

This research has been supported by NIH-NICHD Contract No. 1-HD-3-2776, "Diagnostic and Intervention Studies of High Risk Infants"; and by NICHD Grant No. HD-04112, Mental Retardation Center, University of California at Los Angeles, Los Angeles, California.

REFERENCES

Ainsworth, M. D. S., & Bell, S. M. Mother-infant interaction and the development of competence. In K. S. Connolly, & J. S. Bruner (Eds.), *The growth of competence.* New York: Academic Press, 1973.

Bayley, N. Development of mental abilities. In P. H. Mussen (Ed.), *Carmichael's manual of child psychology* (3rd ed., Vol. 1). New York: Wiley, 1970.

Beckwith, L. Relationships between infants' social behavior and their mothers' behavior. *Child Development,* 1972, *43,* 397–411.

Beckwith, L. Caregiver-infant interaction and the development of the high risk infant. In T. Tjossem (Ed.), *Intervention strategies for high-risk infants and young children.* Baltimore: Univ. Park, 1976.

Beckwith, L., & Cohen, S. E. Preterm birth: Hazardous obstetrical and postnatal events as related to caregiver–infant behavior. *Infant Behavior and Development,* 1978, *1,* 403–411.

Beckwith, L., Cohen, S. E., Kopp, C. B., Parmelee, A. H., & Marcy, T. G. Caregiver-infant interaction and early cognitive development in preterm infants. *Child Development,* 1976, *47,* 579–587.

Berkson, G. Social responses of animals to infants with defects. In M. E. Lewis & L. A. Rosenblum (Eds.), *The effect of the infant on its caregiver.* New York: Wiley, 1974.

Bradley, R. H., & Caldwell, B. M. Early home environment and changes in mental test performance in children from 6 to 36 months. *Developmental Psychology,* 1976, *12,* 93–97.

Bromwich, R. M. Focus on maternal behavior in infant intervention. *American Journal of Orthopsychiatry,* 1976, *46,* 439–446.

Brown, J. V., & Bakeman, R. Relationships of human mothers with their infants during the first year of life: Effects of prematurity. In R. W. Bell & W. P. Smotherman (Eds.), *Maternal influences and early behavior.* Holliswood, New York: Spectrum, in press.

Caputo, D. V., & Mandell, W. Consequences of low birth weight. *Developmental Psychology,* 1970, *3,* 363–383.

Clarke-Stewart, K. A. Interactions between mothers and their young children: Characteristics and consequences. *Monographs of the Society for Research in Child Development,* 1973, *38* (No. 6-7; Whole No. 153).

Cohen, S. E., & Beckwith, L. Caregiving behaviors and early cognitive development as related to ordinal position in preterm infants. *Child Development,* 1977, *48,* 152–157.

Cohen, S. E., & Beckwith, L. Preterm infant interaction with the caregiver in the first year of life and competence at age two. *Child Development,* 1979, *50,* 767–776.

Denenberg, V. H. Paradigms and paradoxes in the study of behavioral development. In E. B. Thoman (Ed.), *The origins of the infant's social responsiveness.* Hillsdale, New Jersey: Erlbaum, in press.

Deutsch, C. P. Social class and child development. In B. M. Caldwell & H. N. Ricciuti (Eds.), *Review of child development research* (Vol. 3). Chicago: Univ. Chicago Press, 1973.

Drillien C. M. *The growth and development of the prematurely born infant.* Baltimore: Williams & Wilkens, 1964.

Dunn, J. How far do early differences in mother–child relations affect later development? In P. P. C. Bateson & R. A. Hinde (Eds.), *Growing points in ethology.* Cambridge: Cambridge Univ. Press, 1976.

Elardo, R., Bradley, R., & Caldwell, B. M. The relation of infants' home environments to mental test performance from six to thirty-six months: A longitundinal analysis. *Child Development,* 1975, *46,* 71–76.

Field, T. Effects of early separation, interactive deficits, and experimental manipulations on infant–mother face-to-face interaction. *Child Development,* 1977, *48,* 763–771. (a)

Field, T. Maternal stimulation during infant feeding. *Developmental Psychology,* 1977, *13,* 539–540. (b)

Fitzhardinge, P. M., & Ramsay, M. The improving outlook for the small prematurely born infant. *Developmental Medicine and Child Neurology,* 1973, *15,* 447–459.

Garai, J. E., & Scheinfeld, A. Sex differences in mental and behavioral traits. *Genetic Psychology Monographs,* 1968, *77,* 169–299.

Golden, M., & Birns, B. Social class and infant intelligence. In M. Lewis (Ed.), *Origins of intelligence.* New York: Plenum 1976.

Hunt, J. V. Environmental risk in fetal and neonatal life and measured infant intelligence. In M. Lewis (Ed.), *Origins of intelligence.* New York: Plenum 1976.

Kagan, J. *Change and continuity in infancy.* New York: Wiley, 1971.

Korner, A. F., Kraemer, H. C., Haffner, M. E., & Cosper, L. Effects of waterbed flotation on premature infants: A pilot study. *Pediatrics,* 1975, *67,* 361–367.

Lewis, M. What do we mean when we say "Infant Intelligence Scores"? A sociopolitical question. In M. Kewis (Ed.), *Origins of intelligence.* New York: Plenum, 1976.

Lewis, M. S., Goldberg, S., & Campbell, H. A developmental study of information processing within the first three years of life: Response decrement to a redundant signal. *Monographs of the Society for Research in Child Development,* 1969, *34* (No. 9; Whole No. 133).

Littman, B., & Parmelee, A. H. Medical correlates of infant development. *Pediatrics,* 1978, *61,* 470–474.

Maccoby, E. E., & Jacklin, C. N. *The psychology of sex differences.* Stanford: Stanford Univ. Press, 1974.

McCall, R. B. Toward an epigenetic conception of mental development in the first three years of life. In M. Lewis (Ed.), *Origins of intelligence.* New York: Plenum, 1976.

McCall, R. B., Hogarty, P., & Hurlburt, N. Transitions in infant sensorimotor development and the prediction of childhood IQ. *American Psychologist,* 1972, *27,* 728–748.

Moss, H. A. Sex, age, and state as determinants of Mother–Infant interaction. *Merrill-Palmer Quarterly,* 1967, *13,* 19–36.

Nelson, K. Structure and strategy in learning to talk. *Monographs of the Society for Research in Child Development,* 1973, *38* (No. 1–2; Whole No. 149).

Parmelee, A. H., Sigman, M., Kopp, C. B., & Haber, A. The concept of a cumulative risk score for infants. In N. R. Ellis (Ed.), *Aberrant development in infancy: Human and animal studies.* Hillsdale, New Jersey: Erlbaum, 1975.

Parmelee, A. H., Sigman, M., Kopp, C. B., & Haber, A. Diagnosis of the infant at risk for mental, motor, or sensory handicap. In T. Tjossem (Ed.), *Intervention strategies for high risk infants and young children.* Baltimore: Univ. Park Press, 1976.

Parmelee, A. H., Kopp, C. B., & Sigman, M. Selection of developmental assessment techniques for infants at risk. *Merrill-Palmer Quarterly,* 1976, *22,* 177–199.

Rosenblum, L. A., & Youngstein, K. P. Developmental changes in compensatory dyadic response in mother and infant monkeys. In M. Lewis & L. A. Rosenblum (Eds.); *The effect of the infant on its caregiver.* New York: Wiley, 1974.

Sigman, M. & Parmelee, A. H. Longitudinal evaluation of the high-risk infant. In T. M. Field, A. M. Sostek, S. Goldberg, & H. H. Shuman (Eds.), *Infants born at risk.* New York: Spectrum, 1979.

Tulkin, S. R. An analysis of the concept of cultural deprivation. *Developmental Psychology,* 1972, *6,* 326–339

Wachs, T. D., Uzgiris, I. C., & Hunt, J., Mc V. Cognitive development in infants of different age levels and from different environmental backgrounds: An explanatory investigation. *Merrill-Palmer Quarterly,* 1971, *17,* 283–317.

Werner, E. E., Bierman, J. M., & French, F. E. *The children of Kauai: A longitudinal study from the prenatal period to age ten.* Honolulu: Univ. Hawaii Press, 1971.

Yang, R. K., & Moss, H. A. Neonatal precursors of infant behavior. *Developmental Psychology,* 1978, *14,* 607–613.

Yarrow, L. J., Goodwin, M. S., Manheimer, H., & Milowe, I. D. Infancy experiences and cognitive and personality development at ten years. In L. J. Stone, H. T. Smith, & L. B. Murphy (Eds.), *The competent infant: Research and commentary.* New York: Basic Books, 1973.

Yarrow, L. J., Rubenstein, J. L., & Pedersen, F. A. *Infant and environment: Early cognitive and motivational development.* Washington, D.C.: Wiley, 1975.

PART IV

INFANTS AND CHILDREN WITH
PERCEPTUAL–MOTOR HANDICAPS

CHAPTER 10

H. ALS
E. TRONICK
T. B. BRAZELTON

Stages of Early Behavioral Organization: The Study of a Sighted Infant and a Blind Infant in Interaction with Their Mothers

INTRODUCTION

The birth of a newborn with a problem such as blindness is a traumatic event for everyone involved. Much has been written about the parents' reactions to such an event (Cohen, 1962; Kennedy, 1969; Michaels & Shuman, 1962; Olshansky, 1962; Solnit & Stark, 1961). They are described as shocked, panicked, overcome by feelings of helplessness, anger, and guilt. The attending physician experiences guilt and helplessness, feeling he has let his patient down by delivering a less than normal infant. He is often at a loss as to how to support the parents. The parents' next reactions include, simultaneously, the wish that the baby will die, the feeling that there must be something that can be done about the condition, and the need to minimize and deny the condition. All these reactions are common and normal, but confusing and difficult to sustain. The intensity of such feelings highlights the degree of psychological preparation during pregnancy that preceeds the actual birth of any infant. Most parents will have thought about the possibility of having a baby with a problem. This may stem as much from the ever-present ambivalence surrounding the question of being competent to become a parent, as it is a preparatory loosening of energies to deal with such an eventuality.

The studies of the emotional development of pregnant women by Bibring and her colleagues (Bibring, Dwyer, Huntington, & Valenstein, 1961) have

181

HIGH-RISK INFANTS AND CHILDREN:
Adult and Peer Interactions

uncovered a process of enormous emotional upheaval and turmoil taking place in the course of normal pregnancies. Yet, when the mother was observed caring for her new infant, this very anxiety seemed to become a force for reorganization and adjustment to her important new role. Brazelton (Brazelton & Als, 1979) calls the prenatal anxiety and distortion in fantasy a healthy mechanism for bringing the woman "out of the old homeostasis, which she has achieved prior to becoming pregnant, to a new level of adjustment." He sees the "shake-up in pregnancy as readying the circuits for new attachments . . . as a method of training her circuits for a kind of sensitivity to the infant and to his individual requirements which might not have been easily or otherwise available from her earlier adjustments." Thus, this emotional turmoil of pregnancy can be seen as a positive force for the mother's healthy adjustment and for the possibility of providing a more individualized, flexible environment for the infant.

If this degree of upheaval is expectable and occurs as a normal process in order to mother a healthy newborn and to adjust to the newborn's specific behavioral organization and individuality, how much more upheaval would one expect when the newborn turns out not to be healthy or normal. Seen this way, the mother's grief reaction in the face of a damaged infant can be taken as an index of the degree of energy available to be channeled toward this infant. Acknowledgement and articulation of the feelings experienced may make it possible for the parent to preserve the energy connected with these feelings so that they can be brought to bear on the developmental process of both the handicapped infant and the new parental role.

In this chapter we discuss our work with normal families and with families where the infant has a problem. Early in our study of normal pairs, it became clear to us that we needed a model for parent–infant organization that allowed for a handicap or damage to the infant's organizational processes. There are many possible pathways to a given developmental outcome. For instance, von Bertalanffy's (1968) principle of equifinality talks about preset biologic goals that the organism seeks to realize, even if there are distortions to overcome. Waddington (1956) speaks of the self-righting tendencies in the developmental process, tendencies to overcome deflection, to return to an appropriate, predetermined developmental pathway. Our study attempts to identify the interactive biologic goals of the infant and parent and to describe the processes of "overcoming deflection." By individualizing the process and by expanding our own ideas of what is appropriate, we can begin to identify the energy that is available within the developing infant–parent feedback system and the behavioral goals negotiated within this system. It seems that the more specifically we can identify the early interactive goals of any infant and parent, the more we will be able to help support parents in this early negotiation process with their infant and diminish the deviances so often observed in the face of a handicap (Fraiberg, 1977).

METHODOLOGY TO STUDY THE PROCESS OF EARLY INFANT-PARENT INTERACTION

Our first study sample consisted of 12 healthy full-term infants and their healthy mothers. They were studied in the laboratory from about age 16 days, in weekly sessions, until 5-months old (Brazelton, Tronick, Adamson, Als, & Wise, 1975; Tronick, Als, Adamson, 1979; Tronick, Als, & Brazelton, 1977). Three-minute, face-to-face play sessions, as well as various experimental conditions (e.g., the mother sitting in front of the infant with a still face), were studied (Tronick, Als, Adamson, & Brazelton, 1978).

To explore the possibilities of applying our knowledge from normal pairs to the dynamics of pairs who have problems, we have studied over the last 3 years the face-to-face interactions of 20 families where the infant had a physical problem such as gross developmental delay, prematurity, small-for-dateness, blindness, cleft palate, or hypothyroidism (Als & Brazelton, 1978; Als, Tronick, & Brazelton, 1977; Als, Tronick, & Brazelton, in press). This study was designed to identify the commonalities of Parent-Infant interaction patterns despite a range of inevitable distortions based on inherent deficits in interactive equipment. Furthermore, it was designed to help us identify the specific effects of the damage on the infant as well as on the parent, and to allow us to identify the process by which mutual interaction and the increasingly autonomous development of both infant and parent is negotiated.

The families in this sample were observed from the infant's first few days of life on. They were videotaped weekly or bi-weekly to age 3 months, then monthly to 6 months, in this face-to-face paradigm. The face-to-face interaction paradigm in the laboratory was used as it provided an opportunity to maximize the displays of social interaction skills between infant and adult. When the infant was alert and calm, he was placed in an infant seat on a table and the mother sat in front of him. The instructions to her were to play with the baby without picking him up. No toys were provided. One video camera was focused on the infant, one on the mother, and their two pictures were fed through a digital timer and a split-screen generator into a single videotape monitor. The resulting split-screen image provides a frontal view of mother and infant, each on one side of the video image, along with a digital time display along the lower margin of the image.

The face-to-face laboratory situation was stressful for the interactants in that it provided no functional goals other than a situation for social interaction

(Tronick et al. 1979). In that way it forced both partners to use all the skills and resources they had in order to engage one another in a mutually satisfying interchange. Furthermore, it brought out the infant's current organizational capacities: his ability to maintain physiological balance (e.g., respiration, color, heartrate, and motor arousal); his ability to maintain postural control; his ability to maintain states of alertness; and his ability to interact reciprocally with his mother. It also brought out the degree to which his mother was capable of helping him regulate his own organization and the degree to which the two partners facilitated each other as they built up and cycled with one another in a rhythmical fashion (Brazelton, Koslowski, & Main, 1974).

MODEL OF HIERARCHICAL ORGANIZATIONAL LEVELS OF THE EARLY DEVELOPMENTAL PROCESS

From our work with the families observed in this interaction paradigm, we learned that in the course of the first month the healthy, well-mothered infant seems to achieve control over basic physiological demands, such as respiration, heart rate, temperature control, color changes, and tremulousness; he or she seems to establish modulated control over his or her movements so that they no longer tax this physiological balance; and he or she seems to achieve increasing control over achieving an alert state. This control over state transitions—from sleep to alert and from aroused crying states to alertness—demands an integration of infant control over physiological and motoric balance (Als, 1979; Als, Lester, & Brazelton, 1979). As state organization becomes more differentiated and regulated, the next newly emerging expansion is that of increasing differentiation of the alert state. Within the alert state, the infant's social capacities can begin to unfold. His or her ability to communicate becomes increasingly sophisticated. The infant's repertoire of facial expressions and their use, the range and use of vocalizations, cries, gestures, and postures, come increasingly into service during interactions with a social partner. On the basis of well-modulated state organization, the infant can negotiate this new range of social skills, and on the basis of rich, well-differentiated social play, a new level of organization emerges. This new level incorporates toys and other objects in play in order to learn about and to expand the give and take of social communication.

From our observations and analyses to date, we have constructed a schematic model of this progression, as Figure 10.1 shows (Als, 1979; Als, Tronick, & Brazelton, in press). Each stage of regulation in this progression can be seen as distinctly different from the preceding one in that a new goal is being tackled. The preceding stage seems to provide the basis from which the new goal emerges. We have observed that the balance and modulation of the

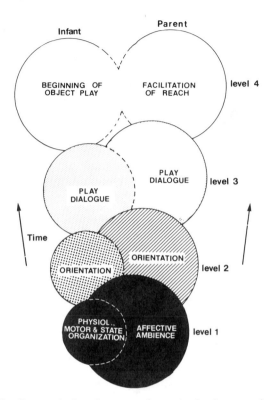

FIGURE 10.1.   The diagram depicts the stages of organization in parent-infant interaction.

previous stage becomes disrupted in order to allow the emergence of the new accomplishment. Apparent disorganization seems to be a necessary precursor to the next stage of growth in the system. However, in the disorganization seems to lie the assurance that the new accomplishment is pressing to emerge.

We have also arrived at a model of the process by which we now think each new stage of organization comes about within the progression of the interaction (Als, 1979; Brazelton & Als, 1979). The fueling drive for this hierarchical emergence of consecutive stages seems to come from two sources: (a) from within the organism and his or her sense of competence achieved as each new step in organization is recognized by the infant, and (b) from the external fueling system, namely, the help for organization provided by the parent. Just as the infant is biologically fueled to accomplish the next stage, the parent, in turn, seems adaptively fueled to support the infant's development. Development is then seen as a mutual process, and both infant and parent facilitate the other's developmental progression. The feedback of completing each cycle acts as fuel for the next (Als, 1979; Brazelton, Als, 1979).

CASE 1: NORMAL INFANT IN FACE-TO-FACE
INTERACTION WITH MOTHER

We would like to present two examples from our study to demonstrate the developmental progression from physiological, motor, and state control to the achievement of mutual orientation (the expansion into the beginnings of play dialogue; the rich and modulated, easily attained play dialogue; and finally to the basis for the eventual incorporation of objects).

The first case is that of a healthy, full-term infant and his mother. This infant was the first-born child of a 26-year-old woman and her 35-year-old husband. The infant weighed 8 lb, 9 oz at birth and had 1- and 5-min Apgar ratings of 8 and 9. Four observation sessions will be discussed here to present the progression of early behavioral expansion observed.

Interaction at 25 days (see Figure 10.2a)

The infant sits slumped back in the seat, head slightly to the side, and chin tucked. His arms are pulled up to his chest, fists closed. His face is serious, brows knitted. As the mother comes in, she first looks down at his trunk, then toward him. He looks at her, and she greets him with a throaty "Hello, there!" sits down, leaning forward, and takes his hands. She cycles them softly, her arms encasing his legs. She leans in closely, her head cocked. In an alluring voice, she smilingly croons "Ooh!" as he lifts his eyes back toward her. Her right hand taps his hand gently. As he averts his eyes again, she moves her left arm up along his body to touch his face. Then her hands softly cycle with his, her voice is drawn out and persuasive, trying to maintain his looking at her. When his gaze averts, she moves after him into his line of vision, her face close to his, rhythmically exercising his hands in small cycles as if to draw him closer. Her voice alternates between drawn-out questions, mock reprimands: "Don't go to sleep!" as he averts his eyes, and acknowledges him with "That's right" when he looks back at her. As he finally continues to look at her with raised eyebrows and pursed mouth, inquisitively monitoring her face for a 10-sec stretch, she builds up to an animated wide smile and greets him with a joyful "Hi!" As he averts again, the cycles of eliciting, drawing him toward her with face, voice, and hand cycling, start up again. She acknowledges his next period of looking with a smile. At this, he averts, puffs out his cheeks, and moves his hands out of hers. His fingers fanning out, his eyes come back briefly to look at her. At this she grasps his hands again, her arms still in the same encasing position, her face close in toward his. She acknowledges his eyebrow raise, cocking her head playfully, smiling sweetly. As he lids down once more, drooping his eyelids, she blows playfully in his face, calling to him, kissing his hand. He strains momentarily with a fussy sound, his lips pouting, as if to get away from the interaction. She moves yet closer in, talking and cycling his hands.

This interaction at 25 days shows the infant moving between averting and briefly monitoring the mother while the mother continuously pursues him, eliciting his attention with animated voice and face. We have developed a systematic behavioral analysis of the interactions described to capture the flow of the displays and the change over time. The scoring system provides for second-by-second scoring on a continuum of involvement in the interaction, ranging from: behavior actively against the interaction (labeled "protest"); behavior indicating passive withdrawal from the interaction (labeled "avert"); behavior indicating serious attention toward the other partner in an attempt to identify what he is doing (labeled "monitor"); active maneuvers designed to heighten the engagement of the other partner, (labeled "elicit"); relaxed readiness to participate in the interaction (labeled "set"); heightened displays of smiling and simultaneous attention directed to the partner (labeled "play"); heightened displays of smiling paired with animated vocalizations and simultaneous attention directed at the partner, (labeled "talk"). The behavioral dimensions considered for each phase are the interactants' eye direction, head position, body position, facial expression, vocalizations, and movements. More explicit methodological directions, including a scoring manual, can be found elsewhere (Als, Tronick, & Brazelton, 1979). This scoring method yields a score per second for each interaction partner. These scores for adult and infant are then graphed along a common time axis, in mirror image to one another, so that the farther apart two points are on the curves, the farther apart interactively the partners are. The closer together the points are on the graph, the closer together the partners are in social interaction. When they are in mutual play dialogue—that is, the phases play or talk—the graphs are overlaid, occupying the same space to indicate the achieved, heightened synchrony (Als, Tronick, & Brazelton, 1977).

As is apparent from the graph in Figure 10.2a, the infant moves mainly from cautious monitoring to averting, then attempts to monitor again, while the mother moves between eliciting and play, attempting to control and drive the infant to attend to her.

Interaction at 46 days (see Figure 10.2b)

The infant sits in his seat in an upright position, head in midline, arms cycling toward the mother as she comes in close to him with a slight smile on her face. His eyes are round and shiny; his mouth opens into an "ooh"; and with a coo he greets her. She returns his greeting, "Oh, you are happy today!" and catches his hands and sits down. As he moves his head to the side and averts his eyes, she moves close in with a wide smile, calling "Hi, there!" He comes back to midline, round eyes back on her, opens his mouth again and lifts his head toward her, off the back of the seat. Jiggling his hands, she repeats at a fast pace: "Hi, hi, hi!" At this he lets his head fall back and now alternates between serious monitoring glances toward her and lidding his eyes. She looks down on his hands, then questions: "What are you up to? What are you up to?" Jiggling his hands rhythmically, repeatedly she tries to move into his line of vision, as he grunts, puffs out his cheeks, and avoids her gaze. She alternately touches his mouth playfully, teasingly,

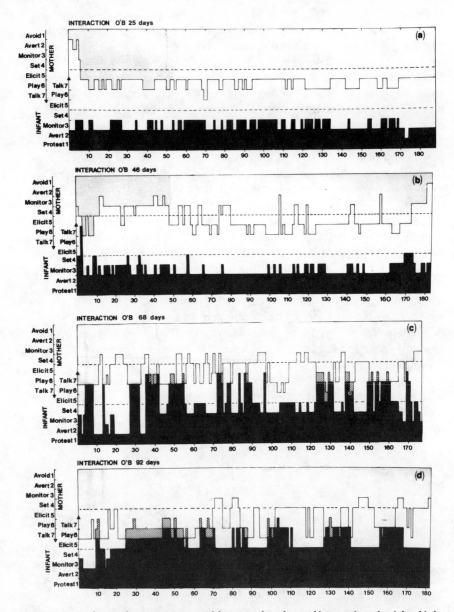

FIGURE 10.2. The graphs represent second-by-second analyses of interaction of a sighted infant and his mother: (a) at 25 days; (b)at 46 days; (c) at 68 days; (d) at 92 days.

with extended finger and calling him a fighter. Then she observes his reaction seriously. He averts for prolonged periods. After each touch, however, he glances at her intently, opening his mouth, raising his eyebrows, and he crosses his eyes. He yawns and looks just past her, keeping her puzzled as to how best to engage him. She gives him time to finish his yawn and then coaxes him to look at her. As he looks back at her intently, his eyes cross again in excitement, and he mouths and swallows. He makes grunting sounds, repeatedly fastening his eyes on her, mouth tense now and cheeks drawn down. She moves in closely each time, smiling and encouraging him to talk to her. Eventually he pulls his lips down in a pout and glances away from her. She touches his face, talks to him with high-pitched voice and cocked head, and cycles his hands. Renewed, he looks back at her, his face more relaxed now, arms and legs opening out towards her as she leaves the alcove.

By 46 days (Figure 10.2b) the infant is now able to maintain a quiet, brightly alert state that is oriented toward the mother for longer periods, and the next emerging coo and play phase is only hinted at in the initial greeting sally. The mother's range of affective level of involvement has also widened by now. She moves from intermittent times of looking away from him, via monitoring the infant, to eliciting and playing. The urgency of continuous prompting and organizing exhibited in the tight cycling of the earlier interaction is no longer as intense. The infant has become more flexible, and the mother can leave some of the modulation to him.

Interaction at 68 days (see Figure 10.2c)

The infant is leaning back in his chair, his right hand open and resting on his thigh, expectantly looking from underneath half-closed eyelids toward his incoming mother. She greets him with a cheerful wide smile: "Hello, there! Hello, there!" His eyelids come down, then he points his foot out toward her, glances at her seriously only to build up to a smiling face, cycling both his arms towards her and pulling up his legs. She continues in her bright greeting as she sits down: "How are you! How are you!" His smile widens and he coos on expiration, head half cocked. She grasps his hands lightly, asking with a wide-mouthed smile, "Are you glad to see me?" His movements become more jerky as his head averts to the side. His cooing changes into a mixture of fussing and gasping. He arches against her momentarily as she becomes serious and watches him. She lets go of his hands, touching his mouth as if to wipe it and asks repeatedly, "What is the matter?" He now alternates between cry faces with fussy vocalizations and sudden smiles, only to return again to a cry face. She alternates from touching him as she becomes serious and inquires empathetically about his "problem," to acknowledging his smiles: "That's it. I know you're trying to smile!" At this they both build up together so that he is cooing and smiling, head toward her, arms open by his side, and legs reaching toward her, while she is close in, smiling widely, and driving him with "That's it, that's it!" Then they both draw back again, momentarily relaxing until she cycles his hands; his eyes widen and they reach another simultaneous peak. She embeds his coos in soft, crooning talking: "That's my boy, yeah!" waiting for the next buildup. Eventually she amplifies his peaks of excitement with a tapping game to his nose: "Beep! Beepeepeep! Beep!" He sobers, she lets up, sitting back, talking to him in almost adult fashion. He coos at her repeatedly. She holds him off, drawing him along until they both build up yet again to simultaneous cooing and talking.

We observe in Figure 10.2c that by 68 days the infant's involvement in the interaction has become increasingly differentiated, moving initially between protest and play, and then, after 35 sec, between monitoring, relaxed readiness, and playing until the very end when he intermittently averts again. His baseline is now at a relaxed readiness for the interaction. The repeated cycling through playing and vocalizing indicates the full emergence of a new differentiated use of his alert state. That he returns to a relaxed readiness regularly after making an excursion into the play levels indicates the degree of organization in the interaction, of his ability to integrate smiling and cooing. He achieves a new amplitude of affective level of involvement in interaction not previously attained. The mother spends more time in relaxed readiness than before, indicating her expectant availability for play and her ability to let the infant take the lead.

Interaction at 92 days (see Figure 10.2d)

The infant sits expectantly in his seat, face intent, right arm waving in midair toward his mother as she comes in with a soft smile and a seductive voice, calling, "Hello, boy! Hello, boy!" He flings his arms over his face momentarily, grunts, and looks away. Both her hands enclose him at his waist as she sits down. She pumps his belly, crooning, "Hello, boy, hello!" He arches toward her, now covering his face with both arms. As his hands slowly sink down, he has burst into a broad smile with narrow, twinkling eyes, cooing at her. She takes his hands and claps them together, smiling broadly, repeating now in a more high-pitched voice, "I know! I know! I know!" He smiles and crows back to her. They engage in a 30-sec long, simultaneous reciprocal smiling and cooing "dance." She kisses his hands, and he shrieks in delight. She acknowledges: "That's right! That's right!" He lids down briefly, relaxing the excitement, as she taps his cheeks and starts the familiar "beepeepeep" game. His eyes remain on her, his mouth opens, his body is stretched out towards her, as he gets ready for the next buildup to renewed smiling, cooing, and gurgling. She waits, then kisses both his hands simultaneously, profusely, with a high-pitched "mmmmmmmm" sound. He squeals. She opens his arms widely, smiling at him broadly. She cycles his arms vigorously as they both relax for a few seconds. She taps his mouth, wipes his chin, all the time looking at him smilingly. He crows, eyes fastened on her every move. Then he starts to smile, crow, and points his tongue toward her, with panting respirations. She exercises his arms in large cycles or kisses his hands, and they achieve another simultaneous cooing and smiling climax. After another 10 sec of mutual gazing, with the mother urging him to "Come on! Come on!" she begins to kiss his ear. He bursts into ecstatic smiling and squealing. She imitates his vocalizations as he relaxes to watch her again in great anticipation.

By 92 days we observed (Figure 10.2d) prolonged play episodes, indicating that the differentiation of the alert state into playing and cooing has become increasingly solidified. This consolidation is evident as both partners return to a relaxed availability after each heightened interaction, rather than to a state of monitoring each other or averting from one another as previously seen. The mother's easy return to readiness seems to indicate her confidence in the infant's self-regulation. The infant's and mother's new baseline is now at the "set" state of alertness with prolonged periods of play and talk.

Figure 10.2a –d shows that the infant's interactive curve has literally moved up by two phases, from averting and monitoring at 25 days, with its peak at the set phase by 46 days, to its base at the set phase and its peaks at play and talk by 3 months. The wavelength of the curve has also considerably increased, pointing to the smooth reintegration of the recent differentiation of both partners who are now ready for new expansion of an increasingly solidifying base. This analysis system, then, gives us a way for a systematic documentation of the process of early development within the matrix of the social interaction.

CASE 2: BLIND INFANT IN FACE-TO-FACE INTERACTION WITH MOTHER

The second case is that of a congenitally blind infant and her sighted mother (Als, Tronick, & Brazelton, in press). This infant was the second child of a 28-year-old woman and her 30-year-old husband. Their first child is a well-developed boy who was 3-years old at the birth of this infant. The blind infant weighed 6 lb., 15 oz. at birth and had 1- and 5-min Apgar ratings of 9 and 10, respectively. Repeated neurological examinations were negative, and the infant was examined in the mother's presence at 3 days and 8 days of age with the Brazelton Neonatal Behavioral Assessment Scale (Brazelton, 1973). Although the infant had some difficulty in controlling her states to achieve a quiet state as she returned from crying, she was eventually consolable with soothing talk from the examiner. Then she would become alert, raise her eyebrows, soften her cheeks, and make an "ooh" face, turning her head to the sound and searching for its source. Her movements would smooth out, her hands open, and she would communicate her availability. The mother was pleased to see this organized communicative behavior. It seemed to help her differentiate the specificity of the lack of vision in her infant from other kinds of damage and to see her infant as a competent newborn. By 10 days the infant had developed a state of awake immobility which occurred especially when there was appropriate auditory input directed toward her from the environment. The mother soon learned to read this immobility as her infant's way of monitoring the environment. She developed a successful way of addressing the infant by touching her softly and continuously calling her name, organizing her with voice and touch.

The initial laboratory observation occurred when the infant was 25-days old, then again in at least bi-weekly intervals until 5 months of age. From 5 months on, she was observed in approximately monthly intervals to 9 months, and then again at 12 and 15 months, in various situations at the laboratory and at home. Four sessions will be discussed here to present the progression of early behavioral expansion observed.

Interaction at 25 days (see Figure 10.3a)

The infant slumps back in her seat, with jerky movements of arms and legs, holding her head tilted to one side. As the mother comes in, she softly repeats in a high, drawn out, crooning voice, "Marci, it's Mommy; it's Mommy." The infant turns her head to midline, her arms open toward the mother, and her arms become somewhat tremulous. The mother changes her voice and says, faster, more pointedly and firmly, "Yes, you know me. Yes, you do. You know me." The mother reaches up with one hand and catches one of the free flailing hands, repeating, "Yes, you do." She moves her face close to the baby. At this the infant becomes still, facing the mother at midline. She raises her eyebrows, her face softens, and she opens her mouth toward the mother. The mother leans in close to her now. Taking hold of the other hand, she cycles it gently three times and makes rhythmical, high-pitched sounds. She imitates the infant's coughing, and than takes hold of both hands simultaneously. The infant faces her straight on and becomes very still. The instant she lets go, the infant throws her head vigorously from side to side. The mother quickly takes hold of her legs and cycles them. The infant's face darkens, her arms tighten up, and she moves her head jerkily from side to side. At this the mother lets go of her legs, strokes her face softly, and repeats in the initial drawn out, rhythmical crooning voice: "Marci, it's Mommy." Immediately Marci stills and orients again toward her. The mother touches her ear, speaking softly, "You are very pretty," then lets go of her. At that Marci throws off a startle. The mother immediately catches both her hands again, cycling them, but Marci fusses, and the mother lets go, sits back a little, and demands: "Tell me! Tell me!" This brings Marci once more to complete stillness, with her body extended toward the mother. The mother softly repeats, "Tell me, tell me!" Marci lies back, still in midline, arms pulled up to her chest with her whole body attending to the mother.

By 25 days this blind infant achieves repeated periods of relaxed orientation toward her mother, although her level of involvement in the interaction is generally low. At her baseline, she has an idiosyncratic "place-holding" pattern, in which there are repetitive head movements back and forth not observed in any of the sighted infants we have studied. By 25 days the mother is already on track with the infant: When the infant is attending, the mother is usually maintaining her attention with soft but animated speech and gentle touch. As the infant disengages, the mother waits, as if to find out what it is she is doing.

In this manner, she alternately builds the infant up when the infant is ready, and decreases her activity when the infant's level of involvement temporarily lessens. It appears that, in contrast to many cases reported in the literature (Fraiberg, 1977), this mother had begun to consciously "read" her infant and work with her by this age and was fostering her organization systematically as early as this, overcoming the severe violation of the interaction that the absence of vision presented to both of them.

The systematic behavioral analyses of the interactions described between this blind infant and her mother again capture the flow of the display and the change over time. To accurately reflect the specific behavior observed in this pair, the infant category place-hold, defined to encompass searching head movements, has been substituted for the category "monitor." Monitor has a visual connotation and seemed inappropriate for the blind infant's behavior. "Eliciting" has been transposed from its original position between monitor and set to place it between set and play, in order to credit the interactive energy expended toward the other partner in attempting to draw him in to the interaction.

Figure 10.3a indicates the repeated efforts the mother makes at monitoring her infant, waiting for her place-holding activity, and then building up to play. In this way, she draws the infant to her optimal state set, which the infant at this stage maintains only briefly (i.e., maximum of 6 sec). After 1 min and 10 sec of interaction, the availability of the infant becomes briefer—the focused attention can no longer be achieved at all after 30 more sec. The mother's final sally of playful building up and expanding the infant's set are finally met by protest and averting. The mother lets up and waits, while the infant demonstrates efforts to stay organized.

Interaction at 60 days (see Figures 10.3b)

As the mother comes in with a cheerful, high-pitched "Hi, Sweetie," the infant startles markedly, throwing both arms out; her head moves from side to side vehemently; her face is turned upwards and tense. The mother lowers and softens her voice. "Hi, Marci, it's Mommy." The mother then moves her face close to Marci, and attempts to pull her to midline by her voice: "Over here, over here!" Marci cycles her arms jerkily and moves her head back and forth, still facing to the right, almost brings it to midline but cannot hold it there. Her face is somewhat softer now. The mother asks in the same animated, high-pitched voice, three times: "Can I have a smile, can I have a smile, can I have a smile?" Marci jerkily moves her head back and forth. The mother changes to "Come over here, come over here," trying again to get her to orient in midline. As Marci almost comes to midline with a jerky, right-left motion of her head, the mother immediately praises her for the success: "Good girl, good girl!" and quickly asks again, "Can I have a smile, can I have a smile?" Her voice is intent at first, then more hesitant, as Marci continues to move her arms about jerkily and fusses slightly. Now the mother moves closer in with her own face, holds her child's hand

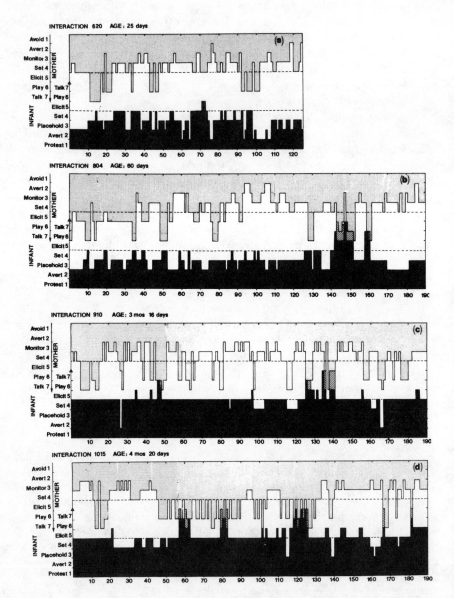

FIGURE 10.3. The graphs represent second-by-second analyses of interaction of a blind infant and her mother: (a) at 25 days; (b) at 60 days; (c) at 3 months, 16 days; (d) at 4 months, 20 days.

momentarily, and runs her finger up Marci's body, all the way to her face, accompanying it by "Boop, boop, boop, boop" sounds in ascending scale. To this Marci stills momentarily and brightens, raising her eyebrows. The mother rewards her with an accentuated "Good girl! What a pretty smile! Can I have another one?" Marci startles slightly and continues to move her head from side to side in fast, sideways turns. She then pulls her arms up to her face. The mother sits back and tries again. "Marci, Marci, I am not over there; I am over *here!* Can I have another smile? Marci, Marci . . ." She touches her gently, moves in closely, and then sits back again, her face getting tenser, waiting for each brief moment of stilling. Marci continues to fling her head from side to side, sticks out her tongue, and flails her arms in tense, small circles.

By 60 days this blind infant's interactive capacities have expanded: After more than 2 min of oscillating between withdrawing and active head movement, she achieves a brief play dialogue with the mother. The goal of the interaction is obviously the same as it was for the mother and the sighted infant: To achieve a mutually satisfying play dialogue. The ease and flexibility with which a sighted infant enacts the new differentiation is not available to the blind infant, for whom even at 60 days state organization as such is still an issue. It requires two minutes of preparatory stage setting before the new accomplishment is achieved.

Overall, (Figure 10.3b) the amplitude of the infant's behavior has become narrowed to a rapid oscillation between averting, place holding, and brief periods of set. The mother's amplitude has become widened, in turn, oscillating more frequently between brief averting, more prolonged eliciting, and bursts of playing and playful talking, enveloping the infant's periods of being set, and attempting to expand them. Finally, at 140 sec, the infant builds up to a 12-sec burst of play, which is climaxed by a coo. This achievement of the infant is embedded in play and talk by the mother.

Interaction at 3 months, 16 days (see Figure 10.3c)

The infant lies back in her seat, leaning to the left, in expectation of the mother's coming in. Her face is lifted up, her right arm extended along her side, her leg stretched out. As the mother comes in with a friendly, somewhat throaty, "Hi, Peanut, hi, Peanut," the infant moves her face even more toward her mother, opens her mouth, and points her index finger toward her mother. She is very still, her face open to her mother. The mother leans in very close, touches her right hand, and with her face almost touches the infant's face. The mother says in her warm, playful, crooning voice, "What are you doing?" several times and nuzzles the infant with her face. The infant lies back, still absorbing every touch and sound. The child's eyebrows and cheeks are raised; every now and then she moves her head in a tiny arc, and she opens her mouth.

The mother sits back a little, touches her on the chin and shirt, flashes her eyes, talks to her in a flattering voice, and then repeats twice, with more emphasis: "What are you doing?" The mother pokes her finger in rhythm at Marci's chin and fiddles with her collar: "Sitting in a big girl seat!" The infant, Marci, has pulled her right arm up somewhat and has moved her right leg in. The mother taps her nose. Marci immediately fusses and pulls back, thrusts out her tongue, and then opens and closes her mouth. The mother lets go of her and says, "Yeah." Sitting further back, she now says softly, "You had a fun ride! You had a fun ride in!" At this, Marci stills again and raises her eyebrows, opens her mouth, face and body drawn to the mother. The mother now walks her fingers up Marci's arm and stomach, saying playfully, "What are you doing? What are you doing?" Marci brings her face even closer to her mother's. The mother switches to moving her own face in and out of Marci's face saying, "Ha-booh! Ha-booh!" in rhythm with her movements. Marci's mouth is wide open. Her shoulders are lifted toward the mother and her right arm moves in rhythm to the mother's voice. Then she breaks into a wide smile, staying fastened onto the mother with her body and face. The mother acknowledges in a gurgling voice: "That's a pretty smile! Ha-booh!" and continues the "Ha-booh" once more. She then shifts Marci's whole body into midline. Marci's face changes. The mother resumes the "Ha-booh" immediately, first putting her head up to Marci's face. Marci relaxes once more, opens her mouth wide, lifts her right arm, raises her eyebrows, and begins to smile again.

By $3\frac{1}{2}$ months, the attainment of a focused, relaxed attending state while in direct interaction with the mother is solidified. Excursions from it as the new base to more animated smiling and cooing are somewhat more likely, although still hard to come by. The richness of modulation of the sighted infant's repertoire is lacking, but the differentiation and modulation are attained.

The infant's main behavior (Figure 10.3c) is now within set. Place-holding behavior has become minimal. Early on in the interaction, she achieves a brief play period, embedded in one of the mother's cycles of play dialogue. The infant achieves another prolonged burst of play dialogue after 2 min of interaction. The main characteristic of this interaction is the prolonged achievement of set by the infant, as well as the relatively few excursions from set.

Interaction at 4 months, 20 days (see Figures 10.3d)

The infant lies back in her chair, her pacifier in her left hand, expectantly turned to the mother. As the mother comes in saying, "Show everybody how you can find your mouth!" Marci passes the pacifier from one hand to the other and puts it back into her mouth, and the mother joyfully acknowledges: "Yes, that's my baby, that's my baby!" giving her time to realize her accomplishment. She strokes her arm, bends her face down toward Marci's hand, which is stretched out to the mother now. Marci flails her arms and legs in excitement, then stabilizes herself with her feet pushed against the mother's body. "Yes, you are very smart! Yes, you are!" the mother praises. She demands: "Say Momma, Momma!" Marci pulls the pacifier out of her mouth, flings the hand out, and with the other hand reaches up to the mother. The mother says in a fast, high-pitched tone, "Oh, you are so excited, so excited!" Marci stretches both her feet against the mother's body. This slows down her movements, and the mother asks in a lower voice, "Can you smile? Can you smile?" She takes both the infant's hands simultaneously, cycles them, releases them, and touches Marci's mouth: "Come on, smile for me," she says. "Can you smile?" she asks while tapping Marci's lips and stroking her mouth. Marci opens her arms widely, stretching them to the mother. The mother bends over her more closely, clicks her tongue in a rapid sequence, and with her index finger taps Marci's mouth and draws circles around it with her finger. She leans her head toward Marci and asks "Oh, can you smile, can you? Come on!" She then clucks and makes rapid kissing sounds. Marci holds her arms stretched toward the mother in midair and her face is continuously turned toward the mother. The mother kisses her several times in quick sequence with audible "Aah-mah, aah-mah, aah-mah!" sounds. Marci smiles. "That's a pretty smile!", the mother immediately acknowledges, speeding up the kisses to the child's hands. The mother then touches Marci's lips with her index finger strokingly and says in rhythm, "Say Momma, Momma!" The mother kisses her again, pushing both of Marci's hands up to her chest. Marci coos and squeals with delight. The mother accentuates her squeal with a high-pitched "Yeah, yeah! Are you talking to me?" kissing Marci again. The mother looks back to her, cycling her arms, kissing her hand, and pulling her to midline: "Where are you going? Do you want to sit up straight?" she asks. As the infant squirms with her legs, the mother opens both the infant's arms simultaneously and closes them again several times in rhythm with Marci's legs; Marci moves away a little. The mother quickly moves her head close in and says, "Can you find my face? Can you find my face?" clicking her tongue and encouraging Marci to reach out. Marci's arms begin to cycle in very small, tight cycles. The mother urges: "Come on! Come on!" in a high-pitched, pressing tone, and moves her face closer to one hand. Marci moves her hand in the air, opening and closing her fingers. When she touches the mother's nose, she grunts instantly. The mother acknowledges her achievement in a drawn-out, guttural, "There it is, yeah, there it is!" nuzzling her face in Marci's hand. Marci feels the mother's face with small, open-palmed pats. The mother pulls back a little and comes back in with a kiss and says ""Mm-ah, Mm-ah!" Marci reaches after her and touches her. The mother responds with "Yeah, go ahead!" Marci leaves her arm stretched out, fingers touching her mother's face. The mother kisses the outstretched hand in a quick sequence of loud kisses: "Mm-ah, mm-ah, mm-ah!" As her mother leaves, Marci's arm stays stretched out after her, and as she loses contact with the mother, Marci vocalizes as if in imitation of the mother's sounds.

By $4\frac{1}{2}$ months, the infant cycles from relaxed attentiveness to more regular smiling and cooing. We can infer that there is broader organization of this interaction for both mother and infant: Since the infant is able to maintain relaxed attention as a base now and can achieve smiling and cooing more readily, the mother can give her longer periods off. In fact, the mother utilizes the infant's improved self-organization to encourage the infant to reach for the mother's face on sound cue. It appears that this comparatively advanced objective was made feasible because of the affective synchrony achieved early between this mother and her infant, and this in spite of the severe violation inherent in the infant's blindness.

Once the mother engages in play (Figure 10.3d), she maintains it for prolonged periods, cycling between set, play, and talk, without drawing back to monitoring or averting. The infant again spends much time in set, frequently elicits the mother's play, only initially showing some place holding, and engages in play dialogue repeatedly and for more prolonged periods. After 80 sec, the mother pulls back and now encourages the infant to reach for her face. She builds the new task into the face-to-face play and seems to be preparing the infant for the later, more demanding task of reaching towards inanimate objects. Once more the mother expands the limits of the developing system just beyond the securely achieved functioning, using that as base. As the infant, after a prolonged (25 sec) effort, reaches for the mother's face, she acknowledges the new achievement profusely and again embeds it in play dialogue, just as she did previously with newly emerging achievements. Figure 10.3a–d shows that this infant in interaction with her mother accomplishes a shift from averting and minimal set over the first 5 months to an easily attained set, to increasing play dialogue, to eventual reaching for the mother's face.

DELINEATION OF THE STAGES OF EARLY INFANT ORGANIZATION IN THE TWO CASES DISCUSSED

The continuum of the hierarchical developmental agenda is similar for the blind and the sighted infant. The negotiation process, by virtue of the sensory handicap, is more explicit, repetitive, and amplified for the blind infant. Figures 10.4 (a–c) and 10.5 (a–d) show sample behavioral sequences of the first stages of the early negotiation continuum for the sighted and the blind infant.

First, an infant tries to integrate his physiological, motoric, and state organization, while the parent provides appropriate, affective ambience for the infant by organizing and enveloping him. The infant is likely to cycle between averting, protesting, and monitoring the interaction (Stage 1).

As figures 10.4a and 10.5a exemplify, the parent envelops the infant with arms, hands, and voice, containing the physiological balance and particularly the motoric arousal engendered as the infant attempts to come to midline and simultaneously look at the mother. For the blind infant, containment is more difficult. The visual focus is missing. Closer tactile contact, nuzzling, and more continuous enveloping with the mother's voice make up for it. The goal is the same, and as it is finally achieved (as demonstrated in the third frame of Figure 10.5a), the mother acknowledges this achievement profusely, allowing the infant to realize that this is their goal. Then they cycle through the process of containment, goal specification, goal attainment, and acknowledgement. The sighted infant's interaction with the mother is similarly structured, yet not as explicit, nor are the cycles repeated as often, as containment and goal attainment are facilitated by visual feedback between mother and infant.

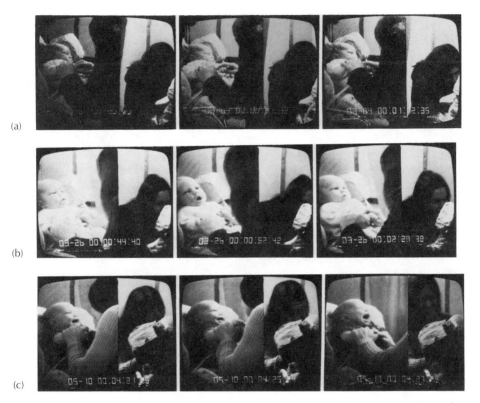

FIGURE 10.4.   The photographs illustrate behavioral displays representing the successive goals of early infant organization (mother and sighted infant): (a) Stage 1—State organization; (b) Stage 2—Mutual orientation; (c) Stage 3—Play dialogue.

Gradually both the blind and the sighted infant differentiate their involvement in interaction by accomplishing the stage of being more easily available for interaction, being oriented without being continuously organized by the adult. The infant comes more frequently and easily to set (Stage 2).

Figures 10.4b and 10.5b show examples of the infant's heightened readiness and active reciprocation by attaining mutual orientation in the interaction. Again, the blind infant's mother facilitates this goal attainment in a more accentuated manner, using hand-holding and close-up heightened talking for more prolonged periods before she can bring the infant to her newly achieved, softened orientation in midline. This orientation, once affirmed, is maintained more briefly than by the sighted infant, yet when attained, the infant's recognition of her own competence seems apparent (see, for instance, Frame 3 of Figure 10.5b).

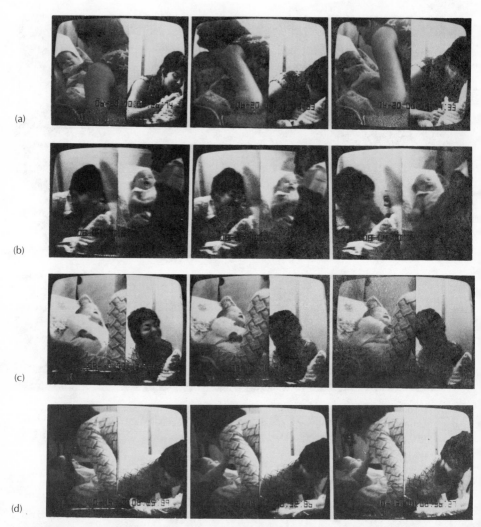

FIGURE 10.5. The photographs illustrate behavioral displays representing the successive goals of early interactive organization (mother and blind infant): (a) Stage 1—State organization; (b) Stage 2—Mutual orientation; (c) Stage 3—Play dialogue; (d) Stage 4—Reaching for mother's face.

The awareness of this new accomplishment and the repeated enactment of it solidifies the new accomplishment and leads to the next expansion of the involvement in interaction, which is the active reciprocal engagement in play dialogue. The infant comes to play and talk more easily, with set as his baseline (Stage 3).

Figures 10.4c and 10.5c exemplify the heightened playfulness and exuberance that characterises the interaction now. The mother and her sighted infant easily, and for prolonged periods, engage in synchronous mutual episodes of interactive "ecstasy," climaxing in simultaneous squeals. The blind infant and her mother's interaction achieve similar heightening, yet again after longer stage setting and affective baseline facilitation. The peaks, although of similar height, are of shorter duration. The readying process shows the toll the absence of vision takes. Yet the same goals are enacted, and the mutual sense of competence grows. Once this is solidified, the next level, an incorporation of objects into the interaction, can begin (Stage 4).

As soon as the mother and her blind infant can achieve the heightened stage of mutual play dialogue, the mother utilizes this new energy to build toward the next step—the reaching out toward objects. She facilitates this goal by the intermediate step of guiding the infant's reach to her own face, thus building closely on the successfully accomplished heightened face-to-face orientation, as Figure 10.5d shows. By now her infant is over 4-months old. The sighted infant and his mother have been engaging in smooth, prolonged, gurgling play dialogues prior to 3-months old. It comes apparent that the successive goal realization is the same for both pairs, yet the process of implementation is much more conscious for the mother of the blind infant. The consciousness derives from her efforts to recognize what her infant is after, despite the distortion in communicative displays. Her efforts to help the infant attain and implement the normal, successive interactive goals are rewarded by the increasing competence and autonomy of the infant. Reaching on sound cue at less than 5-months old is a considerable accomplishment for a blind infant (Fraiberg, 1977). The mother's continued energy for maintaining this degree of sensitive facilitation appears to come from the increasing sense of competence she derives for herself from this expanding growth process in which she and her infant are mutually involved.

DELINEATION OF THE PROCESS OF PARENT SUPPORT TO ENHANCE MUTUAL, INCREASING AUTONOMY

We are attempting to document the process of the developing organization in young infants. More specifically, we are trying to identify how they use social interaction to help themselves regulate attentional processes. We furthermore want to document how, when they become organized, they are able to use this self-awareness to elicit, to further expand, and to differentiate the feedback between themselves and their caregivers. The face-to-face paradigm and the scoring method seemed to be a useful way of identifying the current level of organization of an Infant–Parent interaction and of identifying the specific, individualized features of the regulation process. This process may be based on the temperamental style of each pair or may be due to a distortion when one of the interactants is impaired.

Closely observing the Parent-Infant interaction provides not only an assessment of the level and degree of organization of the systems, but also offers promise for intervention. When the parent can observe the taped interaction, it provides her with an opportunity to stand outside the interaction in order to observe the infant and herself in interaction. This objectivity can help her observe the concrete behaviors necessary to the infant's current organization. Seeing this identifies the options for the parent to modify her own behavior when she is ready to do so. This, in turn, presumably will lead to more autonomous and competent behavior on the parent's part and, in turn, on the infant's part.

Secondly, this opportunity to see herself with discrete goals clearly transmits the message to the parent that her infant can be understood as a person from the beginning. The infant is separated from the parent in the infant seat and is featured as a competent partner with the parent. The child is videotaped and observed as an active, eliciting, and sharing partner, taken seriously in his particular behavioral strategies and in his implementation of current organization, no matter how distorted they may be. The child's and the parent's behavior are always seen in the framework of personal organization seeking to expand and differentiate, to increase mutual competence and mutual autonomy. This interpretation encourages the parent to believe in herself as a competent person and to believe in her infant as separate and competent. The parent more easily identifies those energies taxed by the handicap, energies both of the infant and of the parent. This identification of the behavioral cost of a handicap for both interactants provides the base for reducing this cost by acknowledging its specific reality. The goals become more specific to each infant and become more manageable as a result. By personalizing the infant and by specifying the concrete issues of his current organization on the basis of observable behaviors, one frees energies of both partners to get on with the process of more satisfying interactions, as well as moving toward a more satisfying realization of themselves as competent.

ACKNOWLEDGMENTS

We would like to express our deeply felt appreciation for the privilege of closely observing the parents and their infants over the first months of their evolving relationships. We would also like to thank Lauren Adamson, Dorian M. Greenberg, Susan Palmer, and Nancy Kozak for their great support, for the uncountable hours of videotape analysis, and for their substantial contributions to this work.

This work was supported by grants from the William T. Grant Foundation, New York and the National Institute of Child Health and Development. Parts of this work were carried out at the facilities of the Mental Retardation Research Center at Children's Hospital Medical Center, Boston.

REFERENCES

Als, H. Social Interaction: Dynamic matrix for developing behavioral organization. In I. C. Uzgiris (Ed.), *Social interaction and communication in infancy. New Directions for Child Development.* (Vol. 4.). San Francisco: Jossey-Bass, 1979. Pp. 21–41.

Als, H., & Brazelton, T. B. *Stages of early infant organization: Issues negotiated in interaction with the caregiver. The study of an infant with multiple congenital anomalies.* Paper presented at the meeting of the American Cleft Palate Association, Atlanta, Georgia, 1978.

Als, H., Lester, B. M., & Brazelton, T. B. Dynamics of the behavioral organization of the premature infant: A theoretical perspective. In T. M. Field, A. M. Sostek, S. Goldberg, and H. H. Shuman (Eds.), *Infants born at risk.* New York: Spectrum, 1979. Pp. 173–193.

Als, H., Tronick, E., & Brazelton, T. B. *The achievement of affective reciprocity and the beginnings of the development of autonomy: The study of a blind infant.* Paper presented at the meeting of the Society for Research in Child Development, New Orleans, Louisiana, 1977.

Als, H., Tronick, E., & Brazelton, T. B. Analysis of face-to-face interaction in infant–adult dyads. In M. E. Lamb, S. J. Suomi, and G. R. Stephenson (Eds.), *Social interaction analysis: Methodological issues.* Madison, Wisconsin: Univ. Wisconsin Press, 1979. Pp. 33–76.

Als, H., Tronick, E., & Brazelton, T. B. Affective reciprocity and the development of autonomy: The study of a blind infant. *Journal of the American Academy of Child Psychiatry,* in press.

Bibring, G. L., Dwyer, T. F., Huntington, D. S., & Valenstein, A. F. A study of the psychological processes in pregnancy and of the earliest mother child relationship: I. Some propositions and comments; II. Methodological considerations. *The Psychoanalytic Study of the Child,* 1961, *16,* 7–92.

Brazelton, T. B. Neonatal Behavioral Assessment Scale. *Clinics in Developmental Medicine* (No. 50). Philadelphia: Lippincott, 1973.

Brazelton, T. B., & Als, H. *Four early stages in the development of mother–infant interaction. The Psychoanalytic Study of the Child,* 1979, *34,* 349–371.

Brazelton, T. B., Koslowski, B., & Main, M. The origins of reciprocity: Early mother–infant interaction. In M. Lewis, L. A. Rosenblum (Eds.), *The effect of the infant on its caregiver.* New York: Wiley, 1974. Pp. 49–77.

Brazelton, T. B., Tronick, E., Adamson, L., Als, H., & Wise, S. Early mother–infant reciprocity. In M. A. Hofer (Ed.), *The parent infant relationship.* London: Ciba, 1975. Pp. 137–155.

Cohen, P. The impact of the handicapped child on the family. *Social Casework,* 1962, *43,* 137–142.

Fraiberg, S. H. *Insights from the blind.* New York: Basic Books, 1977.

Kennedy, J. *Implications of grief and mourning for mothers of defective infants.* Unpublished doctoral dissertation, Smith College School for Social Work, 1969.

Michaels, J., & Schuman, H. Observations on the psychodynamics of parents of retarded children. *American Journal of Mental Deficiency,* 1962, *66,* 568–573.

Olshansky, S. Chronic sorrow: A response to having a mentally defective child. *Social Casework,* 1962, *43,* 190–193.

Solnit, A. J., & Stark, M. H. Mourning and the birth of a defective child. *The Psychoanalytic Study of the Child,* 1961, *16,* 523–537.

Tronick, E., Als, H., & Adamson, L. Structure of early face-to-face communicative interactions. In M.

Bullowa (Ed.), *Before speech: The beginning of interpersonal communication.* Cambridge: Cambridge Univ. Press, 1979. Pp. 349–372.

Tronick, E., Als, H., Adamson, L., & Brazelton, T. B. The infant's response to entrapment between contradictory messages in Face-To-Face interaction. *Journal of the American Academy of Child Psychiatry,* 1978, *17,* 1–13.

Tronick, E., Als, H., & Brazelton, T. B. The infant's capacity to regulate mutuality in Face-to Face interaction. *Journal of Communication,* 1977, *27,* 74–80.

von Bertalanffy, L. *General system theory: Foundation, development, applications.* New York: Baziller, 1968.

Waddington, C. *Principles of embryology.* London: Allen & Unwin, 1956.

Prelinguistic Communication Skills in Down's Syndrome and Normal Infants

INTRODUCTION

In recent years the relevance of Mother–Child interaction for the development of social communication has become increasingly apparent. There is currently much emphasis placed on the social origins of linguistic competence operating during prelinguistic stages of development (see reports by Bruner, 1975; Lock, 1978; Schaffer, 1977). The development of language per se can be described as one branch of this social learning process, communication in its full sense involving the developing relationship between infant and mother, or other caregiver. These prelinguistic communication skills ultimately form the basis of language in the formal linguistic sense.

Many children demonstrate a relative difficulty in developing sophisticated communication skills. Such handicapped children include the language retarded, autistic, and mentally deficient. Down's syndrome children are also usually observed to have difficulties in their development of language (see Ryan, 1975). Due to the chromosomal nature of their disorder (usually Trisomy 21) these children are identifiable at birth. They therefore present as a group of handicapped children who have "predictable" language difficulties. In order to follow the prelinguistic stages of communication development, early identification is essential. Many language disorders are only identified once language itself is failing to develop (i.e., around 3-years old). In order to observe the

205

HIGH-RISK INFANTS AND CHILDREN:
Adult and Peer Interactions

progress of prelinguistic communication skills, very young Down's syndrome children were chosen for this study, and their skills compared with those seen in young normal children. In this way we hoped to identify early pointers toward the ultimate language difficulties expected in this mental handicap. It is possible that the Down's syndrome children are only delayed in their development of communication skills, in which case we would not expect any differences of great singificance between their progress and that of a normal child at the same stage of development. However, if the Down's children should show difficulties with communication in particular at this early stage of development, then this presents possibly different implications for "normal" language development.

From the viewpoint of this book, our results may have relevance to the current discussion of the role of the child himself in situations of abuse by parents. There are several studies emphasizing that the children in abuse cases are often physically or mentally deficient before the act of abuse (Johnson & Morse, 1968). The handicapped child himself may act as a catalyst in a potentially abusing situation (Sandgrund, Gaines, & Green, 1974).

METHODOLOGY

Subjects

Six Down's syndrome children at the prelinguistic stage of development were found in the local area. These children were individually matched with six normal children. Matching was on the basis of sex, social class, family position (firstborn, second born, etc.), and developmental age (using the Cattell Infant Intelligence Scale). The chronological age range was between 8 and 24 months, but developmentally the children ranged between 8 and 19 months. The normal children were all slightly younger than their matched Down's syndrome pairs, the age difference varying between 3 and 13 months according to the severity of the retardation in the Down's children.

Procedure

In order to examine, in detail, the exchange of communication between mother and child, microanalysis techniques were employed. In studies of Mother–Infant interaction this technique has proved extremely fruitful (see papers in Schaffer, 1977). We shall present a summary of the technical details of this approach as it was used in this study, but a fuller description can be found in Jones (1977).

The basic source of information was vidotaped recordings of the mothers and children playing together at home with a set of provided toys. Recordings were about 15 min in length and were repeated every 3 weeks for a 3-month period (6 sessions), by which time the Down's syndrome children were beginning to lose their developmental similarity to the normal children due to differences in their rate of development. The mothers were interviewed about their feelings and perceptions of their relationship with their child using a guided interview schedule (i.e., a modified version of one used by Jones in a 1973 study).

Analysis

Analyses were completed under three headings: (a) microanalysis of ongoing communicative events; (b) the children's vocalizations; and (c) mother–child eye-to-eye contact. For practical purposes the microanalysis of Mother–Child interaction was restricted to short samples of the material, although the analyses of particular aspects of the data covered greater quantities of the recorded material. The initial microanalysis involved detailed transcription of the samples of videotape. Simultaneous transcription of both mother and child was a very important feature of this initial analysis. Frequently, interaction studies only follow the action as it flows between the partners. This is, however, an artifact of the observer's role. Consider, for example, a tennis match in which the spectators watch the ball as it goes from court to court. If one really wishes to learn the intricacies of the game, one needs to put oneself in the players' shoes. The observer may be watching the active partner at any one moment, but the player himself is closely observing the behavior (albeit probably passive) of his opponent. Similarly, in interaction, in order to ensure good communication, each partner adjusts his behavior according to the responses of the other. For these reasons the vidotape could be viewed as often as was necessary in order to record the activities of *both* partners simultaneously. In this way we were often able to retrace the activity that elicited a particular response within an exchange sequence and that, by definition, could only be recognized at this "response" stage. For example, the child might be playing, and the mother says, "That's right, clever boy." It is only through rerunning the videotape that the initiatory activity of the child prompting the mother's response could be identified. Mothers frequently "take up" the activities of their children in this way, and consequently it is most important that the full context be recorded. It seems to be through maternal interpretations of children's behavior that children come to associate meaning with their acts and eventually to produce these same acts with more intentional meaning (Newson, 1974). Interactions between mother and child were therefore identified as any act that invited response or was itself a response. Using this operational definition, we were able to identify all exchanges that were intentionally or unintentionally initiated, or for that matter responsive. For example, an interesting form of exchange was one in which the response made by the mother could enclose her child's behavior in a communication sequence without any apparent intention on the child's part (unintentionality being indicated by brackets):

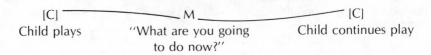

|[C] | M | [C] |
| Child plays | "What are you going to do now?" | Child continues play |

The analysis of the material was therefore performed in two stages. In the first stage data were transcribed from the videotape in such a way as to encompass as full a context as was possible. To aid this transcription, information was recorded in 1-sec blocks under 6 headings: eye direction of child and mother; vocal activity of child and mother; and nonvocal activity of child and mother. Selected samples of the material were taken for the microanalysis. For these purposes two of the earlier play sessions (first and third) were chosen in order to maximize the developmental matching between the pairs of children. Of these play sessions, the first 2-min of play with two of the toys were used for this particular analysis. (Further analyses were completed on the remaining data, but this will be described later.) The toys chosen for this microanalysis of communicative events were a book and a box of cotton reels. It was expected that these might sample different types of interaction, as the book might elicit vocal interaction whereas the box of cotton reels might elicit nonvocal interaction.

The second stage of the analysis involved recording the details of the sequences of interaction. Measurements were made of their overall frequency, their length, the channel (whether vocal or nonvocal) and quality of the communication, and the relative influence of the mother and the child.

The credit for initiating or terminating communication sequences was not always easily assigned. Although the child may seem to initiate a sequence, as we saw in the preceding example, it might be the mother's comment that actually initiated the interactive sequence. There are frequent examples of the mother taking up the child's activity to include him in an interchange:

Child plays ——————— Mother comments on child's play

Similarly, the partner who is last in a sequence does not necessarily terminate it. For example, the mother might respond in such a way as to invite the child to continue, the "opportunity space" being indicated by empty brackets:

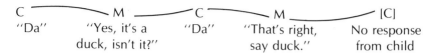

C ———————→ M ———→ C ———————→ M —————————→ [C]
"Da"   "Yes, it's a   "Da"   "That's right,   No response
         duck, isn't it?"   say duck."   from child

If the child then fails to respond, he has effected the termination of the sequence, even though his mother was the last to participate in the communication exchange. The patterns of interaction were carefully traced and described in detail so that we could learn as much as possible about these forms of prelinguistic communication.

In addition to intensive microanalysis of the data, we looked in more detail at the children's vocalizations and how these might be developing toward linguistic speech. We also investigated the use of one particular prelinguistic signal, eye-to-eye contact, and traced it through the taped material. Eye contact was chosen for its obviously powerful role in influencing the interactive findings from the microanalysis.

In addition to observing the communication between mothers and their young children, we interviewed the mothers at the end of the study. In practice, all the interviews were completed within one week of the last filming session. A guided interview schedule was devised based on a combination of the 1-year schedule used by Newson and Newson (1963), the schedule used by Hewett (1970) with mothers of physically handicapped children, and a pilot schedule of the author's for mothers of mentally retarded infants (Jones, 1973). The answers were collated and organized into categories. The major aim of the interview was to collect information on the mothers' perceptions of the children's prelinguistic communication skills, and on their general attitudes toward child rearing in relation to their normal or handicapped children. The questions were divided into three main categories (for full schedule, see Jones, 1979). First, there were questions about very general aspects of practical child rearing, such as sleeping and feeding habits, toilet training, and the management of naughty behavior. Second, a large number of questions concerned the mother's perception of her child's ability to communicate and her future expectations regarding this. Finally, questions were included that looked at more general aspects of living with the child, for example, father participation, the behavior of siblings, the child's personality characteristics, and the general influence of the child on the family's life style.

RESULTS

Mother-Child Interaction

Interestingly, there were few differences between the matched pairs in the frequency, length, variety, and channel (vocal or nonvocal) of the interactions.

Rather than the Down's children being involved in low levels of interaction, we recorded significantly more interactive events with these children than with the normal children. These frequencies did, however, include a large number of failed invitations from the mother. For example, the mother might ask a question or give a directive to which the child failed to respond. There were significantly more of these failed invitations from the mothers of the Down's children than from the mothers of the normal children. There were also significantly more exchanges of two participations in length between the mothers and the Down's syndrome children. These mainly included the mother taking up the child's activity or directing the child. Long exchanges tended to be more common when initiated by the normal children, but the overall result was that the Down's children were being involved in larger numbers of interactions. Apparently, they were by no means being deprived of this experience at equivalent developmental ages. (See Table 11.1).

USE OF SUPPORT TECHNIQUES

Many of the interactions, as we mentioned earlier, were subtly "supported" by the mothers. For example, the mother might respond as if the child has invited her, and she might also provide the child with opportunity spaces for

TABLE 11.1
Mean Frequencies of Mother–Child Interactive Sequences over an 8 Min Period

	Range		Mean		Significance (Wilcoxon)
	DS	N	DS	N	
Total sequences per minute	11–27	9–23	18	15	$p = 0.01$
1 participation in length	1–11	1–9	5	3	$p = 0.05$
2 participations in length	6–17	4–14	10	8	$p = 0.05$
2+ participations in length	1–8	1–6	4	4	n.s.
Mother initiated sequences, total	8–24	6–17	13	10	$p = 0.01$
1 participation in length	1–11	1–9	5	3	$p = 0.05$
2 participations in length	4–10	2–9	6	5	n.s.
2+ participations in length	0–7	1–5	3	2	n.s.
Child initiated sequences, total	2–13	1–8	5	4	n.s.
1 participation in length	0–1	0–1	0	0	n.s.
2 participations in length	2–11	0–6	4	3	n.s.
2+ participations in length	0–3	0–4	1	2	n.s.

Key: DS = Down's syndrome children and their mothers; N = Normal children and their mothers; n.s. = Insignificant difference using the Wilcoxon, matched pairs, signed rank test of significance.

response. We also noted an interesting form of modified invitation where the initial invitation by the mother had failed. The modified form seems to allow the child to participate for example:

M⌒⌒⌒⌒⌒⌒⌒ [C]   M⌒⌒⌒⌒⌒ C ⌒⌒⌒⌒⌒ M
"What is it?"   No response   "It's a duck   Child grunts   "That's right,
                                  isn't it?"   a duck."

In this example, the mother failed to get a response to her first invitation and dropped the level of her question so that the child's response, a simple grunt, became an acceptable reply. Nevertheless, she still provided the child with the opportunity to respond at the higher, more specific level. She then provided him with a sample answer (i.e., "It's a duck"). In this way, the mother not only helped the child participate in the interaction but she also gave him a learning opportunity. These modified invitations were generally very common, but they occurred significantly more often with the Down's children. As seen in Figure 11.1, there was an overall tendency for the mothers of the Down's children to

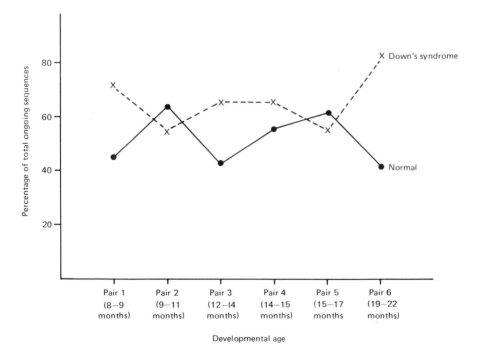

FIGURE 11.1.   The graph shows the proportion of total ongoing interactive sequences that are supported by the mother.

support their children's role in dialogue to a greater extent than the mothers of the normal children.

QUALITY OF INTERACTION

Examination of the overall quality of exchange revealed few differences between the developmentally matched pairs. Generally speaking there was an increase in the use of more sophisticated communication skills over the period of time sampled, but there were few differences between the matched pairs. One difference we did observe was a tendency for the Down's syndrome children to participate in more ritualized nonverbal exchanges, for example putting toys into an offered container, or building up and knocking down towers. In contrast, the normal children showed proportionally more communicative participation of the partially differentiated type such as generalised kicking or screaming in objection, or excited flapping of arms in anticipation.

Finally an overall assessment was made of the relative roles of the mothers and children. Bruner (1975) made an interesting observation about the mothers' styles of interaction. He noted two major types: those mothers who tended to direct the play activity and those mothers who preferred to let their children take the lead, and just give support to their ideas. In this study we made a similar division in which we compared the number of mother-directed sequences with the number of child-dependent sequences. We found significant differences in the frequencies of these types of interaction. The mothers of the Down's syndrome children tended to be more directive, whereas the normal children were more often involved in child-dependent sequences (See Figure 11.2). This difference might be due to the fact that these mothers felt it was better to guide their children's ideas. The Down's syndrome children experienced relatively less responsive interpretation and support of their own activities. Shotter (1978) emphasizes that through such interpretation the child can retrospectively evaluate the consequences of his actions, and learn their socially significant uses. Dunn (1977) also noted that the experience of a caregiver whose responses are promptly contingent upon the child's initiations gives a child a sense of competence and effectiveness that contributes to a developing mastery of the object world. Bloom (1972) remarked that if mothers did not interpret their children's comments, the children might have not learned to talk.

The overall differences in the interactions between these pairs of mothers and children seem to describe a pattern characteristic of the Down's child and his mother. They were involved in relatively more interactive situations, but these consisted mainly of short sequences where the mother was determinedly inviting responses, many of which failed to gain a response from the child. These sequences were frequently followed by a modified, "easier" invitation.

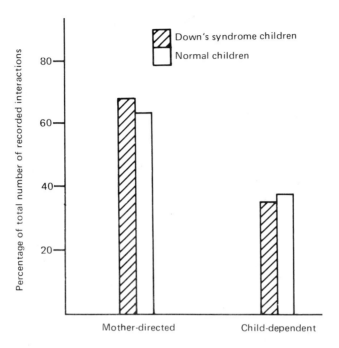

FIGURE 11.2.   The graph shows the proportion of mother-directed and child-dependent interactions.

These types of interaction formed a supportive structure for the Down's syndrome children to participate in dialogue. However, in terms of the child influencing this dialogue, the normal children were seen to be more involved. Therefore, although the mothers of the Down's syndrome children used more support techniques to aid their child's role in dialogue, they did not "support" their children's own initiative to the same extent as the mothers of the normal children, who were more frequently observed to take up their child's idea or allow themselves to be directed by their child. This resulted in the Down's syndrome children experiencing participation in interaction but comparatively less interpretation of their own self-initiated activities. There was a tendency for them to be "steered" through interaction with relatively less chance for them to gain understanding about the communication process in which they were involved. It may have developed through lack of initiative from the child or through attitudes of concern from the mothers to "help" their child's development. Most probably both were involved as this was essentially an interactive pattern, neither the child nor the mother being solely responsible for this particular style of communication. Whatever the reason, the result of this style of interaction was that the Down's children had less opportunity to experience mastery of their world.

The Children's Vocalizations

These were selected for analysis to examine the possible relationship between the children's prelinguistic vocalizations and their development toward linguistic speech. The vocalizations made by the children were individually transcribed from the videotaped material with details of the preceding and following context including any vocalizations made by the mother. Vocalizations were taken from the first 2 min of play with each of the four toys for the alternate sessions, one, three, and five. These were initially described in terms of their frequency, syllable length, variety, and "developmental" level in the traditional forms of babble, jargon, and idiosyncratic words.

In addition to this descriptive data the communicative role of these vocalizations was explored by an interactional analysis in order to study the children's vocalizations in relation to their context. Generally speaking there was little variation between the matched pairs in terms of the descriptive nature of the vocalizations, that is, in their frequency, length, variety, and developmental level. However, when the vocalisations were reexamined for their communicative quality within an interactive context, some interesting variations were apparent (see Figure 11.3). There was a consistent tendency for the Down's syndrome children to vocalize with apparently less consideration of their role in vocal dialogue. Their vocalizations were more repetitive and closer together than those of the normal children. This effectively restricted the mothers' response opportunities. The mothers of the Down's syndrome children produced significantly more acknowledgements and less expansion of their children's vocalizations. This is understandable if one considers that the only polite response when someone is continuing to vocalize is to gently acknowledge their utterances with "mm" or "yes." However, the Down's syndrome children were receiving relatively less informative expansion of their utterances. Newson and Shotter (1974) emphasize the important role of such expansion in providing the child with a meaning for his utterances that he, in turn, learns to use in order to convey this meaning. The poor phasing of the vocalizations made by the Down's syndrome children deprived them of contingent language learning experiences. The mothers of the Down's syndrome children may well have felt "left out" by their infants and found great difficulty in involving themselves with their children in an interesting, expansive, two-way dialogue. The mothers of the Down's syndrome children frequently retired into a monotonous pattern of intermittent acknowledgement. Once the Down's syndrome child initiated a string of repetitive vocalizations, there was little else the

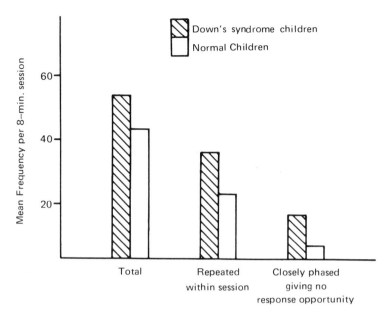

FIGURE 11.3. The graph shows the frequency, repetition, and phasing of children's vocalizations over an 8-min period.

mother could do but simply supply acknowledging remarks. Nevertheless, expansion to single words was still fairly common, for example, "Da"—"Yes, Duck," "Da"—"mm, Duck. . . ." Such strings of dialogue still involved clashing with the child's on-going vocalizations. A further difficulty with these repetitive strings was that the mother was faced with the problem of whether to expand to the same word each time or provide different words, appropriate to the context, for the child's same vocalization, e.g., "Da"—"Duck," "Da"—"Cow."

These differences in vocal dialogue patterns were only evident when the vocal context was considered. The vocalizations themselves were similarly copious and various when compared across pairs. It was the way the children used their vocalizations that differed. For example, although the variety of vocalizations in any one session did not differ between pairs, the Down's syndrome children tended to repeat sounds in strings, (e.g., "Da, Da, Da") in contrast to the normal child's varied vocalizations ("Da, Ga, Du"). To these variations, the mothers of the normal children responded with rich and varied vocal dialogue.

Eye Contact

As a prelinguistic signal, eye contact serves a very powerful role. The frequency of eye contact was only about once per minute. Over a thousand eye contacts were classified into three major types:

1. *Personal eye contact* (Personal), where the mother and child look and smile at each other, for example, as they approach each other.
2. *Game eye contact* (Game), where eye contact serves a definite role in a game such as "peek-a-boo."
3. *Referential eye contact* (Referential), where eye contact serves as a communication signal about a third event outside the communicating dyad, such as a toy. For example, a child bangs a drum and looks up to the mother (eye contact is established). The mother smiles, nods, saying "Yes, you banged it, didn't you?" and the child looks back at the toy.

As can be seen in Figure 11.4 three-fourths of the eye contacts made by the normal children were of the third type, referential eye contact. Only a third of the eye contacts made during the play sessions by the Down's children fell into

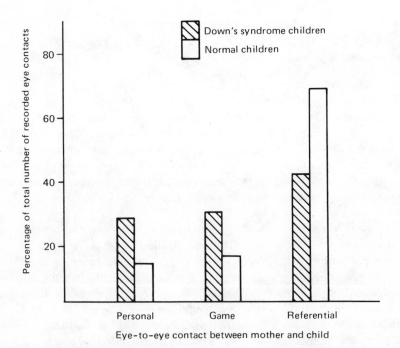

FIGURE 11.4. The graph shows the proportion of eye to eye contact of the personal, gane, and referential types.

this particular category. The onus for establishing eye contact tended to be on the child because generally the mothers were watching their children very closely. Here also we have a further example of the Down's children taking less initiative in communication, as eye contact appeared to be one of the major methods of interaction initiation observed in these prelinguistic children. We are aware of the lack of eye contact in other handicaps such as autism (Hutt & Ounsted, 1966), but unlike autistic children who actively avoid eye contact, the Down's syndrome children in this study simply did not make the most use of their opportunities for eye contact.

The more social types of eye contact, Personal and Game, were used to a similar extent by both the Down's and normal children, although proportionally the Down's syndrome children used these forms of eye contact to a greater extent. Such results suggested that there was something especially difficult about referential eye contact for the Down's syndrome children. The nature of the referential eye contact was its effectiveness as a gesture of reference: the child appeared to be referring to something he was doing. Typically the child would pause at a point in his play and look up at his mother. The mothers characteristically responded to this look by commenting about his previous play activity, for example, "That's right," "Clever boy!," "Did it fall over then?!" The glance from the child seemed to be interpreted by the mothers as a "questioning look" as their response usually involved nodding, smiling, and an encouraging or explanatory "answer." The pattern of this particular form of eye-to-eye interaction is one in which the referential glance from the child acts as a direct invitation that is perceived and responded to by the mother as if it were a sophisticated comment or query, a form of prelinguistic question. The mothers' responses seemed to verbally crystalize for the child the important aspect of the interaction, for example, "Yes you *banged,* it didn't you?" Rather than the "topic" of communication being directed by the mother, it follows from the child's suggestion. The ensuing dialogue therefore involves a mutually agreed upon topic. However, for some reason the Down's syndrome children in this study were not "choosing" to utilize this powerful communication signal to the same degree as the normal children. The Down's syndrome children were therefore seen to be effecting a less rich, less stimulating environment for themselves.

We did not observe any clear relationship between developmental age and frequency of referential eye contact in groups covered in this study (8–19 months), although it probably requires a certain sophistication of cognitive development to be able to consider the three-way relationship between mother, self, and object. Sugarman (1973) noted that by 10 months children usually show an ability to cope with this three-way reference situation, whereas before this they tend to involve themselves in either Self–Person or Self–Object interactions. All the children in this study were observed to use referential eye contact, so they presumably had reached a sufficiently advanced stage of cognitive development to allow for this three-way interaction.

Given that the Down's syndrome children were provided with plentiful opportunities for referential eye contact, that they were physically able to make eye contact, and indeed sometimes did make referential eye contact, why did they not employ this interactive strategy more often? A possible explanation might relate to the child's cognitive capacity to expect responses to his actions. Referential eye contact holds an expectation of a response from the mother. We noted earlier that these children had this type of difficulty in vocal dialogue in that they had more difficulty allowing for their mother's turn in the interaction. Although Pawlby (1977) has recorded turn-taking skills in 4-month-old infants, for some reason the Down's children in this study still appeared to be having difficulty with this very basic communication skill.

Further association of the referential eye contact with language development can be seen in the role it plays in communication. Apart from language itself being the ultimate form of "reference," the referential glance served the role of "comment" from the child about some play situation in which he was involved. From the mother's interpretation, the child appeared to be requesting some sort of confirmation of his "comment," for example, "Yes you *are* a clever boy," "Yes, you *did* bang it." These were not always positive, for example "No you mustn't chew it, that's naughty," but nevertheless this response from the mother was still providing the child with an answer to his glance. In these ways we can see the referential glance serving an important prelinguistic form of later questioning comments of the child—one which attracts a contingent explanation and interpretation from the mother. This can be seen to give the child a meaning for his own activity at a time when he requests such information, a classic "teach me now" situation. Shotter (1978) makes the point that a gesture such as eye contact only becomes a significant symbol when it has the same effect on the individual making it as it does on the individual to whom it is addressed, and in this way involves a reference to the self. The development of language from this stage of joint communication would be a natural progression from this basic understanding of how, when, and where to communicate about what.

Although we only studied the interactions of a small number of children in this project, each of the Down's syndrome children showed the tendency for reduced use of referential eye contact in comparison with the normal children. In doing so they seemed to be depriving themselves of a very rich source of relevant information. These children apparently had not developed a full understanding of the potential communicative role served by this particular signal and could not cope cognitively with the complexities of this referential system. Unfortunately, this has a direct effect on the interactive situation because the mothers of these children are not receiving the appropriate stimulus for providing the rich feedback that we observed to be associated with the referential glance from the child. If the child could in some way be encouraged to make more eye contact in play situations, this at least would provide the mother with the stimulus to provide the feedback. Eventually the child may come to relate the two events and learn to expect, and eventually look for this informative, contingent response from his mother.

Questionnaire

The questionnaire was given in the form of a guided interview to enable the mothers to speak freely about their attitudes and perceptions of their children, including aspects of rearing, communication, personality, and role in the family. The mothers of the Down's syndrome children remembered the birth as a rather frightening experience in that they did not know what to expect from their "mongol" child. As one mother explained:

Mongolism to me meant the child had no hope of ever doing a thing. That was the feeling I had; that this child is never going to know right from wrong, never going to walk or talk. Something I heard said mongolism is something like monsters, they've got this terrible strength and there's nothing you can do with them.

Another mother explained:

The first few days I didn't know anything about it (Down's syndrome) and I kept asking the nurses. They were dead cagey; they had good excuses like, "Oh well, you will be seeing Dr. such and such in a few days" or "Somebody will be round to see you." Well, nobody ever came, so I never got any information out of them anyway. I don't think they knew much themselves, they were only young. It was the first few days I wanted to know what I could. I wanted to know what I could expect from that child; whether he would be a thickie all his life; whether he would ever walk or what.

The mothers of the Down's syndrome children feared the future; they did not know what to expect of their babies. With normal children we have recognized expectancies, not only in terms of child like behaviors, but also in far more basic terms of human behaviors; (e.g., being able to think, walk, and talk). These mothers seemed to think they had another "species" on their hands, and they had difficulty perceiving their child as becoming a person in the way we recognize "personness." The importance of such recognition of personness in babies is that it helps us as adults to treat them as persons and thus encourage their social development. These mothers were obviously having difficulty recognizing this in their "mongol" children. It is impossible to assess the detrimental effect this may have had on the mother-baby relationship in those early weeks or months. Certainly the memories were very vivid for these mothers.

In terms of child rearing, the attitudes and anxieties expressed by the mothers did not vary much across the pairs. There were similar concerns about feeding difficulties, potty training, etc. However, an interesting aspect of this was the tendency for the mothers of the Down's syndrome children to express more concern about the social aspects of child rearing. Although these children were generally treated at an appropriate level for their developmental age, when it came to behaviors that would be socially unacceptable for their chronological age the mothers described these as behavior difficulties. Examples included spitting, throwing, temper tantrums, refusal to use the potty. The behaviors themselves were common to all the normal children as well, but it was the mothers of the Down's syndrome children who expressed the most anxiety. The mothers of the normal children appeared to accept them as part of their child's limited understanding. However, despite the appropriateness of these behaviors to the developmental age of the Down's syndrome children, their mothers were anxious because the behavior appeared socially inappropriate. Unfortunately, the result of this discrepancy was the presence of more conflict between the mother and her Down's syndrome child in these particular areas, resulting in the described "behavior problems."

There were also other examples of the mothers of Down's syndrome children expressing more concern about their children, even though the actual behaviors being described here were little different from those being described by the mothers of the normal children. For example, at night the mothers of the Down's syndrome children felt that they went to their children more readily because they feared breathing difficulties. The mothers of the normal children expressed similar anxieties and went to their children just as quickly. Thus, many of the perceived differences in attitudes and behavior mentioned by the mothers of the Down's syndrome children were not differences in objective terms, especially if the child's developmental age was taken into consideration. However, because the mothers felt they were differences due to their child's handicap, these points warranted recording.

In terms of communication skills, the mothers of the Down's syndrome children expressed some clearly different viewpoints from those of the mothers of the normal children. Although the objective descriptions of the children's skills scarcely differed, the mothers themselves perceived differences. There was evidence of the mothers of the Down's syndrome children expecting less in the way of communication. One mother reported being "afraid to expect any words from her child," explaining that in that way she would not risk disappointment. Although this is a very understandable approach, the difficulty with such an interaction system is that it risks further delaying the development of language as the mother may be reluctant to interpret, expand, and extend her child's vocalizations.

The mothers had not been alerted to the differences in eye contact observed in the videotapes, but several mothers described difficulties with eye contact in communication situations. For example, some of the mothers of the Down's syndrome children mentioned that they had difficulty knowing if their children were addressing their vocalizations to them because the children tended not to look at them when they were speaking. These mothers learned to use alternative cues such as the child's "determined tone of voice," but the communication was obviously less effective in the absence of an eye contact signal. These mothers also described more difficulty interpreting the child's needs due to these limited number of cues. Attracting the child's attention was reported as a problem. The child often needed calling more than once and even then did not necessarily turn to look at his mother. The mothers explained that they knew the child had heard since the child exhibited "stilling" behavior. In these ways the mothers of the Down's syndrome children in this study seemed to receive fewer prelinguistic cues from their children to help their intercommunication. Furthermore, the lack of cues often left the mother unsure about her child's understanding of the communication exchange. Certainly an eye contact signal would have helped in many of the described situations. The lack of eye contact not only made the communication difficult, but it also left the mother confused about the child's participation in the exchange. It could also have had the effect of making the mother feel deliberately ignored.

The mother's descriptions of the ways in which they talked with their children also produced some interesting variations. There was a strong tendency for the mothers of the Down's syndrome children to refer repeatedly to "teaching" their child when in verbal interaction with them. This was in contrast to the descriptions given by the mothers of the normal children who felt that although their children probably learned from these "chats" together, it was the children's company they most appreciated at these times. The important aspect for the mothers of the normal children was this personal aspect of the interaction, whereas the mothers of the Down's syndrome children felt this was a most important teaching opportunity. As one mother of a Down's syndrome child explained, "It's sit him on your knee and talk to him, that's the main object. Play with him, speak to the child, teach him something."

Similarly, when asked what they most enjoyed about their children, the mothers of the Down's syndrome children tended to refer to successes in the teaching situation, whereas the mothers of the normal children more frequently referred to enjoying their children for themselves, enjoying their company. For example, one mother of a Down's syndrome child said, "I enjoy teaching her, getting a response, doing something I've taught her to do, letting other people see what she can do. More than with a normal child, people are doubly impressed." A mother of a normal child reported, "I think I enjoy her altogether, I like her company. I generally enjoy being a mum really. I just think she's super."

These comments made by the mothers gave some confirmation to our own observation that the mothers of the Down's syndrome children in this study tended to be more directive in interaction than the mothers of the normal children. From the clinical point of view, it might be appropriate to advise such mothers to relax a little and allow the child to develop his own ideas. However, we cannot ignore the support that "teaching" might be giving the mother. Having something positive to "do" with a handicapped child can often help a mother participate in interaction with her child when communication might otherwise be difficult and unrewarding. The "rewards" might be justifiably sought in the child's successful progress, which is perhaps a more expected development in a normal child. Unfortunately, the difficulty with this type of interaction is that the child receives less opportunity to experience interpretation and extension of his own activities. Whether one approach is "better" than the other will probably remain a moot point, although a compromise would probably seem the most sensible solution. Certainly an understanding of the difficulties can at least alert the parent and clinician to the problems and provide the most appropriate social environment for that particular handicapped child and family.

DISCUSSION

Our comparison of the communication between mothers and their normal or Down's syndrome children has indicated that although many of the basic activities are similar across the developmentally matched pairs, there were significant differences in the patterns of communication when these were examined in their full interactive context. The Down's syndrome children could and did participate in interaction and they also produced many and varied vocalizations, but there was evidence of problems with some of the more basic communication skills.

The lack of referential eye contact and the poor dialogue phasing of the Down's syndrome children were suggestive of their basic difficulty in being able to predict the response to their own actions. They were not demonstrating a full understanding of their actions as signals and did not seem able to appreciate the role of "the other" in social dialogue. However, the fact that the Down's syndrome children sometimes demonstrated appropriate vocal phasing and referential eye contact may have contributed to their mothers' expectation of these signals and disappointment when they were not forthcoming.

Although these mothers reported that the children did not always look at them, they described an awareness of other subtle cues from the child such as "stilling" when called. The onus was more on the mother to identify these subtle cues as the child was not initiating recognizable prelinguistic signals.

The mothers of Down's syndrome children were observed to "support" their children's role in dialogue to a greater extent than the mothers of matched, normal children. Additionally, the mothers of the Down's syndrome children were more directive in interaction with their children. This was possibly due to the Down's syndrome children initiating communication less frequently, or the mothers wanting to guide their children in the most "profitable" direction, for example through teaching. Despite the increased amount of "support" provided by these mothers, the support was not in the direction of extending the child's activity but more in the direction of suggesting further activities for the child, the child's role in the dialogue being supported by means of making his response slightly easier (e.g., "What is it?. . . It's a dog isn't it?" child grunts in response). Responding to the child's idea was more commonly seen with the normal children.

The resulting pattern of these interactions is one in which the Down's syndrome child is carried along in a fast moving interaction dialogue, but possibly with detrimental effects from the point of view of reducing the child's opportunities to receive meaning for his signals and thereby learn how to influence his environment through communication. The Down's syndrome children demonstrated a relatively limited understanding of their role in social dialogue. The lack of this very basic communication concept could be expected to limit the full development of language as well as the necessary understanding of "self" as distinguished from others.

Although the numbers involved in this study were small, we have highlighted some of the possible problematic areas in Mother–Child interaction with young handicapped children. The implications of these findings for clinical practice could involve providing the child with plenty of opportunities for contingent, informative feed-back. Eye contact for example might be encouraged by physically positioning the child in the face-to-face position when playing with him. Repeated examples of exaggerated, exciting responses to eye contact might encourage the child to expect and then seek eye contact. Similarly, the child could be encouraged to expect interesting and expressive vocal responses with encouragement and extension of their own play activities. It may be important to discourage the mothers of handicapped children from intense "teaching" and encourage them to relax, look, listen, and generally to be sensitive to their child.

The child cannot learn to appreciate his effect on the environment if he is not permitted to experience interpretation of his own activities. Through such interpretation the child comes to recognize the meaning of his own actions

(Newson & Newson, 1976). The child eventually produces these actions to elicit a response, and in this way he demonstrates intention. However, in order for him to develop this independent role, the child needs the example of interpretation. The mother may need help understanding her child's difficulties and the way he is influencing her interaction with him. The mothers of the Down's syndrome children of this study appeared to experience more difficulty interacting with their children. The Down's children were unwittingly barricading interaction with their mothers, which would easily make the mothers feel they were being ignored. We observed with one little Down's girl a situation in which the child was playing with the drum and began to laugh. Her mother bent down to her in an attempt to seek eye contact, smiling and saying "What are you laughing at?." The little girl failed to make the expected eye contact and the mother sat back. This lack of eye contact could not be seen as a neutral event. The mother may well have felt rebuffed in the same way she would if this happened with an adult. Such feelings of rejection might lead to abuse if the mother is hypersensitive to signals of "rejection" from her child.

The mothers in this study referred to making allowances for their children due to their mental handicap. Perhaps a less visible handicap would put a child at greater risk of not receiving such forgiveness. Whatever the variables, the disposition of the mother and environmental stress could make a sensitive situation where difficulties of interaction would be sufficient to tip the balance. For whatever reason, it would seem to be in the interest of the child's development to help mothers of handicapped children to understand their difficulties and be given support in practical terms so that they can enjoy their developing relationship with their children. Urwin (1979), working with blind babies and their mothers, noted the necessity of alerting the mothers to some special signals being given by the babies. For example, the blind infant tends to freeze at its mother's approach. This is a positive signal as it suggests he is trying to hear her, although it normally might be interpreted as a negative signal by the mother. Intervention programs that ignore these interactive aspects of communication and direct the parents mainly to teach their children, are themselves at risk of depriving the mother–child pair of some basic aspects of the learning environment. Nelson (1973) noted that a nondirective parental strategy that was accepting of the child's behavior both verbally and nonverbally facilitated the child's progress and language acquisition. In order to flourish, the mother–child pair need help to understand and support each other. If one member of the dyad demonstrates difficulties in his communication skills due to his cognitive limitations, the ensuing interactive problems can be alleviated by the sensitive and observant clinician. In these ways the mothers of handicapped children might be helped to give appropriate support and encouragement to their children's development.

REFERENCES

Bloom, L. Semantic features in language development. In R. L. Scheiflbusch (Ed.), *Language of the mentally retarded.* Baltimore, Maryland: Univ. Park Press, 1972.

Bruner, J. The ontogenesis of speech acts. *Journal of Child Language,* 1975, *2,* 1-19.

Dunn, J. B. Patterns of early interaction: Continuities and consequences. In H. R. Schaffer (Ed.), *Studies in mother-infant interaction.* London: Academic Press, 1977.

Hewett, S. *The family and the handicapped child—a study of cerebral palsied children in their homes.* Illinois: Aldine, 1970.

Hutt, C., & Ounsted, C. The biological significance of gaze aversion with particular reference to the syndrome of infantile autism. *Behavioural Science,* 1966, *11,* 346-356.

Johnson, B. & Morse, H. Injured children and their parents. *Children,* 1968, *15,* 147-152.

Jones, O. H. M. Unpublished master's thesis, Univ. Nottingham, 1973.

Jones, O. H. M. Mother-child communication with pre-linguistic Down's syndrome and normal infants. In H. R. Schaffer (Ed.), *Studies in mother-infant interaction.* London: Academic Press, 1977.

Jones, O. H. M. *Mother-child communication: A comparative study of prelinguistic Down's Syndrome and normal infants.* Unpublished Doctoral thesis, Univ. Nottingham, 1979.

Lock, A. (Ed.) *Action, gesture and symbol: The emergency of language.* London: Academic Press, 1978.

Nelson, K. Structure and strategy in learning to talk. *Monographs of The Society for Research in Child Development,* 1973, *149.*

Newson, J. Towards a theory of infant understanding. *Bulletin of The British Psychological Society,* 1974, *27,* 251-257.

Newson, J., & Newson, E. *Infant care in an urban community.* London: Allen & Urwin, 1963.

Newson, J., & Newson, E. On the social origins of symbolic functioning. In V. P. Varma & P. Williams (Eds.), *Piaget, psychology and education,* London: Hodder & Stroughton, 1976.

Pawlby, S. J. Imitative interaction. In H. R. Schaffer (Ed.), *Studies in mother-infant interaction.* London: Academic Press, 1977.

Ryan, J. Mental subnormality and language development. In E. Lenneberg (Ed.), *Foundations of language development.* New York: Academic Press, 1975.

Sandgrund, A., Gaines, R., & Green, A. Child abuse and mental retardation: A problem of cause and effect. *American Journal of Mental Deficiency,* 1974, *79,* 327.

Schaffer, H. R. Early interactive development. In H. R. Schaffer (Ed.), *Studies in mother8 infant interactions.* London: Academic Press, 1977.

Shotter, J. The cultural context of communication studies: Theoretical and methodological issues. In A. Lock (Ed.), *Action, gesture and symbol: The emergence of language.* London: Academic Press, 1978.

Sugarman, S. *A description of communication development in the prelanguage child.* Unpublished study project thesis, Hampshire College, Massachusetts, 1973.

Urwin, C., Unpublished Ph.D. Thesis, Univ. Cambridge, England, 1979.

CHAPTER 12

KATE L. KOGAN

Interaction Systems between Preschool Handicapped or Developmentally Delayed Children and Their Parents

INTRODUCTION

There has been a rapid expansion of evidence that the process of child development is a reciprocal interpersonal phenomenon, and that the interactive milieu in which growth and change take place is an essential component. Britton and Thomas (1973) point out that a child, whether normal or disabled, begins life with a relatively small number of behavior patterns, and that his repertoire expands as he learns to do more things for himself. In addition to simple physical maturation, the child learns through social interaction, and this is colored by the common standards of conduct and behavior that a culture expects from its members. Thus, the role of the parents or caretakers in the social learning of the child is undeniably important, and its importance in the development of the handicapped child is grossly magnified. Society helps to define the behavior expectations and standards for normal children. There are few, if any, available guidelines to help parents set appropriate behavioral goals for their disabled child.

Recognizing that socialization of the child is rooted in his or her experiences in social interaction requires that one also recognize the two-way, reciprocal character of interaction. Bell (1968) was one of the first to document the extent to which mothers respond differentially to variant qualities of infant

227

behavior. That concept has been widely endorsed, and Lewis and Rosenblum (1974) have provided many appropriate examples of its application.

It is apparent, and readily confirmed, that the mother of the handicapped or slowly developing child participates in transactions that are less rewarding and provide far less positive feedback than received by mothers of normal children. Lax (1972) pursued these implications even further, using the concept of the narcissistic trauma to explain a mother's protracted, self-perpetuating cycle of guilt, anger, rejection, and depression. A number of studies have been concerned with the impact of handicapped children on their families and have attempted to analyze and describe parental attitudes and adjustment processes. Most of the problems of family impact and adjustment are common to a variety of handicapping conditions. Wolfensberger (1967) pointed out that repetitive stereotypes and clichés characterized many of the statements. Studies appear to fall loosely into two clusters; one is concerned with the immediate impact of acceptance of the child's handicap on family members' adjustment, whereas the other deals with their later long-term adaptations. Families may experience difficulty over the unexpectedness of the diagnosis, over the extent to which its implications conflict with their established goals and values, or over the practical difficulties of coping with and caring for the handicapped child.

Cummings, Bayley, and Rie (1966) concluded that the situation caused ongoing stress for the mothers of deficient children, and that one needed to find means to maintain parents' self-esteem and confidence in their ability to care adequately for their children and to offer psychological climates conducive to the children's optimal development. Terdal, Jackson, and Garner (1976) compared the interactions of normal and developmentally delayed groups and pointed out that mothers of delayed children may need added support and assistance to manage the behaviors of their children. Cook (1963) demonstrated that parental rejection was more likely to be associated with a mild handicap, whereas parental overprotection was associated with more severe conditions. Farber (1968) reported that the initial stress of mental retardation was sex-related and that mothers were more disturbed when the retarded child was a girl. Poznanski (1973) questioned whether the psychological limitation of handicapped youngsters could be traced to the parenting process. Buda, Rothney, and Rabe (1972) went so far as to suggest that the mother–child relationship not only affected the child's development, but might even affect aspects of his physical functioning such as muscle tone.

Kogan, Tyler, and Turner (1974) studied a group of young cerebral palsied children longitudinally. Observations were recorded and analyzed at the beginning, middle, and end of a 2-year period. Mother–Child interactions while mother and child played together and while they were engaged in therapy were compared. The results demonstrated that when mothers were performing therapy, both mother and child displayed greater amounts of negative behaviors than when they were playing; mothers also became excessively controlling during therapy. These behaviors proved not to be temporary reactions to a new situation, but persisted over the total time period covered by the study. Furthermore, there was a progressive reduction in friendly, warm, and positive behaviors during play sessions as well as during therapy sessions, over the period covered by the study.[1]

On the basis of the studies just described, it seemed important to develop techniques for helping mothers become more comfortable in their interactions with their handicapped children. The goal was to help them augment their interactive repertoires, acquire more positive and rewarding attitudes, and thus modify the interpersonal climate in which they were communicating. It was a logical step to move from the recognition of the reciprocal behavioral elements in the interactions between handicapped children and their parents to the utilization of behavioral approaches in dealing with some of the problems they encountered.

Kogan and associates had developed an individualized program for teaching parents to alter their interactions with their children, and had demonstrated its effectiveness in guiding parents of children with behavior problems to rehearse more effective styles of responding to their children (Kogan & Gordon, 1975a; Kogan, Gordon, & Wimberger, 1972). These procedures were adapted for use with a new sample of cerebral palsied children in a study which began in 1973. A report of the results of that study and of a subsequent project dealing with developmentally delayed children constitute the main body of this chapter.

By the time the developmentally delayed study was initiated, it was clear that, although the approach was unquestionably effective clinically, it was too time consuming to have practical utility on a large scale. Efficient as well as effective treatment is an ultimate goal for clinicians. The literature suggests group approaches as a means of economizing professionals' time and enhancing the rapport between mothers and their children. Rose (1969) reported using group treatment to increase parents' repertoires of management procedures. Most of the parents in his study indicated that following treatment they felt more skillful in handling the problems they had worked on and better able to cope with any new problems their children might have. Carkhuff and Bierman (1970) described a group training approach with parents of emotionally disturbed children. Mash and Terdal (1973) demonstrated the effectiveness of behavior modification principles in training parents to play effectively with their mentally retarded children, using videotaped samples to teach groups of parents. Mash, Lazere, Terdal, and Garner (1973) used group instruction in behavioral management skills with parents whose primary complaints were about the behavior of their children.

[1]This study was supported by Grant #08815 from the National Institute of Neurological Diseases and Stroke.

Three major themes are prominent in these studies: (a) parenting children with developmental disorders contains risks for a variety of distortions of Parent–Child interaction; (b) behavioral techniques have been shown to be appropriate approaches to averting or ameliorating interactive distortions; and (c) there has been evidence to suggest that group instruction can provide parents with behavioral guidance on a scale that has practical clinical utility. The two studies reported in this chapter were based upon the recognition of and response to these themes.

PROCEDURES AND METHODS USED IN TEACHING PARENTS TO ALTER INTERACTIONS WITH THEIR CHILDREN[2]

System for Recording and Analyzing Dyadic Interactions

At the first two contacts, usually a week apart, two unstructured half-hour play sessions were videotaped. The same toys were provided in all of a dyad's recorded observations, and were brought into the playroom on a fixed schedule that subdivided each half-hour session into one 6-min period followed by two 12-min sections. The small playroom was furnished with only a table and two chairs, and was equipped with a one-way mirror and a microphone. The videocamera was in the adjacent room and the recording was taped through the mirror. Time unit markers were superimposed on the tape every 4 sec during the observation period.

Videotapes were analyzed in 40-sec time units according to the Interpersonal Behavior Constructs system (Kogan & Gordon, 1975b). This system utilizes a 22-item checklist of behavior transactions that are assessed for their occurrence or nonoccurrence in each 40-sec time unit. Three main portions of the checklist assess the focus of the participants' attention (primarily on the other person, on his own activity, or on joint activity), amount and type of vocal or verbal activity (absent or limited, onesided, or responsive and related), and lead taking (a variety of behaviors conveying authority, assertiveness, or expertise). Items are checked when their duration characterizes the major portion (70% or more) of the 40-sec time unit being reviewed.

The remaining items refer to momentary occurrences and are summarized under five headings as follows:

1. Positive affect: Smiling or animated voice: praise; physical warmth
2. Negative affect: Negative voice or face; ambiguous affect; physical hostility

[2]These procedures were developed under Grant #19642 from the National Institute of Mental Health.

3. Nonacceptance: Frustration; ignoring; contradicting or refusing
4. Control: Physical intrusion; directing; competing
5. Submissiveness: Seeking approval or guidance; actively following; ambiguous status

As the checklist is applied to each 40-sec time unit, a half-hour play session yields 45 sets of codings.

Parent Instruction Techniques

Behavior frequency tabulations were compared with clinical expectations based on experience with healthy, normal populations of comparable ages. Samples of the taped observations were edited so that a summary of the findings could be shared with the parents at the next meeting. They were shown examples of effective response behaviors, and it was recommended that these be used more frequently in a variety of situations. They were also shown examples of less effective interactions for which alternative response behaviors were suggested. Behaviors deemed problematic by the parents were discussed, and the observations were related to the problem areas. This joint information was translated into specific behavioral suggestions for the parent to try to follow while in the playroom for weekly guided practice sessions. Whichever parent was the principal participant was also asked to spend at least 15 min a day at home rehearsing the suggestions in daily, individual play sessions. For the next 8 weeks the parent participated in a half-hour play session during which he or she wore a "bug-in-the-ear" which permitted the observer to comment while the interaction was taking place. The observer recognized when suggestions were carried out successfully, suggested further opportunities for the use of the desired behaviors, or suggested specific things that might be said or done. Behavior observations were recorded at the end of the series of parent instruction sessions, and again at the end of a year.

MOTHER–CHILD TRANSACTION IN CEREBRAL PALSY THERAPY[3]

Subjects

The subjects of this study were 20 children enrolled in the Children's Clinic and Preschool in Seattle, all of whom had been diagnosed as having

[3]This study was supported by Grant #MC-R-530248 from the Maternal Child Health and Crippled Children's Services of the Department of Health, Education, and Welfare. Co-investigator on both studies reported in this chapter was Nancy B. Tyler, M.O.T., Assistant Professor, Rehabilitation Medicine, University of Washington.

motor disorders. Subjects were chosen from that facility because it was the source from which a study sample of 10 cerebral palsied children had been drawn 3 years earlier (Kogan, Tyler, & Turner, 1974). The earlier study had indicated that when the mothers conducted therapy with their handicapped children there was evidence of interpersonal stress regardless of the child's age or the nature or severity of the disability. The present group contained 13 boys and 7 girls whose age ranged from 21 to 61 months. Their motor disabilities ranged from one child with almost no head, trunk, or extremity control to a mild hemiplegic who had acquired most of the motor skills expected of a child his age. The form of data analysis selected provided for each mother–child pair to serve as its own control, so that the wide range of age and motor development constituted no problem in data analysis. Practical considerations precluded the use of matched, untreated control subjects.

Procedures

In the videotaped observation sessions the mother was asked to play and do therapy with her child as she normally would at home. Each child was provided with the same functionally appropriate toys and therapy equipment for all observations. The experimental schedule consisted of two baseline observations, followed by eight guided "bug-in-the-ear" sessions, followed by two postinstruction recorded observations. A final pair of observations was videotaped a year after the initial contact. The method of data analysis chosen for this study was a nested analysis of variance procedure. This procedure permitted comparison of the frequency of occurrence of a single behavior checklist item in the behavior records of an individual dyad at the three points in time considered.

Results

NEGATIVE BEHAVIORS

There were seven behavior constructs that were considered to be mother stress indicators in the earlier longitudinal study. These were high amounts of "control," "lead taking," "negative content," "negative voice," "ambiguous affect," "physical hostility," and "physical intrusion." Analyses of variance indicated that 14 of the 19 mothers who completed the instruction sessions exhibited decreases in from one to six of the stress-indicating behaviors.

Changes in the behavior of the children were less numerous. Five behavior items were identified as stress indicators for children—"negative content," "negative voice," "ambiguous affect," "physical hostility," and "physical intrusion." Significant changes were noted in one or two of these in seven children.

For the total group there were 50 significant changes out of 228 comparisons made—well above the chance level. Of those 50 significant changes, 40 were still manifest in the observations recorded 9 months later. There were also 5 additional changes in the predicted direction at the end of the year in items in which the change had not reached significant proportions immediately after instruction sessions.

Therefore, it was concluded that the parent instruction procedures had reduced stress and conflict in the interaction between mother and child while they were playing and doing therapy. Most of the change was in mother behaviors. In accordance with the view that interaction is a reciprocal process, changing one element in a dyadic relationship effects change in the second element also. Instructing a mother not only made the mother more comfortable with her child, but also made her, to the limited extent noted, a change agent for the child's behavior and effected some reduction of stress on the part of the child.

POSITIVE BEHAVIORS

The earlier longitudinal observations on a similar population sample had demonstrated reduction of positive behaviors on the part of all mothers over a 2-year period. The specific behavioral items examined were "smiles and enthusiasm," "praise," and "physical warmth." According to the Wilcoxon Matched-pairs, Signed-ranks Test, none of these measures decreased significantly for the 18 mothers who participated in the study over the 1-year period. When the analyses of variance of the observation records of individual dyads were examined, one mother exhibited less praise at the end of the study, but there were no other significant decreases in the selected items. The evidence implied that the mother-instruction series had helped to avert any decrement in expressions of positive feelings, such as had been noted in the earlier study of a similar population sample.

OTHER BEHAVIORS

Analyses revealed a cluster of behaviors in which half or more of the subjects exhibited extreme frequencies (as compared with normative standards) at all three time-points. The behaviors in question included high child "quiet," high mother "comment," low "shared conversation"; a number of the children either had no speech or only limited speech. Also included in this category were high "physical warmth" and "physical intrusion" on the part of the mothers; only five of the children were capable of independent ambulation, and there was, therefore, a high occurrence of physical interaction. The third cluster, remaining unchanged during the year, was low child "control and direct" and low mother "actively follow." Because of their combined verbal and physical limitations, the children appeared to be restricted to more passive interactive roles, and their mothers' low occurrence of following was undoubtedly a direct corollary of the children's inability to impose structure on the activity.

ADJUNCT ASSESSMENTS

The Minnesota Child Development Inventory (MCDI—a developmental assessment instrument with normative standards as the reference point) was completed by the parents just before the behavioral instruction sessions, and again 6 months and 1 year later. The records were examined to explore whether there were any systematic changes in the child's relative position with respect to developmental standards for his age over the 6-month interval during which parent instruction took place, or in the subsequent 6-month interval. In both of the intervals, 70% of the classifications remained unchanged, and the remainder were scattered between scores that moved further from age standards, scores that moved closer to age standards, and incomplete data. It had been hypothesized that improvement of the interactive milieu in which the children were functioning might result in their being able to better maximize their potential. This would lead to an acceleration of their achievement within the limits set by their handicap. In assessing the results one must recognize the fact that the measuring instrument chosen had never been used with handicapped children, and that there is a complete absence of appropriate developmental assessment tools for this purpose. The results suggested primarily that use of the MCDI with children with motor disabilities was nonproductive. The final conclusion to be drawn from the findings was that the mother-instruction sessions had no direct measurable effect on any aspect of the child's developmental rate as measured by the MCDI.

The Washington Symptom Checklist also uses age standards as its reference point, although not in a normative sense as does the MCDI. This instrument is a modified form of the checklist described by Wimberger and Gregory in 1968. Parents were asked to indicate which of 63 behaviors they believed their child exhibited more than most children his age, which ones about the same as most children, and which ones less than most children. The checklist was completed before behavioral instruction sessions and at the end of the year. The responses were construed as constituting the parents' perception of the number and kind of problem behaviors their child exhibited, as compared with most children his age. Clinical experience had demonstrated that parents of children with behavior problems (nonhandicapped) reported a high number of problem behaviors before parent-instruction sessions and about half as many afterward. In the sample of handicapped children in this study, parents' reports prior to the behavioral instruction sessions reflected a much lower mean number of "more than most" behaviors than had been found in any other clinical group. Their mean was not significantly different from that of a healthy, normal, comparison group. In addition, the parents perceived significantly fewer problem behaviors than staff therapists and teachers did when they assessed the behaviors of the same children using the same instrument.

The low level of sympton reporting by parents was unexpected and made it a practical impossibility to document any systematic reduction over the course of time. Because of the discrepancy between staff and parent perceptions, one cannot escape the possible inference of defensive attitudes and denial on the part of the parents.

SUMMARY

An overall summary of the findings of this study and its implications stresses the importance of making a distinction between behavioral characteristics that are amenable to change, largely in the areas of positive and negative interpersonal expressions, and behaviors that are directly associated with the handicap or disability and are presumably irreversible. In the case of those parents and their children with motor disabilities, it was possible to demonstrate that either being or parenting a severely handicapped child carries high risk of negatively toned interpersonal transactions. Such transactions can be averted or ameliorated by behavioral instruction and guidance to parents. The behavioral changes were not, however, accompanied by any measurable change in the child's development of skills or independent function. These findings led the investigators to pursue the third and final project in the series. In this study a population of less severely disabled or delayed children was followed with similar procedures and assessments in order to evaluate whether behavioral training might, under other circumstances, bring about broader interactive and developmental changes.

COMPARING WAYS OF ALTERING PARENT-CHILD INTERACTION[4]

The study that will be described was designed to answer two questions. Were the findings of the previous study generalizable to a more mildly disabled population? And, would the introduction of more economical and less time-

[4]This study was supported by Grant #MC-R-530373 from the Bureau of Community Health Services of the Health Services Administration of the Department of Health, Education, and Welfare.

consuming, group parenting-instruction procedures be as effective as the program that used only individual parent-instruction sessions?

Subjects

Sixty 3-, 4-, and 5-year-old children and their parents were referred to the study by professionals or concerned parents. Referral information identified the child as developmentally delayed or mildly to moderately retarded (IQs no lower than 60). There were 38 males and 22 females, of whom 17 were 3 years of age, 29 were 4-years old, and 14 were age 5. According to the Hollingshead Two-Factor Index of social position, 19 families were classified in Social Classes 1 and 2, 18 in Class 3, and 23 in Classes 4 and 5. The primary participant in parenting instruction was the father in two cases and the mother in the remainder.

Procedures

Subjects were divided into three groups: One group experienced only individual parenting instruction; a second group experienced 50% individual parenting instruction and 50% group instruction and discussion; and a third group received no instruction. The distributions of sex, age, and social class in the three groups were not matched, but, according to the χ^2 test, their distributions were not significantly different from chance.

Group 1 experimental subjects experienced two observation sessions followed by six individual "bug-in-the-ear" monitored play sessions, following the parent instruction techniques already described. Reduction of the initial series of instruction sessions from eight to six was based on our past observation that most parents had mastered basic response-techniques by that time. Group 2 experimental subjects experienced two observation sessions followed by one "bug-in-the-ear" session and four parent discussion sessions. Together with four or five other parents they were shown videotaped illustrations of other parents' effective and ineffective responses to child behaviors. Each illustrative tape was organized to demonstrate a distinctive facet of Parent–Child interaction. They then had a second "bug-in-the-ear" session. Both groups were observed again in the two weeks following their six instruction sessions. Both groups also had two additional "bug-in-the-ear sessions" 3 months later, an innovation that was based on our experience that after a few months some parents begin to be less conscientious about paying regular positive attention to their children, and their children again display problem behaviors. Both groups were observed a third time at the end of a year. Group 3 comparison subjects participated in behavior observations at the beginning and at the end of a year with no intervening instruction.

Results

COMPARISON WITH NORMATIVE BEHAVIOR STANDARDS

Another study, as yet unpublished, has provided normative behavioral data on 96 3- to 5-year-old healthy, normal children evenly divided for age, sex, and social class. Although the developmentally delayed subjects were not selected so as to be stratified for these demographic variables, their distributions, detailed earlier, were not significantly skewed or distorted. In order to define whether the clinical group examined in this study had special characteristics, the initial observation records of the 60 developmentally delayed children and their mothers were compared with these normative standards. Note was made of behavior frequencies falling more than one standard deviation above or below the mean of the normative group; note was also made of extreme frequency scores that were outside the range of the normative group. Both the single checklist items and the additive summary scores were compared. The following list consists of single items on which one-fourth or more of the delayed children or their parents had frequency scores more than one standard deviation above or below the mean of the normative sample.

Smile: Sixty-five percent of the delayed children scored more than 1 *SD* below mean; 18% below the normal range. Fifty-eight percent of the parents of delayed children scored more than 1 *SD* below mean; 20% scored below the normal range.

Ignore: Sixty percent of the delayed children scored more than 1 *SD* above the mean; 13% scored above the normal range.

Negative voice: Forty-five percent of the delayed children scored more than 1 *SD* above the mean; 15% scored above the normal range.

Giving orders: Thirty-five percent of the delayed children scored more than 1 *SD* below the mean; none scored below the normal range.

Comment: Thirty-five percent of the parents of delayed children scored more than 1 *SD* above the mean; 7% scored above normal range.

Lead taking: Thirty-two percent of the parents of delayed children scored more than 1 *SD* above the mean; 5% scored above the normal range. Twenty-eight percent of the parents of delayed children scored more than 1 *SD* below the mean; none scored below normal range.

Additive summary scores clarified and corroborated the parallel affective imbalance of the delayed children and their parents by indicating that 68% of the children and 43% of their parents were low in positive affect expressions, and 55% of the children and 40% of their parents were high in negative affect expressions. In addition, 40% of the children were high in nonacceptance behaviors, and 28% of them were low in controlling behaviors. These figures suggest that the back-and-forth transactions between parents and delayed children were best summarized as having more than usual amounts of struggle between resistant or avoiding children and lead-taking mothers in an atmosphere with strong, negative, emotional flavor.

BEHAVIOR CHANGES ASSOCIATED WITH PARENT INSTRUCTION

In past reports utilizing the Interpersonal Behavior Constructs, the investigators had given priority to the unique and individual interactions of each parent–child dyad. In the present report, the effects of parenting instruction on measured interactions were assessed by means of group results rather than individual dyad data.

The hypotheses to be tested were

1. Behavior observations before and after parenting instruction sessions would reveal an increase in positive behaviors on the part of both parent and child and that the recorded changes would persist to the end of a 1-year period.
2. Parents and children who participated in parenting instruction sessions would exhibit greater interactive behavior changes than parents and children who had not participated in the programs.
3. A combination of individual and group parenting-instruction sessions would result in as many interactive behavior changes as would accompany individual instruction sessions.

Hypothesis One

The initial observations of the three groups of subjects were compared by analysis of variance. There were no significant differences between the groups on any of the behavior measures.

Behavior changes from before instruction to immediately after instruction were assessed in each of the experimental groups (Groups 1 and 2), using a paired t test with an alpha level of .05. There were 12 mother behaviors (out of 22 comparisons) in which significant differences were noted. Nine of them indicated that parallel changes were exhibited by both experimental groups as follows: mothers watched more, engaged in separate activity less, took the lead less, smiled and praised more, contradicted and corrected less, gave less orders, intruded physically less, and followed more. In addition, Group 1 mothers reduced their nonresponsive talking; Group 2 mothers reduced both negative and mixed affect, but these were very low frequency occurrences, and the notation of significance may be an artifact. There were significant changes in all of the summary behavior combinations.

The paired *t* test was also used to examine changes over the 1-year experimental period in both experimental and comparison groups. The results are detailed in Table 12.1. Again there were changes in 12 of 22 mother behaviors, 7 of them appearing in both treatment groups, and one of those also appearing in the untreated comparison group. In addition, Group 1 mothers engaged in independent activity less and became more quiet. Group 2 mothers reduced their use of negative voice, reduced the number of times they sought approval, and increased their following of the child's lead. However, two of these items ("negative voice" and "seeks approval") were low frequency occurrences. Additive summary scores changed significantly in all five areas in Group 2, but only in three of them in Group 1.

Child behavior changes numbered 8 out of 22 at the end of the year. Of the six changes exhibited by the treatment groups, three were common to both groups, one occurred only in Group 1 and two occurred only in Group 2.

The data just reviewed supported the hypothesis that the parenting instruction programs would be accompanied by positive interactive changes that would persist over time.

Hypothesis Two

The data contained in Table 12.1 suggested that there were more numerous interactive changes in experimental groups than in the comparison group.

Group 3 mothers, who received no instruction in this research, exhibited only three changes in the 22 single behavior measures. Only one of their changes, reduction in giving orders, corresponded with the changes exhibited by mothers who participated in the instruction sessions.

Two significant shifts occurred only in comparison children, one of them in a low-frequency item, which may make the finding an artifact. Comparison children also exhibited two other shifts, reduction of ignoring and reduction of actively following. These shifts also occurred in both treatment groups, a fact which suggests that some changes might be attributable to increased age as well as to having provided parent instruction.

Direct comparisons between the three groups' year-end observations were now made by 1-way analyses of variance, with identification of the source of the differences by the Scheffé Multiple Range test. The differences are detailed in Table 12.2.

It will be remembered that a 1-way ANOVA revealed no differences between the three groups in their initial behavior observations. Table 12.2 indicates that treatment groups were clearly different from the comparison group at the end of the program. Differences were found in 7 mother behaviors and 3 child behaviors and in 5 of their 10 additive summary scores.

TABLE 12.1
Paired t-test Significant Changes Time 1 to Time 3

	Group 1	Group 2	Group 3
	Mothers		
Single behaviors			
1. Watch	$p = .015$[b]	$p = .001$[b]	
2. Does own thing	$p = .047$[c]		
			$p = .043$[b]
3. Quiet	$p = .025$[b]		
4. Lead	$p < .001$[c]	$p < .001$[c]	
5. Smiles, enthusiasm	$p < .001$[b]	$p = .002$[b]	
6. Praise	$p = .001$[b]	$p = .004$[b]	
7. Negative voice[a]		$p = .001$[c]	
8. Negative content	$p < .001$[c]	$p < .001$[c]	
9. Physical intrude	$p < .001$[c]	$p = .006$[c]	
10. Control and direct	$p < .001$[c]	$p < .001$[c]	$p = .002$[c]
11. Seeks approval[a]		$p = .034$[c]	$p = .040$[c]
12. Actively follows		$p = .014$[b]	
Additive combinations			
13. Positive affect	$p < .001$[b]	$p = .001$[b]	
14. Negative affect		$p = .005$[c]	
15. Nonacceptance	$p < .001$[c]	$p < .001$[c]	
16. Control	$p < .001$[c]	$p < .001$[c]	$p = .007$[c]
17. Submissive		$p = .006$[b]	

	Group 1	Group 2	Group 3
	Children		
Single behaviors			
1. Watch[a]			$p = .002$[b]
2. Does own thing		$p = .008$[b]	
3. Quiet			$p = .029$[c]
4. Smiles, enthusiasm	$p = .001$[b]	$p = .002$[b]	
5. Negative voice	$p = .035$[c]		$p = .027$[c]
6. Ignore	$p = .005$[c]	$p = .003$[c]	$p = .004$[c]
7. Control and direct		$p = .025$[b]	
8. Actively follow	$p < .001$[c]	$p < .001$[c]	$p = .005$[c]
Additive combinations			
9. Positive affect	$p = .001$[b]	$p = .001$[b]	
10. Negative affect	$p = .023$[c]		$p = .016$[c]
11. Nonacceptance	$p = .033$[c]		
12. Submissiveness	$p < .001$[c]	$p < .001$[c]	$p = .003$[c]

[a] The significant change may be an artifact of this item's having low frequency occurrence; means were less than 1 on these items.

[b] Represents significant frequency increase.

[c] Represents significant frequency decrease.

TABLE 12.2
Comparisons of Groups at Year-End Observations

Single behaviors	F probability	Scheffé Multiple Range test
M: Watch	$p = .008$	$3 < 1$ and 2
C: Watch	$p = .0126$	$3 > 2$
M: Do own thing	$p < .0001$	$3 > 1$ and 2
C: Do own thing	$p = .0490$	NS[b]
M: Lead	$p = .0026$	$3 > 2$ and 1 [a]
M: Praise	$p = .0033$	$3 < 2$
M: Negative content	$p = .0009$	$3 > 1$ and 2
M: Intrude	$p = .0028$	$3 > 2$ and 1 [a]
M: Control and direct	$p = .0003$	$3 > 1$ and 2
C: Actively follow	$p < .0001$	$3 > 1$ and 2
Additive summary scores		
M: Positive affect	$p = .0060$	$3 < 2$
M: Negative affect	$p = .0405$	$3 > 2$
M: Nonacceptance	$p = .0009$	$3 > 1$ and 2
M: Control	$p = .0005$	$3 > 1$ and 2
C: Submissive	$p = .0001$	$3 > 1$ and 2

[a] Although the means for Groups 1 and 2 were not significantly different the Group 1 mean was more different from Group 3 than the Group 2 mean.
[b] This item did not exhibit significant differences on the Scheffé procedure, the most conservative measure, but Groups 2 and 3 were different according to the Duncan Multiple Range test.

Hypothesis Three

Table 12.2 also supports the hypothesis that a combination of group and individual parenting instruction would be as effective in producing interactive changes as individual instruction alone. In five of the measures listed in Table 12.2 only Group 2 was significantly different from Group 3. In another eight measures, Group 2 differences were just a little greater than Group 1. In only two measures did Group 1 results surpass Group 2. Thus, combining group and individual instruction, which was originally intended as an advantage in economy, appeared also to constitute a slight but consistent advantage in effectiveness.

ADJUNCT ASSESSMENTS

In the MCDI the parent indicates whether the child has ever displayed each of 320 behaviors or skills. Items represent seven specific areas of development, as well as providing a scale that measures general development. Fifty-nine mothers completed the inventory at the beginning of the study. According to their responses on the General Development Scale, 16% of them perceived their child as being 31% or more below his age standards, 24% perceived their child as being 21–30% below age standards, 41% perceived them as being 1–20% below age standards, and 19% perceived them as at age or above. There were only two mothers who did not report their child as being below the age standard in at least one of the seven facets of development assessed by the inventory. When year-end inventory responses on the General Development Scale were compared with preinstruction scores in the experimental subjects, there were no systematic changes. Therefore, it appears that mothers viewed their child's development realistically and were not denying the presence of delay; their perception of the child's developmental delay did not change essentially over the year.

There were, however, three scales whose results suggested that the behavioral coaching may have been accompanied by specific developmental changes rather than general ones. In the Expressive Language, Conceptual Comprehension, and Situation Comprehension scales, the percentage of comparison mothers who attributed average or better skills to their child, changed by no more than 3% between the beginning and end of the study. In each of the experimental groups, the percentage of mothers who attributed average or better skills to their children on these three scales increased by from 8 to 22%. The facts presented here are crude and further research focusing directly on this issue is worthwhile. It would be fruitful to explore whether behavioral coaching of mothers to assist them in providing positive interactions and in fostering independence may help to maximize expressive language and social comprehension growth. The primary implications of the findings, however, were that despite marked changes in Parent–Child interactions, so that parents could be helped to live more comfortably with the problems of parenting a delayed child, the fundamental delays and inherent problems were not dissipated by behavioral procedures.

The Washington Symptom Checklist was again chosen to index the parents' perceptions of the extent of deviant or problem behavior and its area of focus. The hypothesis was that parents who had participated in parenting instruction would perceive fewer behavior problems at the end of the study than they did at the beginning. Sixty mothers and 44 fathers completed the checklist at the beginning of the study; 55 mothers and 32 fathers completed it a year later. There were no significant differences between experimental and comparison subjects either at the beginning or end of the study. There were no significant differences between initial and final reports for any of the groups. Additionally, there were no differences between data for mothers and for fathers.

These results were unanticipated. The mothers' responses at the beginning of the year were therefore compared with the responses of two other population samples available: 30 children referred because of behavior problems (matched for sex and age with the developmentally delayed) and 49 healthy, normal comparison subjects between the ages of 3 and 6.

When the mean number of "more than most" responses in pretreatment reports were compared for the three groups, the children with behavior problems were reported as having 17.17 problem behaviors, the developmentally delayed 11.83, and the normal children 4.76, a difference that was significant at the .0005 level. Therefore, mothers of developmentally delayed children reported more deviant behaviors than mothers of normal children, but less than mothers of children with behavior problems. In this respect they differed from the mothers of the more handicapped children in the earlier study who had reported no more problems than the nonclinic group.

An item-by-item comparison was made between the reports of the mothers of the developmentally delayed children and the nonclinic mothers, using a 1-way analysis of variance. Significant differences were found on 29 of the 63 items, and with only one exception, the differences were in the direction of higher problem incidence in the delayed subjects. There was little uniformity in the particular behavioral items reported as being deviant; only two items were marked by half or more of the group ("has speech difficulty" and "stubborn"). In a series of varied clinical samples over the past 7–8 years, "stubborn" has been one of the most frequently marked items by parents of preschool-aged children.

SUMMARY

Mothers of developmentally delayed children perceived them as being different from most children in a number of ways—as indeed they were. The results suggest that the parents of the delayed children were aware of the many differences and problems presented by the child's delay. These kinds of statements were based in part on instructions to compare the delayed child with normative expectations (i.e., to compare him with most children his age). Behavioral intervention may have made the parents more competent and self-assured, and more positive toward their child, but it could not change the fact that these children were still delayed and therefore continued to exhibit behaviors that differentiated them from normal subjects.

DISCUSSION AND IMPLICATIONS OF RESEARCH FINDINGS FOR PARENTS

One of the most important issues raised by this report is differentiation between the direct primary effects and the indirect secondary effects of the behavioral counselling techniques used in these studies. Primary effects were relatively clearcut. The parenting instruction programs were designed to teach parents to alter their interactions with their children, and the resulting measurable and demonstrable behavior changes can be construed as being direct and primary results of the teaching. But changes in child behaviors, whether rated by careful analysis of videotaped records, by parent reports of behaviors or events at home, or by outside observers in other settings would have to be considered to be secondary or indirect effects.

In the study of families with young cerebral palsied children, behavioral coaching was followed by a reduced occurrence of stressful interactions and by maintenance of behaviors that expressed warmth and acceptance. Behavioral changes were most clearly demonstrated and best maintained in the affective realm. Relative status relationships were temporarily altered in some instances, but the child's verbal and physical limitations made independent activity more difficult to achieve and many mothers easily found themselves in extremely lead taking and controlling roles. There were many indications that the Parent–Handicapped-Child interaction was necessarily different from that of parent and normal child. The mothers of the handicapped children were actively involved more constantly than their counterparts, and yet were experiencing fewer numbers of interactive behaviors from their children, with the exception of negative affect. Primary effects were partial and were restricted to certain areas of behavior within the physical limits set by the handicapping condition.

Consequently, interaction standards and guidelines based on normal children may be no more appropriate and no more within reach for handicapped children than are normal development standards. The extent to which social development depends on normal growth is often overlooked. In the first 2 years of normal growth, interaction skills develop quickly and have facial, gestural, and verbal components. There is a rapid transition toward independence, mobility, communication, and self-entertainment. These in turn elicit positive interaction both from the mother and from other adults in the social environment. As the normal preschool child acquires skills and independence, he spends less time with his parents. However, physically handicapped children have more difficulty participating in reciprocal interaction, especially in a positive or active way, and thus the mother is "stuck" in interactions that do not change at the rapid rate of the normal child, nor are they as rewarding. The phenomenon of reduced warmth noted in the first study in this series may have been a self-protective defense on the mother's part. Their more active involvement in interaction may make it harder for mothers to disengage from their handicapped child as he passes through the preschool years. They may need considerable help in accepting the appropriateness of reducing the quantity of their involvement in interaction rather than its quality.

In the study of families with less severely handicapped children, primary behavioral changes were more extensive and were reflected in a greater variety of interactive behaviors. Parents who participated in the training program exhibited clearcut behavioral changes. In addition, there were demonstrable changes in the interactions between parent and child so that interactions became less stressful and more positive and friendly. Parent and child "got along together" better, and parents were more comfortable and secure about the appropriateness of their child-management techniques. However, parents continued to appraise their children with realistic recognition of their developmental delay, and they continued to perceive their child as being different from other children in a variety of ways. Those differences and delays did not disappear.

This study also provided the opportunity to examine the similarities and differences among the developmentally delayed subjects, their more severely handicapped counterparts, and a healthy, normal comparison sample. Mothers of delayed children tended to be more controlling than comparison mothers, while their children exercised low amounts of direct control as compared with nondelayed children. However, the developmentally delayed children exhibited high amounts of ignoring and nonacceptance. Terdal et al., (1976) noted similar differences between normal and developmentally delayed groups. However, the interaction-analysis system employed by those authors did not permit analysis of the affective dimension of the interpersonal transactions. The results of the present studies suggested that the most prominent behavioral differences between the delayed subjects and normative samples lay in the high negative affect and low positive affect exhibited by both mothers and children. The affective elements of the interactions proved to be at least as susceptible to change following parent instruction as the control elements were. Bromwich (1976) has described an approach to infant intervention that focuses on enhancing the quality of Mother-Infant interaction. She concluded that the relationship must be positive in affect and grounded in mutual enjoyment and satisfaction in order to be consistently growth promoting for the child and the mother. It should be noted that high control, high negative affect, and low positive affect had also been described as typifying the interactions between the children with motor disabilities and their mothers. The similarity between the findings in the two populations studied is striking.

In the last study in the series reported here, two methods of providing parenting instruction were compared. The results suggested that there was not only an economic advantage to replacing some individual instruction with group experience, but an advantage in effectiveness as well. McMahon and Forehand (1978) describe a study of the effectiveness of "nonprescription behavior therapy"—a brochure to teach mothers to correct their children's inappropriate mealtime behaviors. They documented substantial decreases in inappropriate behavior, maintained at 6-week follow-up. The instructional materials utilized in the group discussion meetings in the study described here probably warrant being called nonprescription therapy, in that they dealt with appropriate responses to problem behaviors in people and situations not directly based on the participants' personal experiences. Further exploration in this direction is clearly indicated. I still have a conviction that immediate personal feedback is also an important component of the most effective program and that the two approaches need to be balanced for optimal results.

Finally, the results reported here appear to confirm the original premise of the projects that were carried out. Parents of developmentally delayed children encounter many problems not experienced by other parents. Often they have little concrete and specific guidance in responding appropriately to behavior of their children, which is, in fact, different from the behavior of their age mates. There are many tensions and areas of conflict, and self-esteem, confidence, and competence of both parent and child may be at risk. Although in this research the fundamental condition of the child was generally unchanged, the affective climate of daily interactions became more positive and more enjoyable, and parents were helped to encourage and accept independence and confidence on the part of their children within the limits of their capacities.

REFERENCES

Bell, R. Q. A reinterpretation of the direction of effects in studies of socialization. *Psychological Review,* 1968, *75,* 81-95.

Britton, J. O., & Thomas, K. R. Rearing the disabled child: A framework for further research. *Journal of School Psychology,* 1973, *11,* 105-109.

Bromwich, R. M. Focus on maternal behavior in infant intervention. *American Journal of Orthopsychiatry,* 1976, *46,* 439-446.

Buda, F. B., Rothney, W. B., & Rabe, E. F. Hypotonia and the maternal-child relationship. *American Journal of Disabled Children,* 1972, *124,* 906-907.

Carkhuff, R. R., & Bierman, R. Training as a preferred mode of treatment of parents of emotionally disturbed children. *Journal of Counseling Psychology,* 1970, *17,* 157-161.

Cook, J. J. Dimensional analysis of child-rearing attitudes of parents of handicapped children. *American Journal of Mental Deficiency,* 1963, *68,* 354-361.

Cummings, S. T., Bayley, H. C., & Rie, H. E. Effects of the child's deficiency on the mother: A study of mothers of mentally retarded, chronically ill, and neurotic children. *American Journal of Orthopsychiatry,* 1966, *36,* 595-608.

Farber, B. *Mental retardation: Its social context and social consequences.* Chicago, Illinois: Houghton-Mifflin, 1968.

Kogan, K. L., & Gordon, B. N. A mother-instruction program: Documenting change in Mother-Child interactions. *Child Psychiatry and Human Development.* 1975, *5,* 189-200. (a)

Kogan, K. L., & Gordon, B. N. Interpersonal behavior constructs: A revised approach to defining dyadic interaction styles. *Psychological Reports,* 1975, *36,* 835-846. (b)

Kogan, K. L., Gordon, B. N., & Wimberger, H. C. Teaching mothers to alter interactions with their children: Implications for those who work with children and parents. *Childhood Education,* 1972, *49,* 107–110.

Kogan, K. L., Tyler, N., & Turner, P. The process of interpersonal adaptation between mothers and their cerebral palsied children. *Developmental Medicine and Child Neurology,* 1974, *16,* 518–527.

Lax, R. Some aspects of the interaction between mother and impaired child: Mother's narcissistic trauma. *International Journal of Psychoanalysis,* 1972, *53,* 339–344.

Lewis, M., & Rosenblum, L. (Eds.). *The effect of the infant on its caregivers.* New York: Wiley, 1974.

Mash, E. J., Lazere, R. L., Terdal, L., & Garner, A. M. Modification of Mother–Child interactions: A modeling approach for groups. *Child Study Journal,* 1973, *3,* 131–143.

Mash, E. J. & Terdal, L. Modification of Mother–Child interactions: Playing with children. *Mental Retardation,* 1973, *11,* 44–49.

McMahon, R. J., & Forehand, R. Nonprescription behavior therapy: Effectiveness of a brochure in teaching mothers to correct their children's inappropriate mealtime behaviors. *Behavior Therapy,* 1978, *9,* 814–820.

Poznanski, E. O. Emotional issues in raising handicapped children. *Rehabilitation Literature,* 1973, *34,* 322–326.

Rose, S. A behavioral approach to the group treatment of parents. *Social Work,* 1969, *14,* 21–29.

Terdal, L., Jackson, R. H., & Garner, A. M. Mother–Child interactions: A comparison between normal and developmentally delayed groups. In E. J. Mash, L. A. Hamerlynfk, L. C. Handy (Eds.), *Behavior modification and families.* New York: Brunner-Mazel, 1976.

Wimberger, H. C., & Gregory, B. S. A behavior checklist for use in child psychiatry clinics. *Journal of the American Academy of Child Psychiatry.* 1968, *7,* 677–688.

Wolfensberger, W. Counseling the parents of the retarded. In A. A. Baumeister (Ed.), *Mental retardation.* Chicago: Aldine, 1967.

Peer and Teacher Interactions
of Children at Risk

Peers, Play, and Pathology: Considerations in the Growth of Social Competence[1]

Children live in a social world—a world inhabited by millions of other people. Only a few of these individuals have a direct impact on the child but, without them, there is a risk for survival as well as a risk that full human potential will not be achieved.

The psychological and pediatric literatures have long stressed the importance of the parent-child relationship to the development of social and intellectual competencies in children. Much less attention has been given to peer relationships—to the child's acquisition of competence in encounters with other children and to the occupation of a comfortable niche within the peer culture. No one has ever doubted that peer interactions are common events (we all remember something about the role played by other children in our own growing up), but few scientists have given much thought to the functions of peer relationships in human development. Often, social scientists seem to consider children's peers as subversive agents of the counter culture who entice the child into delinquency and other antisocial activities. Such notions are the basis for countless television dramas, stories in the daily newspapers, and novels that range from *Huckleberry Finn* to *Kinflicks*.

[1]Adapted from an article published under a similar title in the *Newsletter*, Society for Research in Child Development, Fall, 1977.

HIGH-RISK INFANTS AND CHILDREN:
Adult and Peer Interactions

In point of fact, it is difficult to conceive of normal human development in the absence of peer interaction. New evidence shows that, without an opportunity to encounter individuals who are co-equals, children do not learn effective communication skills, do not acquire the competencies needed to modulate their aggressive actions, have difficulties with sexual socialization, and are disadvantaged with respect to the formation of moral values. Peer relationships are not luxuries in human development, but necessities. In fact, one's competence in engagements with other children and one's centrality in the peer group are nearly as predictive of later difficulties in development as intellectual competence. I am persuaded by a variety of recent literature that poor peer relationships in childhood are among the most powerful predictors of later social and emotional maladies (Hartup, 1976).

Now, with research material, let me elaborate these themes: (a) the importance of peer relationships to children's development; (b) the kinds of research strategies utilized by developmental psychologists in acquiring basic knowledge about social development; and (c) the manner in which psychologists, like their biomedical colleagues, move from clinical observations to clinical trails in the effort to ameliorate adaptational difficulties among children.

In 1951, Anna Freud and her colleague, Sophie Dann, published an extremely interesting series of observations on six 3-year-old German-Jewish children who had come to Britain and into their care in August, 1945. Earlier that summer, these children—three boys and three girls—had been found living by themselves in a "motherless" ward in a concentration camp in Moravia. Various scraps of information revealed the following: Each of the children had been in concentration camps since before its first birthday; the mothers of each had been killed within a short period of the confinement; and the children had mostly been passed from camp to camp until they ended up at Theresienstadt. Their care, in terms of food and facilities, was impoverished but not extreme. Socially, however, the children had essentially reared themselves. Adults had not cared for them other than minimally. Thus, one may regard these 3-year olds as peer reared.

After being discovered, the children were removed to a relocation center in a nearby castle and fed lavishly for several weeks until they were flown by bomber to a children's facility established by Miss Freud in England. The significance of this "natural" experiment is recorded in the following three excerpts from the report. First, the children's behavior toward adults was bizarre.

> They showed no pleasure in the arrangements which had been made for them and behaved in a wild, restless, and noisy manner.... They destroyed all the toys and damaged ... the furniture.... Toward the staff they behaved either with cold indifference or with active hostility. ... At times they ignored the adults completely [Freud & Dann, 1951, p. 130].

Second, the children showed a high degree of mutual attachment.

> Positive feelings were centered exclusively in their own group. . . . They cared greatly for each other and not at all for anybody or anything else. They had no other wish than to be together and became upset when they were separated. When separated, a child would constantly ask for the other children, while the group would fret for the missing member [Freud & Dann, 1951, p. 131].

Last, and the most important observation from this study:

> They were neither deficient, delinquent, nor psychotic. They had found an alternative placement for their [attachments] and, on the strength of this, had mastered some of their anxieties and developed social attitudes. That they were able to acquire a new language in the midst of their upheavals, bears witness to a basically unharmed contact with their environment [Freud & Dann, 1951, p. 168].

Despite the horrendous deprivations experienced by these children, peer rearing had kept their social repertoires intact and preserved a large measure of what may be called "social competence."

In 1972, Harry Harlow and his colleague, Stephen Suomi, published a protocol for ameliorating the effects of social isolation in young rhesus monkeys. This work, completed at the University of Wisconsin, is one of the more recent studies in a series that has examined the debilitating effects on this species of early isolation from maternal stimulation. There is no doubt that prolonged periods, during which infant rhesus monkeys are cutoff from social and sensory stimulation, produce withdrawn, depressed animals who manifest high anxiety when exposed to other animals and who engage in a variety of behaviors that can only be labeled atypical. Over the years, Harlow and his colleagues have tried a number of different methods of restoring the capacity for normal social activity to them. Gradual introduction to adult animals or to animals of the infants' own age have each failed to restore social competence. Therefore, it has seemed as though the early deprivation leaves irreversible scars—scars that persist into the animal's adulthood and that leave it vulnerable to reproductive and parenting malfunctions, as well as debilitations in ordinary social give-and-take.

However, using four experimental animals that had spent their first 6 months in total isolation, these investigators tried a new kind of intervention. It consisted of successive exposures to a normal infant monkey who was only 3-months old—3 months younger than the experimental animal itself. The results were dramatic: (a) self-stimulation, huddling, and other sterotypic behaviors declined; (b) locomotion and exploration of the environment increased; and, (c) social contacts and social play began to emerge. The initial overtures were made by the therapist monkeys who would approach the isolate infants and cling to them. But then (unlike the case when agemates were used as therapists), the isolates reciprocated, and play behavior emerged. Once these interaction patterns were established, the isolates themselves initiated play bouts with progressively increasing frequency. Replication work (Novak & Harlow, 1975) has been published involving other animals whose initial isolation extended over 12 months, the effects of which were even more severe than in the other study.

Previous work in this series of studies suggested to some investigators that, without early socialization, certain social competencies never develop; there would seem to be a critical period in primate development in which social interaction must occur in order for social behavior to emerge normally. Now, it appears that this is a "sensitive" rather than a "critical" period. The social pathology induced by early isolation *can* be reversed through a carefully managed program of play with peers who are younger than the subject.

Just how does children's interaction with agemates differ from their interaction with children who are not their same age? To answer this question, we conducted observations of pairs of nursery school children who differed by not more than 2 months, or by an average of 16 months in chronological age (Lougee, Grueneich, & Hartup, 1977). We watched their play behavior on two occasions (using a concealed video camera) and subsequently tabulated their social activity using the videotapes. First, we found striking differences in the sociability of same-age and mixed-age pairs. The mixed-age pairs were intermediate, in number of social contacts, between younger and older children observed in same-age pairs. The appropriateness of the verbal behavior varied as a function of age mixture in this same manner. Accommodation by individual children to the developmental status of the companion occurred, but this accommodation was more extensive in relation to the *appropriateness* of the communication than to the *amount* of social interaction. Thus, there seems to be a capacity, even among very young children, for making subtle adjustments in social behavior according to the needs and demands of other children. Obviously, normative data based on same-age interaction may not be generalized to mixed-age situations.

Does play with a younger child possess different functions from play with a same-age child? Does play with younger children possess the same kind of therapeutic potential for a socially retarded human child that it seems to possess for the socially debilitated rhesus monkey? Can we devise a protocol that will demonstrate the efficacy of this intervention strategy in human development? Can we demonstrate that play and peer contact have unique importance in the development of social competence in human children? A study constructed with preschool children (Furman, Rahe, & Hartup, 1979) was designed to answer these questions.

Using double-blind procedures and an appropriate control group, we examined the social development of 24 4- and 5-year-old children who may be described as "noninteractive," resembling, in some respects, children to whom labels like "socially withdrawn," "socially isolated," or "nonsociable" are typically applied. (They may not be described as "autistic" or "disturbed.") The children were located in seven day care centers in 19 different classrooms and were identified on the basis of observations conducted over a 5–8 week period. In all cases, the children selected were observed to engage in social interaction in less than 30 of the 90 observation periods completed on each child.

The treatment protocol for one-third of the children consisted of participation in 10 special play sessions (covering 4–6 weeks) with one other child who was 15 months younger than the subject. For a second group, the protocol involved playing with another child who was within 3 months of the subject's own age. A third group received no treatment. The center personnel did not know which children had been selected for the research or assigned to which group, nor did the research staff who conducted the follow-up observations. These observations were conducted in the day care center during the 2 weeks following treatment.

Statistical analysis revealed that the children exposed to both same-age and younger peers were significantly more sociable in the posttreatment observations than in the pretreatment observations, whereas this was not the case for children in the nontreatment condition. Also, children exposed to younger peers were significantly more sociable than the control children in the posttreatment observations, whereas this was not the case for the children exposed to same-age peers. Indeed, unique socialization potential resides in play with younger peers for children who are at risk in the development of social competence. No effects were noted in the behavior of the "therapists" as a function of having participated in the experiment. These "clinical trials" illustrate both the theoretical value and the health potential of recent work on peers, play, and pathology. This work also supports the contention of the Committee on Maternal and Child Health Research (1976) that social competence should receive a much higher priority in policy deliberations during the next few years than it has received previously.

An appreciation of the role of peer interaction in the growth of social competence is only beginning to emerge, although the ubiquity of children's societies has long been recognized. Even now, the contributions of peer interaction to the child's capacities to relate to others, to regulate emotional expression, and to understand complex social events are not well understood. Most commonly, the scientific literature has emphasized the conflict and contentiousness presumed to exist between the peer culture and the core (adult) culture with such contentiousness serving as the basis for innumerable treatments of childhood and adolescence in Western fiction.

Family relationships and peer relationships are very different social systems. Although the social interaction occurring in each system becomes more complex and more differentiated as children grow older, the nature of the social interaction differs greatly between the two systems. Parent–child relationships, especially the mother–child relationship, produce an affective and instrumental base from which the young child can explore the wider social world without undue anxiety or distress. Specific competencies, such as language and role-taking skills, as well as self-esteem, also emanate from this system and are later elaborated in other contexts. But the major function of family relationships seems to be the provision of a basis for environmental exploration. Such exploration then brings the child into commerce with many different social objects, among which are other children. Through interaction with other children, the child then extends his or her competencies in communication and role taking. These associations also result in the direct acquisition of a constellation of unique attitudes and affects—each essential to social adaptation.

Parents also exercise managerial functions with respect to the social lives of their children, selecting particular sociobehavioral contexts to which the children will be exposed. Mothers determine the timing and circumstances under which their offspring will have contact with child associates, teachers, and other individuals. In most instances, this management maximizes exposure to socializing agents who can extend, elaborate, and multiply the child's adaptive potential—far beyond what family relationships could do alone.

REFERENCES

Freud, A., & Dann, S. An experiment in group upbringing. In R. Eisler, A. Freud, H. Hartmann, & E. Kris (Eds.), *The psychoanalytic study of the child* (Vol. 6). New York: International Univ. Press, 1951.

Furman, W., Rahe, D., & Hartup, W. W. Rehabilitation of socially withdrawn preschool children through mixed-age and same-age socialization. *Child Development,* 1979, *50,* in press.

Hartup, W. W. Peer interaction and the behavioral development of the individual child. In E. Schopler & R. J. Reichler (Eds.), *Psychopathology and child development.* New York: Plenum, 1976.

Hartup, W. W. Peer relations and the processes of socialization. In M. J. Guralnick (Ed.), *Early intervention and the integration of handicapped and nonhandicapped children.* Baltimore: Univ. Park Press, 1978.

Lougee, M. D., Grueneich, R., & Hartup, W. W. Social interaction in same- and mixed-age dyads of preschool children. *Child Development,* 1977, *48,* 1353–1361.

Maternal and child health research. Report of the Committee on Maternal and Child Health Research, Assembly of Life Sciences, National Research Council. Washington, D.C.: National Academy of Sciences, 1976.

Novak, M. A., & Harlow, H. F. Social recovery of monkeys isolated for the first year of life: 1. Rehabilitation and therapy. *Developmental Psychology,* 1975, *11,* 453–465.

Suomi, S. J., & Harlow, H. F. Social rehabilitation of isolate-reared monkeys. *Developmental Psychology,* 1972, *6,* 487–496.

CHAPTER **14**   MARY MARTINI

Structures of Interaction between Two Autistic Children

INTRODUCTION

Early childhood autism is considered to be a severe developmental disturbance characterized by faulty development of communication processes and by what Kanner (1943) originally described as "an inability to relate." Although recent research has considered many other features of this disturbance, atypical social behavior remains the salient diagnostic feature of autism (Wing, 1971). Systematic description and theoretical explanation of the social behavior of autistic children has proven difficult. Clincal and research descriptions emphasize a number of interaction abnormalities such as lack of language, use of language in noncommunicative ways (e.g., echolalia, stereotyped speech, and idiosyncratic language), abnormal prosodic and paralinguistic features of speech, lack of gestural communication, inability to imitate others, lack of anticipation movements, gaze aversion, social avoidance tendencies, and the isolating effects of continuous stereotyped behavior.

Descriptions of autistic children vary in the degrees and forms of social isolation observed. Some children are described as totally withdrawn from the outside world, to the point of being unaware of external events. Their unresponsiveness to painful stimuli or to aversive auditory or visual stimuli are cited as examples of this breakdown of contact. They are also said to remain isolated through the continuous performance of stereotyped behaviors. Other children

257

HIGH-RISK INFANTS AND CHILDREN:
Adult and Peer Interactions

are described as being aware of the external world, but as using this awareness for the sole purpose of avoiding contact. Others are described as being highly aware of their physical and social environments, and as initiating some contact. This contact, though, is considered to be purely mechanical, with the child manipulating the other as if he is an object. Still other children are described as having developed the mechanics of social interaction, such as grammatical speech, but as using these in rigid, hollow ways, with little appreciation for the subtleties or complexities of human relating.

These descriptions vary in terms of the imputed awareness of the autistic child, the degree to which he is seen as altering his actions in relation to others, and his capacity to engage in essential interactive processes. Variability in these descriptions may stem from variations in the ages of the children observed, problems with mixed diagnoses, observation of children under abnormal conditions, and lack of specification of the particular interaction processes and disruptions considered. The descriptions are generally unclear as to the exact nature of the avoiding behaviors of these children. In view of this, an important research goal is to specify the particular processes involved in this breakdown of contact and to more carefully delineate what we mean by the "inability to relate."

Theories of Etiology

Theories of the etiology of autism are similarly variable, differing in terms of the organizational level at which the underlying disturbance is believed to occur. These range from physiological theories of sensory-processing deficits, right-hemispheric dominance, and arousal-regulation deficits; to psychological models of deficits in cognitive and linguistic processing; to psychodynamic theories of faulty ego development, or of autistic withdrawal as a higher-level defense mechanism. Most theorists consider the autistic child to be incapable of dealing with complex interaction demands and explain social withdrawal as a defense against overload.

Physiological theories posit that behavioral abnormalities arise from deficits in the ways in which these children perceive the outside world (Condon, 1975), process this input (Ornitz & Ritvo, 1968, 1978), or regulate their level of arousal in relation to this input (DesLauriers, 1969; Hutt, Hutt, Lee, & Ounsted 1964). According to these models, autistic children withdraw from the world in an attempt to avoid excessive sensory stimulation or neurological arousal.

Cognitive and linguistic theories posit that basic sensory and processing mechanisms are intact, but that higher levels of processing, involving the ability to abstract and use symbols, are deficient (Hermelin & O'Connor, 1970; Rutter, 1978; Wing, 1976). These theorists feel the children are unable to deal with the complexities of social interaction and avoid contact in an attempt to avoid cognitive overload.

Psychodynamic theories posit that autism is an affective cognitive disorder based on faulty ego development in children predisposed for difficulties in separation or individuation (Mahler, 1968) or identity formation (Bettleheim, 1967). Cognitive deficits such as lack of internal labeling, problems in conceptualizing time, space, and causalty (Ekstein, 1954), as well as the fragility of their rudimentary egos, are believed to arise from the lack of differentiation of self from outside. The resultant chaos requires defensive attempts to maintain order, such as withdrawal from novelty, complexity, ego-threatening others, and the ritualization of behavior.

A common feature of these theories is that social behavior is believed to be extensively disrupted by these deficits, and is therefore either totally disorganized (Rimland, 1964) organized for the sole purpose of defensive avoidance (Richer, 1976), or organized around low-level mechanisms such as arousal regulation (Hutt, Hutt, Lee, & Ounsted, 1968). One consideration of the present study is that their social behavior may be organized to higher degrees, but in ways that differ from those of normal interaction.

Research in Social Behavior

Until recently the strategy of observational research on autism has been to compare specific aspects of autistic behavior with those of normal, retarded, or differently-disturbed children. In this way, their social behavior was found to be lacking in normal organizational features, as well as different from the behavior of other disordered children. Recent studies, however, have turned to studying the possible functions and organization of these behaviors within the system of autism itself, and have demonstrated the limitations of the comparative strategy. The comparative studies typically have not considered constellations of behaviors, nor the possibility of organized connections between various abnormal features. For example, early clinical descriptions stressed that autistic children constantly gaze averted and did not visually attend to their outside world. Hutt and Ounsted (1966), however, found that some autistic children visually scan their environment but do so via fractional glances that are apparent only in slow-motion viewing of films. Similarly, Richer and Richards (1975) have described how the typical responses of adults to these children serve to elicit avoidance responses in the children, and DesLauriers and Carlson (1969) have observed that autistic children enjoy and even initiate rough and tumble play. Wing (1976) indicates that avoidance behavior in general diminishes in some of these children as they approach middle childhood. Through the strategy of trying to understand the possible functions and connection of abnormal behaviors, the assumption that autistic children are basically motivated to avoid social contact is being questioned. Howlin (1978), for example, asks, "What . . . is the exact nature of the 'avoiding behavior' shown by autistic children? Is it avoidance in the active sense, with the child deliberately pulling away from the adult? [p. 65]."

Orientation of This Study

This study considers the question of the nature of "avoiding behaviors" via careful consideration of how two autistic boys make and maintain nonverbal contact while playing side-by-side at a basin of water. The study is an exploratory, structural analysis of this optimal interaction between the boys. The purpose is to discover and describe as many elements of interaction organization as possible and to generate hypotheses from these structural findings. These hypotheses relate not only to the possible organization of how autistic children coordinate and maintain contact, but also to the possible organization of how coordination "breaks down" or fails to be achieved.

Face-to-face interaction is considered to be the basic unit of interpersonal relating, and it is assumed that disturbances in relating will be reflected in interaction abnormalities at this level of contact. A further assumption of the study is that the dysfunctioning of a system is best understood via careful description of the optimal functioning of that system and subsequent delineation of the processes that break down or occur in modified form when the system malfunctions. In view of this, an optimal interactive sequence was selected from a large body of videotaped data on interactions among five autistic children. The selected film is of waterplay between two of the most disturbed children and involves a clearly coordinated pouring game between the boys. The research strategy was to study how they achieve this coordination, and then to compare this to segments of the film in which they do not achieve coordination. The microanalytic methodology and structuralist framework described by Duncan and Fiske in *Face-to-face Interaction* (1977) is followed closely in this study.

BACKGROUND

Clincial Description of the Children

The two boys filmed in this study are 8-years old and entered their current day-school for disturbed children 4-years ago. They have been repeatedly diagnosed as autistic and display many of the features of childhood autism, which are described in the following section using the format of Wing (1976). Though neither boy has been formally tested (because both were considered to be untestable), their day-to-day responses to various cognitive tasks indicate that they would probably function in the low-retarded range on such tests.

SETH

When Seth entered the school at 4-years-old, he had not developed speech. At 8-years old, he remains nonverbal. He repeats long chains of syllables and hums tunes for long periods. Receptively, he responds to "no," can carry out a simple, one-step command, and under constant conditions executes much longer but familiar routines. Seth does not use gestures for communication, though he pulls the teacher's arms toward him when he wants to be picked up. Also he leads adults by the arm. Over a 10-month period he learned one hand sign in a signing program but did not use this spontaneously.

Seth spends much of his unstructured time running from one corner of the room to the other, skipping in circles, spinning objects, and, whenever possible, pouring water. He also performs a number of stereotyped hand movements (e.g., finger twiddling at his chin and mouth) and some self-hurtful behaviors, such as biting his hand and forcefully poking his mouth.

Seth responds in an atypical way to painful stimuli—for example, when he falls from a height, he stands up, giggles, and runs in circles. When he first came to the school he alternated between periods of "out of control" giggling (in which he limply fell to the ground and wet his pants), and periods of extreme agitation in which he whined, screamed, thrashed with his arms, threw his body around, and hit and bit himself and anyone approaching him. It was rarely clear what had precipitated his agitation.

Seth maintains eye contact from a distance of about 10 ft., but avoids gaze and uses fractional glances in closer contact. In very close contact, he stares blankly at areas of the face other than the eyes. As he skips back and forth in the room, he darts glances at ongoing activities and particularly at the teachers. He intently watches his ritualized pouring of liquids and twirling of objects, but does not visually inspect other objects. He uses fleeting glances to check where he is running, and in this way seems not to be looking.

Seth's motor coordination in ritualistic activities is precise and elaborate, but he coordinates poorly on unfamiliar tasks. With a pencil, he produces random scribbles or dots, and his fine-motor coordination, in general, is poor. On cognitive tasks he can complete a form-puzzle and large peg-board, but does not stack rings in sequence. He shows some ability in matching pictures to sounds. Seth's self-help skills are minimal: He partially dresses himself and eats with his fingers. For long periods of time he will eat only certain foods.

Over the 4-year period at this school, Seth made most progress in terms of social relatedness. He developed physically close ties with three teachers and now wants to sit close to them, lay on their laps, and be carried by them constantly. He initiates tickling and wrestling play with teachers and engages in extended, nonverbal contacts with Brad.

BRAD

Brad, also, does not talk, though his repetitive vocalizations approach the sound of English syllables and words, and, when slowed down on videotape, sound like certain phrases ("look-up," "shut-up," "don't wanna," "me me me," "go 'way"). Brad's receptive language is developed to the extent that he performs exact-opposite, negativistic responses to commands. He does not use gestures to communicate—instead, he pulls teachers to what he wants and pushes at the juice can for more juice. He does not imitate gestures even when physically modeled to do so.

Brad shows little response to pain and little awareness of danger (e.g., runs into the street; wanders out into the snow, barefoot). Brad produces repetitive auditory stimulation by bouncing balls, cartons, and metal objects for long periods. He squints and stares at fluorescent lights, performs rapid hand movements in front of his eyes, and pushes against his eyeballs with his fingertips.

Brad performs a large repertoire of stereotyped behaviors, including jumping up and down, rocking, head banging, pounding, bouncing objects, elaborate hand flapping, and finger-twiddles. He performs a number of self-hurtful behaviors, such as head banging, hitting his head and face with his fists, and poking at his eyes. When he is upset, he moans, rocks in a frog-like position, jumps up and down, hits his face and head, and tries to bang his head against sharp edges. Similar to Seth, his motor coordination is very good at ritualistic activities, but poor on unfamiliar tasks. In contrast to his elaborate hand flapping, which looks like rapid sign language, his fine-motor coordination at other tasks is extremely undeveloped.

Brad maintains eye contact, though seems to be staring blankly or with a puzzled expression, while doing so. He watches other children and teachers from a distance, and visually attends to his stereotyped activities. As with Seth, no symbolic play or appropriate use of toys was observed over the 4-year period. On cognitive tasks, Brad can complete form puzzles and simple pegboards. He refuses simple discrimination, sorting, and sequencing tasks, but obeys one-step commands and shows some ability in matching pictures to sounds.

He eats frantically with his fingers, does not inspect what he puts in his mouth, and drinks large quantities of liquids. He has an abnormal sleep cycle and tends to rock extensively at night. In terms of self-help skills, he partially dresses himself, but cannot button, or put on his shoes.

Brad spends much of his unstructured time bouncing balls or objects while hand flapping, running back and forth, frantically eating whatever is available, teetering on the climbing structure, or sitting passively, watching others while hand flapping and pushing at his eyes. He plays in the water whenever allowed, putting his hand under the faucet, splashing water on the table, or running through puddles. He has begun to initiate chase games with teachers and a blanket game and push-pull physical play with them, Seth, and another boy.

Group Dynamics

Seth and Brad have remained in the same group of six severely disturbed, nonverbal children, with two teacher-therapists, since they entered the school. Observations of this group over time indicated a slow progression toward social interaction. Initially, when the children were together they made little eye contact, did not watch each other, and seemed oblivious to what was going on around them. Eventually they became at least minimally aware of each other's actions, and carefully watched the one child who tried to hit and bite. One nonautistic child manipulated the others by leading them around, sitting them down, and undressing them. The other children rarely spontaneously interacted and seemed uncomfortable when in close proximity to each other.

Films of the group, taken 4 months prior to the filming that is the subject of this chapter, indicate that the children now remain in proximity to each other, that they wander at the periphery of activities and watch each other, and that they make fleeting, dis-synchronous eye contact. Stereotyped hand movements—by two children watching each other—sometimes occur in synchrony and there are indications that the children alter their behaviors in relation to each other. In one film, for example, four of the children run rapidly and repeatedly through a puddle, yet only one collision occurs in the 4 min of activity. Film analysis reveals deference patterns as to "who runs through first" in a conflict situation.

In terms of peer contact, Brad and Seth interact the most. Initial interactions involved much push and pull, running away and back, threatening to hit, but then touching softly, looking toward each other, then looking away. They initiate contact by backing into each other or by placing their heads close together. The interactions are choppy, uncomfortable to watch, but continue for up to a few minutes.

In summary, though displaying many of the classical features of childhood autism, these children also present many social-approach tendencies. They exhibit several prerequisites to social interaction, such as indications of awareness and interest in each other, examples of altering their behaviors in accordance to others, and the development of some direct, social-approach behaviors. Progress in these children, in general, occurred in social relatedness.

Specifically, gaze aversion and isolating behaviors dropped out over the 4-year period. This is in keeping with observations cited by Wing (in Rutter & Schopler 1978), that some autistic children "lose their indifference to people, and want to join in social life," as they move into later childhood. In this particular case, the extreme consistency and familiarity of their school environment may have played a large role in enhancing this progression toward interaction behavior.

The Waterplay Interactions: Background

A month prior to this film, a daily waterplay time was set up for Seth, who, when given the opportunity, tried to play at the sink for hours. Brad began to watch Seth from the other side of the room and, over the weeks approached the area, darted back and forth, and eventually stood next to Seth, quietly watching him. At some point Brad put his hand under the faucet and engaged in his typical water activities (splashing on the floor, etc.). Seth, at first, ignored Brad's presence, but then became increasingly upset when Brad interrupted and began to pour wildly, throw pots, screech, bite his own hand, and threaten to hit Brad. Attempts were made to set up separate times for the boys, but then each child became upset when the other was allowed to play in the water. Another attempt involved putting two basins on a low table and letting them both play at once. It was assumed they would play in separate basins, but Brad continued to stand next to Seth and, at one point, put his hand in the stream that Seth was pouring. Seth ignored this and continued to concentrate on the bottom pot into which the water was supposed to flow, ignoring the fact that it was being deflected by Brad's hand. Eventually, Seth attended to Brad's hand, and dropped the bottom container out entirely. He quickly returned to his idiosyncratic play, however, as soon as Brad turned away. This first waterplay session was filmed, but a technically clearer film (taken face-on instead of from behind). made the next day was analyzed for this study.

Film Description

The film is a color, sound movie, running 5 min 44 sec. Conditions were naturalistic in that the boys were filmed during a normal morning session, in their classroom, at an activity which would have occurred anyway. They were accustomed to being filmed, and I was very familiar to them. The film runs from soon after the teacher has placed the basins on the table to when he says it is time to clean up. The boys stand side-by-side at one basin, facing the camera. Seth pours from various containers and Brad either attends to him or turns away to his own activities. Their play is undirected and uninterrupted.

At the beginning of the film, Seth pours from a very low level, lowers the pot into the basin, or pours directly into the mouth of another bottle. He begins pouring when Brad is turned away, and stops pouring or lowers the stream when Brad turns back. Brad watches Seth for short periods, and then becomes involved in his own activity of taking mouthfulls of water and spitting it on the floor.

At a certain point, Seth begins pouring from a slightly higher level and Brad makes some tentative reaches toward the stream, but Seth then lowers the stream or moves away. Brad finally forces his hand into the stream for the first "hand-in-stream" game of this session. The general sequence of the game is that Seth pours the water, Brad puts his right hand in the stream, and they both watch the water flow over it. After this first game, Seth begins to pour in a way conducive for Brad to insert his hand (pours at a medium or high level), and the synchronized game is repeated several times. The next few pouring sequences are then characterized by fits and starts until the mutual game is again synchronized. By the end of the film Seth pours from a high level and attends to Brad's hand, rather than to the pots he pours into. The game runs smoothly and quickly and is reset immediately. Near the end of the film, however, Brad becomes involved in splashing in a puddle and leaves Seth and the game. The film ends as Seth pours a pot of water over his own head, Brad reattends and watches, and the teacher intervenes to clean up. Over the $5\frac{1}{2}$ min period Seth pours 39 times, of which 20 result in hand-in-stream games.

An important feature of this sequence is that it provides many examples of apparent coordination (e.g., the hand-in-stream games) and presents these side-by-side with pouring sequences that do not result in this game but that occur under identical conditions. In this way, the film provides a kind of natural experiment in which successfully coordinated sequences can be compared to all other sequences. This is an important arrangement for exploring questions such as: How is interaction coordination achieved between these children, and in what cases does it breakdown or fail to be achieved? The actions and sequences on this film are also relatively simple and repetitive. It can be easily postulated, for example, that one goal of their interaction is simply to synchronize actions to result in a hand-in-stream game, as each boy has many other options in this situation yet participates in repeating this game many times. Also, the game is new and developmental changes can be seen during the 5-min period. This is important for exploring the question, What is the process by which coordination is developed between these two boys? i.e., How are coordination rules or shared sets of expectations about this game established over the 5-min period?

Research Questions and Strategy

At this point, the relevant research questions seemed to be:

1. Is the interactive synchrony observed in this film due to actual coordination between the boys, or does it reflect a kind of mechanical en-

meshing of both children's idiosyncratic patterns? Does interaction
occur or do the boys engage in an elaborate but sterile form of parallel
activity?

2. If these sequences are coordinated, what structural regularties are observed in the smoothly coordinated games? What forms of interaction
organization account for these regularities?

3. How do these structural features differ from those of the non-hand-in-
stream sequences?

4. How do early, "successful" games compare with later ones? What
structural changes occur over time?

5. Are there behavioral and sequential regularities in the "unsuccessful"
sequences, and can an alternate form of interaction organization account for these failures to synchronize?

A fairly straightforward research strategy was derived from these questions: Compare the 20 hand-in-stream games with the remaining 19 pouring
sequences in the film and then compare early forms of this game with later
ones.

METHODOLOGY

Many aspects of this method are derived from Starkey Duncan's work on
interaction analysis, particularly as described in Duncan and Fiske (1977).
Briefly, analysis of the waterplay film involved the following:

1. Detailed transcriptions were made of each child's stream of behavior
for specific behavior modalities, such as hand movements, visual orientation,
etc., using frame numbers (equal time periods in fractions of seconds) as points
of reference.

2. Pattern analysis of each child's stream of behavior was done for the
purpose of describing elements of internal organization or self-synchrony.

3. Pattern analysis of the 19 hand-in-stream games, via analysis of antecedent probabilities, was done for the purpose of delineating rule-governed
sequences of back-and-forth moves between the boys.

4. A hypothetical system of interaction organization was derived to account for the observed regularities, and the hypotheses were tested by comparing the presence or absence of its postulated elements in the hand-in-stream
versus non-hand-in-stream situations.

5. Structural features of the early versus the later forms of the hand-in-
stream game were compared.

6. The 19 remaining sequences were analyzed for structural regularities

and a second hypothetical system of "interaction strategy" was derived to account for these regularities.

The final step of this research, testing the interaction-strategy hypotheses, has not been completed, and is not reported here. In general, this is not a definitive statement on optimal analyses techniques or conceptualization of findings.

Transcribing the Stream of Behavior

Each child's stream of behavior was transcribed, modality by modality for four behavior modalities: (a) movements of the right hand; (b) movements of the left hand; (c) body posture and orientation to the other; and (d) gaze direction. The modalities encompassed all observable behavior in the film. Vocalizations were considered to be important, but could not be carefully transcribed, due to the lack of slow-motion audio equipment. The onset, offset, and content of the occasional teacher comments were noted in the transcriptions.

Comprehensive lists of behaviors were made for each modality for each child via repeated viewings of the film. The behaviors transcribed in this study were at the organizational level of behavioral shifts such as TAKES POT, LIFTS POT, POURS, MEDIUM HEIGHT, REACHES TOWARD STREAM, and PUTS HAND IN STREAM.

A hand-driven, editor-viewer with a frame counter was used for the slow-motion viewing and transcribing of this film. A child's behavior stream was transcribed, modality by modality, in the following way. To transcribe the actions of Seth's right hand, for example, the film was moved through the editor-viewer until a shift in the action of this hand was observed. The onset of the action was marked by frame number on ruled paper for which each line represented 5 frames or one-third of a second of the behavior stream. The film was then continued through the editor-viewer until this hand movement ended, and the offset was noted in the same way. In this way, the onset and offset of behaviors in all modalities for both boys could be transferred to one transcription sheet, with Seth's stream of behavior on one side and Brad's on the other; and this could be visually scanned for patterns.

Unit of Analysis

The pouring sequence was chosen as the unit of analysis and was defined as that segment of the behavior stream beginning when Seth made his first move to pour and ending when he turned from that pouring bout to a new activity. The pouring sequence included both boys' actions within that segment, and also stretched over the reset period between two distinct pouring bouts.

Pattern Analysis

Typically pattern analysis involves determining the probability that B will follow A in the sequence A → B. This technique is particularly effective, yielding high probability when sequences involve obligatory rules such as every time that signal A occurs the response must be action B. Another form of rule, however, is the optional rule, which provides the interactant the option of responding with B or not. In conversation turn taking (Duncan & Fiske, 1977), the speaker may relinquish the speaking turn to the auditor, but the auditor is not required to take it; he can remain silent or indicate that he is listening but has no comment at that time. Analyzing conversations for the probability that he will take the turn every time it is relinquished may yield very low probabilities. Duncan and Fiske (1977) found that the exchange of speaking turns is rule governed, however, in the sense that when a turn-exchange occurs smoothly, it is almost always the case that the auditor has attempted to take the turn at the appropriate time (i.e., after the speaker has relinquished the turn). In this case, the rules designate where in the behavior stream an attempt to take the turn will occur when it does so. In order to determine this, we must look at the occurrences of action B and determine what actions consistently precede these. Pattern analysis in this study was conducted in this backward searching way (i.e., antecedence probabilities were figured for actions occurring just before the behavior in question). Analysis questions were of the nature, "What actions consistently occur immediately before Seth starts pouring?"

Rules of Evidence

Once sequence regularities are discovered, the analysis turns to the question: Could this pattern have occurred by chance, or can we assume that its regularity is due to behavior- or interaction organization? Duncan and Fiske (1977) suggest the use of statistical tests to determine the probability that an observed pattern could have occurred by chance. The stated hypothesis is that interaction organization exists, that there is an organized relationship between an action by Seth and an antecedent action by Brad. The null hypothesis is that no organization exists, and χ^2 are used to test this null hypothesis.

ANALYSIS AND RESULTS

Self-Consistency: The Organization of Each Child's Behavior

Two forms of internal organization appeared in the behavior transcriptions. Within each child's repertoire there were actions that consistently cooccurred with specific external events and behaviors that consistently fit together into patterns. The most striking example of self-consistency involved Brad's stereotyped behaviors. Brad performs three kinds of stereotyped behavior: repetitive hand movements near his mouth or chin (i.e., "hand flapping" with his left hand), brisk mouth-rubs with the left hand, and ear tapping with his right hand. In the film, he also spends a great deal of time watching water flow over his hand, onto the table or floor, or down his upraised arm. Pattern analysis revealed that Brad consistently begins hand flapping when the water he is watching begins to flow (93% of all hand-flapping bouts) and ends hand flapping when water stops flowing or when he stops watching it (85%). Similarly, he rubs his mouth at the end of an ongoing activity (100%), (particularly at the end of a hand-flapping bout, 53%), and stops mouth rubbing when he begins a new activity. In much the same way, Brad taps his ear when he shifts his visual attention from one activity to another. These findings are summarized in Table 14.1.

Viewed in this way, Brad's stereotyped behaviors temporally frame other events and actions: His hand flapping encompasses the flowing of water, mouth rubbing frames the pause between activities, and ear tapping marks shifts in his attention. His stereotyped behaviors are consistent and are temporally related to certain external events, but we can say nothing as to "why" Brad starts hand flapping when the water begins to flow, and stops when it stops. Minimally, however, these behaviors seem to be incorporated into his larger

TABLE 14.1
Self-Consistency: Co-Occurrence[a] of Bs Stereotyped Behaviors with Other Events

	Begin	End
Bouts of hand flapping (N = 40)		
When water starts flowing	37 (93%)	
When water stops flowing		29 ⎱
When B stops watching water		5 ⎰ 34 (85%)
At any other time	3 (7%)	6 (15%)
Bouts of mouth rubbing (N = 34)		
At end of hand flapping bout	18 (53%) ⎱	
At end of other activity	16 (47%) ⎰ 34 (100%)	
At beginning of new activity		33 (97%)
Bouts of ear tapping (N = 10)	Occur	
When B shifts his visual		
attention from one activity		
to another	10 (100%)	

[a] Co-occurrence within 1 sec (18 frames).

behavioral organization, and may also be organized in relation to outside events. Further hypotheses (e.g., that Brad's stereotyped movements may serve as behavioral markers for fleeting, external events or for temporal features such as "ongoing activity," "shift in activity,") would need to be explored using a large body of data as to how Brad uses these behaviors in a range of situations.

The findings are perhaps most useful as indications of the importance of studying the specific context in which a child performs stereotyped behaviors, the ways in which he uses these in his day-to-day life. This does not suggest that stereotyped behaviors have specific etiologies or underlying functions for each child, but rather considers the possibility that each child incorporates these behaviors, whatever their etiology or basic function, in systematic ways into his repertoire, and in ways that may serve secondary functions. Study of this organization may provide us with clues as to how he is trying to structure his perception of and contact with the outside world.

EMBEDDED ACTIONS

Self-consistency was also reflected in the "embedded" nature of each child's stream of behavior. In Table 14.2 the sequence of actions Seth performs in pouring a stream of water and the sequence Brad performs in putting his hand in the stream are described. The seemingly simple act of pouring water involves a number of actions that are started at the beginning of the sequence and then stopped at the end (e.g., Seth takes a pot at the beginning and then lets go of it at the end; he pours at one point and stops pouring at another). In Table 14.2 the starting and stopping of each action are connected with a line, and it becomes apparent that the starting and stopping of some actions frame or embed that process in others. For example, Brad's visual attention frames his body orientation, which, in turn, frames his hand movements.

SELF-CONSISTENCY AND INTERACTION PROCESSES

Given the repetitive and ritualistic nature of autistic behavior, it was not surprising to find elements of internal organization, although it was interesting to note the extent to which external events were reflected in it. In another sense, though, self-consistency processes are important for face-to-face interaction as they provide a level of predictability about what an interactant will do. Some degree of mutual predictability is necessary for coordinating two people's actions. In this sense, grammatical embedding in language is useful for providing the listener with cues as to what might come next in the flow of speech and for facilitating the flow of comprehension. The behavioral embedding observed here may have a similar value. One action in the embedded sequence, such as Brad leaning toward the basin, may serve as an indication of

TABLE 14.2
Self-Consistency: The Embedded Pattern of Each Child's Actions

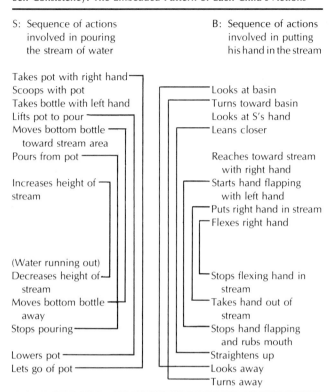

S: Sequence of actions involved in pouring the stream of water

B: Sequence of actions involved in putting his hand in the stream

Takes pot with right hand
Scoops with pot
Takes bottle with left hand
Lifts pot to pour
Moves bottom bottle
 toward stream area
Pours from pot

Increases height of
stream

(Water running out)
Decreases height of
 stream
Moves bottom bottle
 away
Stops pouring

Lowers pot
Lets go of pot

Looks at basin
Turns toward basin
Looks at S's hand
Leans closer

Reaches toward stream
 with right hand
Starts hand flapping
 with left hand
Puts right hand in stream
Flexes right hand

Stops flexing hand in
 stream
Takes hand out of
 stream
Stops hand flapping
 and rubs mouth
Straightens up
Looks away
Turns away

the next action, putting his hand in the stream. Whether such indications are actually used by Seth and Brad to predict each other's actions or to regulate their own actions accordingly is a question considered in detail in the next stage of the analysis.

Interaction Synchrony

Analysis then turned to describing patterns of back-and-forth actions that occurred between the boys during the hand-in-stream games. The purpose was to describe structural regularities that could account for the outcome of successful coordination in these games. The stream of behavior was analyzed for patterns in a backward, searching way. An important element in the game was selected, such as Seth beginning to pour, and the question "Which actions by Brad consistently occur immediately before Seth begins to pour?" was asked.

The analyis was continued backward until each significant action or group of actions was considered. This process was particularly helpful in discovering certain actions that, from a forward analysis, seemed insignificant.

Using this method, patterns were found at various phases of the hand-in-stream games (i.e., at the beginning of each game, when the boys prepare to play; in the middle-stages, when the hand-in-stream activity is occurring; at the endings; and during reset periods between games). Patterns became stablized for the different phases at different times across the 5-min contact. Coordinated beginnings of the game were stablized first and then were repeated in fairly consistent form 19 times in the film. For the sake of brevity and because the essential interaction processes of rule formation and strategic ways of playing the game can be explored within this segment of the game, only the findings pertaining to the beginnings of the games are described.

REGULARITIES IN BEGINNING OF THE GAME

A step-by-step pattern was found to characterize the beginning of these games. In Figure 14.1 this pattern is presented as a flow diagram in which each diamond represents a possible "move" in the sequence and in which the action flows in the direction of the arrows. Specifically, the following was observed:

1. Brad performs a number of actions associated with finishing-up an activity (i.e., he stops hand flapping, rubs his mouth, and straightens up from his play.
2. At this point, Seth takes a pot, scoops with it, and lifts it to pour.
3. Brad then turns toward him, looks at his hands, and may also crouch toward the basin, reach with one hand, and hand flap with the other.
4. At this point, Seth starts pouring, usually from a medium or high level.
5. Brad puts his hand into the stream.

In Figure 14.1, the antecedent probabilities that each step precedes the next are noted above the arrows.

An interesting aspect of this pattern is that it consists of a series of preparatory moves by each child. For example, Seth takes the pot, scoops with it, and lifts, in preparation for pouring; Brad turns toward the basin, leans forward, and gets his hands ready, in preparation for putting his hand in the stream. The fact that their preparation moves are intermeshed suggests two possibilities: Either the boys perform these actions so regularly that their streams of behavior

FIGURE 14.1. The diagram illustrates the observed sequence of behaviors leading up to hand-in-stream games. The numbers represent the probabilities that A occurs before B in the sequence A → B.

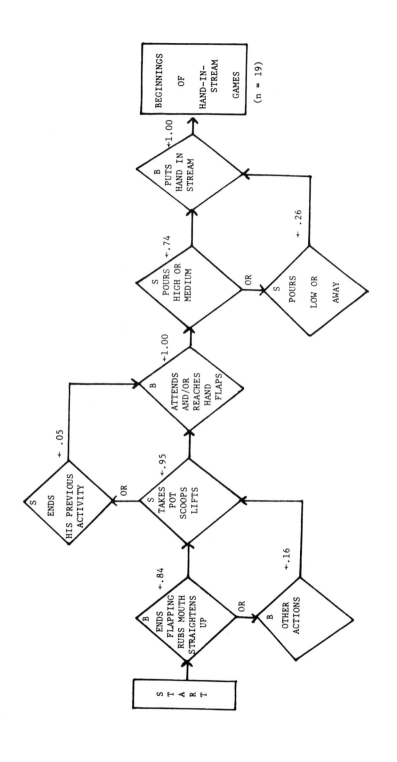

mechanically enmesh, or they are anticipating each other's actions and are regulating their own behaviors in relation to the other. In support of the second possibility is the observation that, in all of the coordinated games, Seth starts pouring only when Brad is attending and is already positioning himself to play, and, in cases when Brad is not already watching, he returns to the basin immediately after Seth takes the pot and scoops. From these observations a system of coordination was posited. This was based on the possibility that Brad's actions are read by Seth as cues to what Brad might do next and how ready he is to go on to the next step in the sequence. Seth may then regulate his own actions accordingly. This would apply similarly to Brad. Although this process of anticipation–regulation is one of the most basic processes of human, face-to-face interaction, it is interesting to note whether, and to what extent, it occurs between these two children.

ACHIEVING COORDINATION

Although the above pattern seems simple and straightforward, Seth and Brad have numerous options at each step of this sequence, which they in fact exercise at other times in the film. Seth, for example, could start pouring whether Brad was attending or not, and Brad could turn toward the basin and get ready to play regardless of Seth's readiness to pour. In the coordinated games, however, they manage to stay in step. The next stage of the analysis involved hypothesizing *how* they do this, and testing this hypothesis.

A system of coordination was hypothesized, based on the anticipation–regulation processes described. The elements of this system are presented, in detail, in Table 14.3, but briefly consist of hypothesized readiness signals; the specific behaviors or cues making up these signals; and the subsequent action by the partner that is consistantly preceded by the signal. In this system, it is not necessary that the signaler intend to send a message, but only that the partner read his behaviors as such.

RULES OF THE GAME

The basic rule of this system is hypothesized as "Wait until the other is ready before proceeding to the next step of the sequence." Specific rules of the game are

1. Seth begins the game *only after* Brad displays cues that he is ending his current activity.
2. Brad reattends to the game *when* Seth starts preparing to pour.
3. Seth lifts the pot to pour *only when* Brad is attending.
4. Brad positions himself to play *when* Seth has indicated that he is ready to pour.

TABLE 14.3
Interaction Coordination: Hypothesized System for Coordinating Hand-in-Stream

Hypothesized signal	Behavioral cues making up signal	Related to subsequent
B: "ENDING PREVIOUS ACTIVITY" signal	Withdraws hand from stream (if in) Straightens up Rubs mouth Ends hand flapping	S: BEGINS new sequence
S: "BEGIN" signal	Looks at basin (if away) Leans toward basin Puts hand(s) in (if out) Takes pot or bottle SCOOPS with container	B: REATTENDS (if away) B: Starts READY behaviors (if already attending)
B: "ATTENTIVE" signal	Turns toward basin (if away) Looks at basin Performs a "quick-away" sequence (i.e., ends mouth rub, holds onto S, glances away, looks back at S, and rubs mouth again)	S: Lifts pot to pour
S: "PREPARING TO POUR" signal	Lifts the container (either HIGH, MEDIUM, or LOW, with or without other container underneath)	B: Performs READY BEHAVIORS
B: "READY TO PLAY" signal	Looks at S's hands (if not before) Lets go of S (if holding him) Ends mouth rub REACHES toward stream area Begins hand flapping, flexes hand Leans forward	S: Pours
S: "PLAY" signal	POURS (either HIGH, MEDIUM, or LOW, and with or without bottom bottle)	B: Puts hand in the stream
B: "PLAY" signal	Puts hand in stream (either while hand flapping with other hand, or flexing the hand in the water)	S: Continues pouring
(Water running out)		
S: "ABOUT TO STOP POURING" signal	Water running out, and/or Lowers stream, moves pot away from B's hand Straightens up Tips pot up to end stream	B: Withdraws hand
B: "READY TO END"	Removes hand from stream Ends hand flap and flex	S: Stops pouring
S: "END GAME"	Stops pouring Leans away Lets go of containers	B: Straightens up Rubs mouth "ENDS PREVIOUS ACTIVITY" signal (see above)

5. Seth starts pouring *only after* Brad had indicated that he is ready to participate. Seth pours *in a conducive way.*
6. Brad puts his hand in the stream *if* all of the preceding steps have occurred.

The hypothesized moves and options of this system are presented in the flow-diagram in Figure 14.2. Each diamond in the diagram represents a possible move or decision point in the sequence. The "yes" arrows indicate that the move was made, and they then lead to the next decision point. The "no" arrows indicate that the action was not performed, and lead to alternative moves in the system. The smoothest running game occurs if each child promptly performs his actions in the correct sequence. In this case, the interaction flows directly across the diagram, from "start" to the outcome of a hand-in-stream game. This is the optimal, "expected" sequence and is taken as a baseline from which deviations and variations occur, some of which are analyzed in terms of "interaction strategy." Less smooth running, yet coordinated, games require waiting by one child or both, or other behaviors (e.g., Seth's attention-getting behavior of pouring over his own head) for drawing each other back into the expected sequence. Some of the side branches from the expected stream may result in a loss of contact if one child or the other quits the game entirely. This diagram represents a hypothesized system in which "waiting" is an inferred process included as a possible explanation of how coordination is achieved.

Testing the Hypothesized System

An alternate hypothesis considered in this study was that the observed back-and-forth regularities occurred by chance (via the enmeshing of rigid behavior patterns of each child). In this case, a system of interaction coordination would not be necessary to account for the consistencies. One strategy for testing this was to see if the hypothesized rules or steps of the system could significantly differentiate the hand-in-stream from non-hand-in-stream games. It was hypothesized that these steps would consistently occur in the coordinated games but would consistently *not* occur in the non-hand-in-stream sequences. For this analysis, X^2 were figured for 2 by 2 contingency tables, and the results are presented in Table 14.4. A second strategy was to examine the rigidness of the behavior by comparing the early hand-in-stream games to the later ones.

FIGURE 14.2.   The diagram illustrates the options in the sequence of behaviors leading up to hand-in-stream games.

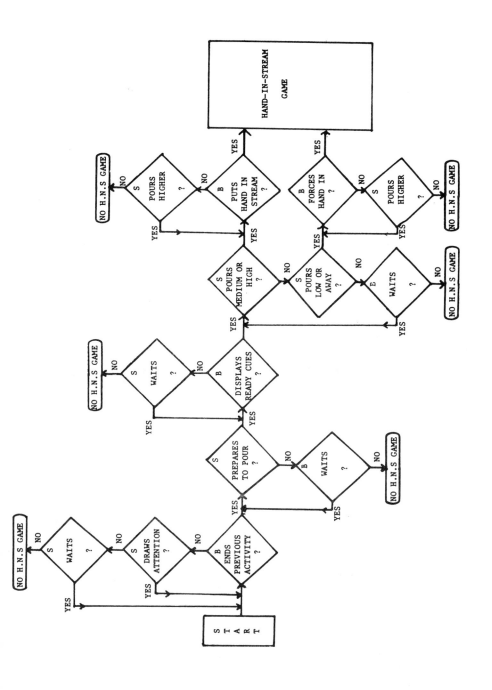

TABLE 14.4
Interaction Coordination: Comparing Hand-in-Stream Games with All other Sequences for Presence or Absence of Hypothesized Rules Relating Moves to Signals

Move: Antecedent signal	Present in hand-in-stream games (N = 19)	Present in all other pouring bouts (N = 19)	
Step 1: S BEGINS (scoops); N = 38			
1. Only after B "ENDS PREVIOUS ACTIVITY"	16	6	
2. While B is engaged in other activity, with NO "ENDS" cues	3	13	$\chi^2 = 8.74$ $p < .005$
Step 2: B REATTENDS, if away; N = 25			
1. Immediately after S, "PREPARING TO POUR" signal	10	5	
2. At other time, or fails to reattend	1	9	$\chi^2 = 6.88$ $p = .017$
Step 3: S LIFTS TO POUR; N = 38			
1. Only when B is attending	14	4	
2. When B is looking away	5	15	$\chi^2 = 8.55$ $p = .003$
Step 4: B displays "READY" signal N = 38			
1. Only after S "PREPARING TO POUR" signal	18	2	
2. At other time	1	17	$\chi^2 = 23.75$ $p < .00007$
Step 5: S start POURING			
1. Only after B gives "READY" cues	20	5	

TABLE 14.4 (continued)

Move: Antecedent signal	Present in hand-in-stream games (N = 19)	Present in all other pouring bouts (N = 19)	
2. When B displays no "READY" cues	0	14	$\chi^2 = 19.89$ $p = .00007$
Step 6: B PUTS HAND IN STREAM: (B attending when S Pours = 33)	S POURS HIGH or MEDIUM	S POURS LOW or NO SPACE	
1. Yes	15	5	
2. No	2	11	$\chi^2 = 8.96$ $p = .0028$

FINDINGS: INTERACTION COORDINATION

As indicated in Table 14.4, each step in the hypothesized system of interaction coordination significantly differentiated the hand-in-stream from non-hand-in-stream sequences. The hypothesized relationships between moves and antecedent readiness signals consistently occurred in the hand-in-stream games but did not characterize the other pouring sequences. Therefore, the null hypothesis was rejected and the hypothesis that coordination is achieved when each boy proceeds only when the other is ready to do so, gains support.

On Seth's part, this hypothesis was supported as follows.

1. In 84% of the coordinated games he begins the game *only after* Brad displays ENDS PREVIOUS ACTIVITY cues. In 68% of the other sequences, Seth begins the game *while* Brad is engaged in other play, or exactly when Brad turns away to play by himself.
2. Similarly, in 75% of the coordinated games, Seth lifts to pour *only when* Brad is watching. In 79% of the other sequences, he lifts to pour when Brad is looking away.
3. Most significantly, in 100% of the coordinated games, Seth begins pouring *only after* Brad has displayed one or more READY cues. In 74% of the remaining sequences, he begins to pour *before* Brad has displayed any READY cues.

The findings indicate a parallel awareness of responsiveness on Brad's part:

1. In 91% of the coordinated games that begin when he is away, Brad reattends immediately when Seth starts scooping or lifting. In 64% of

the unsuccessful sequences, he either fails to reattend at all, or turns toward the basin much later in the sequence.

2. Similarly, in 95% of the hand-in-stream games, Brad displays READY cues *only* in the appropriate time slot (i.e., after Seth prepares to pour, but before he actually pours). In 89% of the remaining bouts he displays this signal out of sequence.

3. Brad's responsiveness to how conducively Seth pours the stream is also indicated by the findings. Brad puts his hand in the stream 90% of the time when Seth pours HIGH or MEDIUM (and when Brad is watching), but only 31% of the time when Seth pours LOW, leaves no space for his hand, leans away from him, or makes him reach over his arm.

SUMMARY: THE HAND-IN-STREAM GAME

It was hypothesized that Brad and Seth coordinated their actions by being sensitive to each other's readiness cues and regulating their own actions accordingly. The findings support the hypothesis that Brad and Seth have developed a rudimentary rule system or set of expectations that functions in organizing their interaction. It is important to delineate the specific processes of this coordination both for understanding how it occurs and for examining what happens when coordination does not occur.

The shared expectations of this coordination system can be thought of as effecting different organizational levels of their interaction. Following the Duncan and Fiske terminology (1977), there are (a) sequence rules that define a particular back-and-forth sequence of moves as optimal for producing a hand-in-stream game; (b) signal rules that define the relationship between a readiness signal by one boy and the expected response by the other, as well as between this signal and the subsequent actions of the signaler, and; (c) signal definition rules defining the particular behaviors that make up a readiness signal, as well as the appropriate place in the behavior stream for these actions to take on this signal value.

Once an expected sequence of moves and signals is established, it is then possible to consider each boy's readiness to participate in this system. Duncan and Fiske (1977) have considered this in terms of *transition readiness,* or the readiness of each interactant at any point in the contact to continue to the next expected unit of the interaction. It is assumed that a person's transition readiness can fluctuate greatly across an interaction and is dependent in part on his purposes for interacting and his perceptions of the situation. Up to this point, transition readiness has been considered only in the limited sense of one child reading the readiness cues of the other. These cues were assumed to be straightforward reflections of the child's readiness, without requiring that he be actively sending these messages. Readiness was most important in terms of its regulating function in the hand-in-stream game. In the analysis of interaction strategy, however, each child's transition readiness becomes an important interactional feature in and of itself, and an important focus of their interaction.

In summary, structural, relational elements of the proposed rule-system have been described and some of its degrees of freedom have been specified. This was considered to be a necessary preliminary to exploring their "uncoordinated" sequences and actions. The strategy for further analysis was to consider the hand-in-stream game as a baseline of expectations from which to note variations or violations.

Interaction Strategy

Interaction organization has been considered in terms of coordination—mutual awareness and regulation of behavior for the purpose of coordinating a hand-in-stream game. The structural features produced by these coordinating efforts were described and contrasted with the lack of such organization in the other sequences. The non-hand-in-stream sequences were described as unsuccessful coordination attempts, but this label referred only to their lack of *that* particular form of hand-in-stream organization. Simply because they are lacking in this form of organization does not mean that they are generally disorganized. This is an interesting issue because it is reflected at a different level in much of the research on autistic social behavior. Specifically, because autistic contact is rarely organized for the purpose of cooperation or coordination, it is assumed that the social behavior of autistic children is either disorganized in general, or is organized solely for the purpose of social avoidance.

Duncan and Fiske (1977) emphasize that coordination is not the only organizing goal of interaction. They describe interaction strategy as another source of organization and contrast it with convention: "As opposed to conventions, which serve only to facilitate coordination of action, interaction strategies may serve any human purpose, such as competition, deceit, ingratiation, and, of course, coordination [1977, p. 248]."

The possibility of alternate forms of interaction organization is based on the observation that there are multiple sources of variability in how closely the rules are followed in even a fairly stable system of shared expectations. Duncan and Fiske (1977) state that a human rule system, even if it consists of obligatory rules, will never be perfectly proficient in predicting the actions of the people using it. There are many sources of variability: (a) variability due to unintentional mistakes, human fallibility, forgetting the rules, or being insensitive to the subleties of the system; (b) behavioral variability due to any options provided by an optional system (e.g. the person's decision *not* to respond in the expected but optional way); (c) variability related to the degrees of freedom or permissible limits provided by the rule system; and (d) variability due to blatant rule violation, going against the expectations or transgressing the limits provided by the degrees of freedom. The last three sources of variability have at least the potential of being very organized in and of themselves. Alternate rule systems may influence an interactant's decision to take or leave an option, to perform his signals with particular intensity, or to violate this or that rule.

VARIATIONS ON PLAYING THE GAME

Once a set of expectations is established between two interactants, their range of communication increases enormously. Signals are no longer limited to observable actions, but now include omissions and modifications of the expected actions. The message value of omitting or modifying an expected behavior is frequently discussed in communication studies. Subtle variations such as failing to shake hands when meeting someone, or hesitating a second too long when asked one's opinion all carry important communicative messages. In order to understand the meanings of these omissions or variations, however, we need to understand the basic set of expectations.

In this analysis of interaction strategy, the coordination system just described is considered to be a baseline of expectations between the boys. The back-and-forth sequence of moves typically leading to a hand-in-stream game is considered the baseline of expected moves. The signal rules and signal definition rules presented in Table 14.3 reflect the expected relationships among elements. From this starting point, further analysis consisted of (a) describing the ways in which Seth and Brad deviated from the expected patterns, signal intensities and display timing; (b) describing regularities in the ways in which they combined these variations into sequences; and (c) postulating a system of interaction strategy that could account for the observed structural regularities.

Observed Variations

Brad and Seth deviate from the expected patterns, signal intensities, and display-timing in many ways. Specifically, they (a) perform actions earlier or later than expected in relation to the readiness of the other; (b) perform actions with greater or less intensity than indicated in the rules; (c) violate or break sequence by performing a move blatantly out of sequence (i.e., doing something exactly when it should not be done); and (d) transgress the limits or range of permissible features for a signal. The first two deviations are permissible variations provided for by the degrees of freedom within the rule system; however, the last two represent blatant violations of the rule system.

In Table 14.5 variations in signals and moves performed by Brad and Seth during different stages of the hand-in-stream game are presented. Seth, for example, performs an action early or just before Brad displays his readiness cues. He scoops just before Brad displays ENDS PREVIOUS ACTIVITY cues, or pours after Brad has displayed only one weak, READY cue. He tends to "jump the gun" in these cases. Similarly, Seth performs an action late when he waits until all of the readiness cues are displayed by Brad. He does not begin to pour even though Brad has displayed a number of READY cues; or, he fails to reset a game immediately, even though Brad is ready for a new game.

Seth displays weak signals when he emits a minimal number of cues or introduces nonconducive elements into the display. For example, he pours low, leaves no space for Brad's hand, or leans away while pouring. Strong signals are the opposite of these and include some attention-drawing behaviors such as pouring over his own head. Seth breaks the sequence when he performs an action that is blatantly unexpected such as pouring exactly when Brad turns away to his own play.

Brad's rule violations and variations are more subtle than Seth's. Each boy seems to have a different modality for expressing variation. Seth controls the stream of water and his deviations and violations center around this. Brad's control involves attending to the game, putting his hand in the stream. Early actions consist of responding to minimal number of cues by Seth (e.g., positioning himself to play the moment that Seth touches a pot). At other times, Brad attends late (i.e., he remains away even though Seth has performed many readiness signals).

Patterns of Strategic Variation

These variations were observed to form structually regular sequences. Pattern analysis for this phase of the study was conducted in a forward-searching direction and consisted of describing sequence variations from the baseline pattern. In analyzing the hand-in-stream game, it was assumed that one goal of the boys' actions was to produce a hand-in-stream game, and because of this the analysis could trace backward from the outcome. For the present analysis, the viewpoint is that the goal of their actions is unclear. Thus, the strategy was to consider the expected sequence as a baseline and study deviations from this. The questions were "When do Seth and Brad deviate from the expected sequence?" and "What is the response of the second child to this deviation?"

VIOLATING SEQUENCE RULES

On Seth's part, a frequently repeated rule violation was of this form: (a) Brad turns away to play by himself; (b) Seth immediately lifts and pours; (c) Brad reattends; and (c) Seth immediately stops pouring or lowers the stream. In

TABLE 14.5
Interaction Strategy: Variations on Signals and Sequences Hypothesized Rules for Indicating "Willingness to Play"

	As game begins	During the game	As water runs out
		Ways to Indicate High Willingness to Play	
S:	Draw B's attention if necessary	Keep pouring conducively	Finish pouring gradually;
	Wait for B to be READY	Increase height of stream	Give many WITHDRAWAL signals
	Hurry up if B already READY	Lean closer to B	Scoop for reset immediately
	Pour high, with no bottle under stream, with outside hand	Follow B's hand with stream	
	Lean toward B while pouring	Keep pouring, even if B leaves; increase stream if B comes back.	
	Keep pouring, even if B turns away	Draw B's attention if necessary (e.g., Pour over own head)	
B:	Attend to S immediately	Keep hand in stream	Remain attentive for the RESET of next game
	Give early READY cues	Flex this hand	WITHDRAW hand gradually
	Give many READY cues	Hand flap with other hand	Give many withdrawal cues
	Wait until S is ready before reaching toward stream	Keep hand in stream, even if S lowers the height	Then, give END PREVIOUS cues
	Reach immediately when S gives READY cues	Remain attentive even if S stops pouring	
	Force hand into stream even if S has left		

S:		
Begin game when B not ready	Keep pouring unconducively	Stop pouring abruptly
Begin game exactly when B turns away	Decrease height of stream	Drop pots abruptly
Stall, if B is READY and waiting	Insert bottom bottle into stream	Stall on RESET
Pour LOW or leave no space for B's hand (e.g., lower pot into basin while pouring or pour into mouth of bottle)	Redirect stream over bottle	Shuffle pots aimlessly in the basin
	Nudge B's hand out of stream	Do not scoop
Pour into or over a bottle	Lean away from B	Scoop briefly but then drop pot
Lean away from B while pouring	Become self-absorbed if B leaves, even briefly	
Pour with inside arm so that B has to reach across	Lower stream if B returns	
If B is away and reattends, STOP lifting or pouring		

B:		
Remain AWAY, absorbed in own activities (e.g., splash on floor or table, or play in other basin)	Take hand out at slightest withdrawal by S	Leave basin area as soon as water runs out and become self-absorbed
Do not reattend, even if S does "attention" behaviors	Turn away at slightest distraction	
	Look around while hand in stream	

this sequence Seth begins pouring and stops pouring blatantly out of the expected sequence. This pattern, and slight elaborations of this, were repeated 20 times in the 5-min period.

Brad performs a similar breaking of sequence in this way: (a) Seth scoops and lifts; (b) Brad reattends; (c) Seth pours; and (d) Brad immediately turns away. Brad breaks the sequence by abruptly turning away when Seth is beginning to play. This pattern, and slight variations of it, were repeated 17 times in the film.

In both these patterns the back and forth action is proceeding as expected when suddenly one boy stops playing the game. It is interesting that in many cases the boy who quits the game is also the one who had initiated the activity. When Brad turns away, Seth starts pouring which draws Brad back to the game. However the moment that Brad returns, Seth drops the pot. Seth indicates that he is going to do one thing (play), but then does another (stops playing). In normal children this is a common teasing pattern. Through patterns such as these, Brad and Seth invite contact, but then cut it off.

Brad responds in one of three ways to an abrupt break in sequence. He either turns away, waits attentively, or makes moves to continue the expected sequence in spite of the disruption. Seth in turn responds in different ways to each of Brad's reactions. If Brad leaves, Seth either quits the game also, or performs attention-drawing behaviors. If Brad waits or increases his game activity, Seth tends to continue the sequence as expected.

VARYING SIGNAL INTENSITY

Another frequently repeated pattern is (a) Brad displays ready signals; (b) Seth pours, but into a bottom bottle instead of over Brad's hand; (c) Brad puts or forces his hand into the stream; and (d) Seth immediately increases the height of the stream and drops out the bottom bottle. In this sequence Seth performs the expected actions in sequence but displays ambiguous cues by pouring into a bottle instead of over Brad's hand. As described in the earlier pattern, Seth continues the game with increased commitment as soon as Brad forces his hand into the stream.

VARYING TIMING OF DISPLAY

Variations of signal display frequently occurred in terms of timing. Actions performed late result in patterns similar to those described. Performing an

FIGURE 14.3. The diagram illustrates the system of interaction coordination where the direct flow represents baseline, sequences, the top branch represents conducive variations, and the bottom branch represents nonconducive variations.

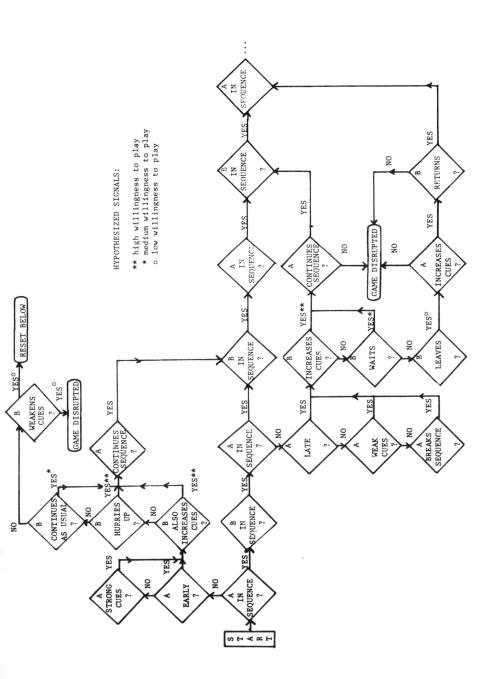

HYPOTHESIZED SIGNALS:

** high willingness to play
* medium willingness to play
o low willingness to play

287

action early—but within the sequence limits—produces a different effect. For example (a) Seth scoops and lifts; (b) Brad turns slightly toward Seth; (c) Seth immediately pours at a medium height; (d) Brad looks at Seth's hands, crouches forward, hand flaps and puts his hand in the stream; and (e) Seth increases the stream height to a higher level. In this sequence, Seth starts pouring as soon as Brad displays only one weak readiness cue. Seth acts in rapid sequence that Brad attempts to match by condensing his actions into one step (d). Seth then increases his pouring.

SUMMARY: PATTERNS OF VARIATION

In the above patterns, we have seen that one child varies the expected behaviors by breaking the sequence of events, displaying weak cues, or varying the timing of actions. In this way, he departs from the expected sequence of actions. Both boys tend to react to such departures in one of three ways. They either leave the sequence, remain attentive, or actively continue the game in spite of the disruption. If the child responds by waiting or continuing the game, the first child generally returns to the expected sequence. The second child has responded in a way that results in pulling them back into sequence. The range of possibilities in these variation patterns is presented in Figure 14.3.

In this figure, the direct flow of action represents the baseline sequence of actions leading up to a hand-in-stream game. Along this line each child performs his actions in sequence, at the appropriate time, and to the appropriate degree. Branches off of this baseline represent potential variations of the sequence. The branch above the baseline reflects conducive variations such as a child displaying early or strong cues. The branch below the baseline reflects nonconducive cues such as late, weak, or sequence-breaking cues. In this diagram, sequences are carried out to three or four steps, whereas in the interaction these are elaborated into longer patterns.

PROPOSED SYSTEM OF INTERACTION STRATEGY

Based on these observations, the possibility was considered that the way in which each boy responds to rule departures may serve as a further indication of his readiness to participate in this game. A departure from the rules of the game by one child may provide a similar option to the other. When Seth quits in the middle of the game, Brad is provided a legitimate option to also quit, as the typical expectation is that if Seth displays "no cues" Brad will then display "no cues." Whether or not Brad takes this option may indicate how willing he is to continue this game.

Rule violation may produce a kind of testing situation in which Brad indicates a high degree of willingness to continue if he tries to continue the game in spite of the violation, but a lower degree of willingness if he simply turns away. For example, if he remains attentive in spite of the fact that Seth has abruptly stopped pouring, or if he speeds up his own actions to match Seth's quick actions, he indicates high willingness to play. In summary, pattern analysis indicated that a second form of game emerged in their play. This game was organized around testing each other's readiness to participate in the hand-in-stream game and the contact in general. The moves and signals of this strategy were based on expectations developed in coordinating the hand-in-stream game, but also are organized in and of themselves.

Development of the Interaction

The two interrelated games of coordination and strategy emerged simultaneously in this waterplay. A problem with structural descriptions of organized behavior is that they present organization in static terms as if the structure "appeared" and then was either adhered to, elaborated, or violated. Comparison of early and later pouring sequences revealed that to the contrary, structural changes occurred across the interaction.

Elaboration of the Hand-In-Stream Games

Different segments of the hand-in-stream game were stabilized at different times across the 5-min period. Also, once a specific pattern was minimally established, it was elaborated. Coordination was achieved systematically so that first the beginning sections of the games were stabilized, then the endings became synchronized, and finally the middle sections gained smoothness. Elaboration of this game occurred within the already established sequences, rather than in terms of extending a particular sequence. From a macroanalytic point of view, the hand-in-stream game remained fairly stereotyped throughout the 5 min: Seth poured and Brad inserted his hand. They did not introduce novel aspects such as role reversals, novel use of containers or water. The elaboration occurring consisted of refining the steps of the game, and involved increasingly complicated preparation and readiness cues. Each step was elaborated into a number of substeps, each of which then required mutual coordination. A number of substeps were developed that seemed to have little function in the game other than that of mutual regulation. For example, the following 3-step sequence performed in the early games was elaborated into a 5-step pattern by the end of the film: (a) Seth takes and lifts the pot; (b) Brad reattends; (c) Seth begins to pour. The elaboration was (a) Seth takes the pot and scoops;

(b) Brad reattends, rubs his mouth, glances at a third child, ends his mouth rubbing, and looks back at Seth; (c) Seth lifts the pot; (d) Brad displays ready cues; and (e) Seth pours. In the elaborated pattern Brad performs a "quick-away" action of glancing at another child. This was not present in early games and did not serve any apparent function, but Seth consistently responded to this action as part of the ready signal instead of as Brad turning away.

Elaboration of the Testing Games

As the expectations were progressively elaborated in this game, so were the ways in which the expectations could be broken. Signal and sequence violation could now be performed with very small behavioral shifts. In the early sequences, variations were gross sequence violations. For example, Seth would begin to pour the moment that Brad turned away, and would stop pouring the moment he turned back. By the end of the film, very subtle rule variations were occurring (e.g., Seth simply moving a bottom container toward the stream, without even placing it in the stream). A theoretically interesting possibility is that the message value of the early, gross signals may be similar to that of the later, subtle moves, and that the mode of transmission has been refined (i.e., the potential of the system for carrying messages has been increased). This is what typically occurs as two interactants build up a shared set of expectations.

In terms of the development of the contact between them, however, this kind of elaboration indicates that the focus of the interaction shifted from concentrating on the object of the game—pouring and inserting a hand—to concentrating on the regulation of this game. The strategy game of testing each other's transition readiness became as prevalent, if not more prevalent, than the pouring game. Two games were being played simultaneously, a hand-in-stream game and a regulation game. Therefore, interaction was occurring on at least two structural levels. Bateson (1956) has described this interactive situation as *metacommunication,* or transmitting messages about messages, in this case playing a testing game to determine readiness to play the pouring game.

This is a theoretically important observation with regard to the boys' general inability to establish and maintain contact. The regulation of the game (requiring acute awareness by each child of the subtle cues of the other) became the focus of their interaction and resulted in very restricted elaboration of the objective game. Normal interaction minimally involves both kinds of organization, coordination for an objective goal and strategy that involves any number and kind of goal. A possibility suggested by this study is that interaction between these boys may involve an overconcern for regulation at the expense of developing contact of a more objective nature. The problem with interaction strategy and mutual testing is that they frequently result in the break-off of contact if both parties are not well aware of the dynamics of the strategy. Also, the forms of elaboration and contact that occur in this game seem to be different from those that develop around a more objective activity.

OVERVIEW AND IMPLICATIONS

In summary, the findings indicate some of the interaction competencies of these two autistic boys. Interaction prerequisites such as self-synchrony, awareness of other's actions, and self-regulation were observed. Coordination between the two boys in an objective activity was noted. Furthermore, sequences in which objective cooperation did not occur were found to be organized in other ways. These sequences constituted metacommunications about mutual involvement. The elaboration and subtlety of such signaling was striking.

The emphasis on contact regulation, as opposed to developing objective cooperation, is significant—given that these boys were unable to establish and maintain normal contact. It was suggested that coordinated contact is difficult to maintain when each interactant's readiness to participate is constantly being tested by the other. It was also suggested that the degree of emphasis on interaction regulation as compared to objective coordination, may distinguish autistic interaction from that of normal children.

This study suggests a hypothesis for further research, namely what has been seen as disorganization and withdrawal may be partly accounted for by structures of interaction concerning the coordination of committment rather than the coordination of objective actions. Although inferences were not made as to why this particular organization characterizes interaction between these boys, the study indicates the importance of studying *how* deviations are organized to facilitate examination of why these deviations occur.

ACKNOWLEDGMENTS

This research was supported by an NIMH training Grant #1F31MH05970-01.

I would like to express thanks to Starkey Duncan for help in conceptualizing and carrying out this study, John Kirkpatrick for extensive conceptual and editorial comments, and also to the director, staff, and children of STEP School for facilitating extensive filming and study of these children.

REFERENCES

Bateson G. The message: This is play. In B. Schaffner (Ed.), *Group proccesses*. New York: Josiah Macy, Jr. Foundation, 1956.

Bettleheim B. *The empty fortress: Infantile autism and the birth of self*. New York: Free Press, 1967.

Condon W. Multiple response to sound in dysfunctional children. *Journal of Autism and Childhood Schzophrenia*, 1975, *5*, 1.

DesLauriers, A. M. & Carlson, C. F. *Your child is asleep*. Homewood, Illinois: Dorsey Press, 1969.

Duncan, S. & Fiske, D. *Face-to-face interaction: Research, methods, and theory*. Hillsdale, New Jersey: Erlbaum, 1977.

Duncan, S. Working the other side of the sequence: Studying interaction strategy. In S. Weitz (Ed.), *Nonverbal communication* (2nd ed). New York: Oxford Univ. Press, 1979.

Ekstein, R. The space child's time machine. *American Journal of Orthophychiatry*, 1954, *24*, 492–506.

Hermelin, B., & O'Connor, N. *Psychological experiments with autistic children*. Oxford: Pergamon Press, 1970.

Howlin, P. The assessment of social behavior. In M. Rutter & E. Schopler (Eds.), *Autism: A reappraisal of concepts and treatment*. New York: Plenum, 1978.

Hutt, C., Hutt, S. J., Lee, D., & Ounsted, C., Arousal and childhood autism. *Nature*, 1964, *204*, 908–909.

Hutt, C., & Ounsted, C. The biological significance of gaze aversion with particular reference to the syndrome of infantile autism. *Behavioral Science*, 1966, *11*, 346–356.

Kanner, L. Autistic disturbances of affective contact. *Nervous Child*, 1943, *2*, 217–250.

Kanner, L. Irrelevant and metaphorical language in early childhood autism. *American Journal of Psychiatry*, 1946, *103*, 242–246.

Mahler, M. *On human symbiosis and the vicissitudes of individuation: infantile psychosis*. New York: International Univ. Press, 1968.

Ornitz, E. M. Neurophysiologic studies. In M. Rutter & E. Schopler (Eds.), *Autism: A reappraisal of concepts and treatment*. New York: Plenum, 1978.

Ornitz, E. M., & Ritvo, E. R. Perceptual inconstancy in early infantile autism. *Archives of General Psychiatry*, 1968, *18*, 76–98.

Richer, J. The social avoidance behavior of autistic children. *Animal Behaviour*, 1976, *24*, 898–906.

Richer, J., & Richards, M. Reacting to autistic children: The danger of trying too hard. *British Journal of Psychiatry*, 1975, *27*, 526–529.

Rimland, B. *Infantile autism*. New York: Appleton-Century-Crofts, 1964.

Rutter, M. Language disorder and infantile autism. In M. Rutter & E. Schopler (Eds.), *Autism: A reappraisal of concepts and treatment*. New York: Plenum, 1978.

Rutter, M., & Schopler, E. (Eds.) *Autism: A reappraisal of concepts and treatment*. New York: Plenum, 1978.

Wing, L. (Ed.) *Early childhood autism* (2nd ed.), Oxford: Pergamon, 1976.

Wing, L. Perceptual and language development in autistic children: A comparative study. In M. Rutter (Ed.), *Infantile autism: Concepts, characteristics, and treatment*. London: Churchill-Livingstone, 1971.

Wing, L. Social, behavioral, and cognitive characteristics: An epidemiological approach. In M. Rutter & E. Schopler (Eds.), *Autism: A reappraisal of concepts and treatment*. New York, Plenum, 1978.

CHAPTER 15

CAROL GEORGE
MARY MAIN

Abused Children: Their Rejection of Peers and Caregivers

INTRODUCTION

During the past decade child abuse research has sparked interest in the psychological development of the battered child. An almost exclusive interest in the abusing parent is gradually shifting toward examining family interaction patterns, particularly in intervention and treatment programs. The purpose of this chapter is to describe one aspect of the psychological development of the abusing family—styles of social interaction of the battered child. Attention will first focus on the question of why knowledge of the social behavior of abused children is important. A summary of the research that has been concerned with this aspect of development will then follow, highlighting studies that examined social interaction patterns quite closely. Finally, the importance of applying this knowledge to the development of child treatment programs will be discussed.

THE NEED FOR UNDERSTANDING SOCIAL INTERACTION PATTERNS

One widely recognized component of the abusive relationship is the parents' perception of the abused child as particularly "difficult" (Galdston, 1965; Kempe & Kempe, 1978; Lynch, 1976; Morse, Sahler, & Friedman, 1970; Parke

293

& Collmer, 1975; Smith & Hansen, 1975). Not every child in a family is abused, but rather one child is usually singled out (Lynch, 1976; Sameroff & Chandler, 1975) and one child may consistently be the target of abuse in several different environments (Milow & Lowrie, 1964). Parents, as well as researchers, suggest that a particular child may possess negative characteristics contributing to its own abuse (Friedrich & Boriskin, 1976; Martin, 1976).

What are the characteristics that predispose some children to trauma? One type of evidence has been sought from the perinatal histories of battered infants. Physical limitations such as low birthweight (Fontana, 1964; Green, Gaines, & Sandgrund, 1974; Klein & Stern, 1971) and prematurity (Lynch, 1976) have been associated with infant trauma. Comparing abused infants with their nonabused siblings, Lynch (1976) emphasized a variety of medical problems that seemed to catalyze abuse. These included the mother's illness during pregnancy, a difficult labor and delivery, congenital birth defects or injuries (particularly brain damage), prematurity, and illness during infancy. The physical limitations of one infant may violate the unreasonable or inappropriate expectations of its parents and eventually lead to abuse (Parke & Collmer, 1975).

Certainly a parent's perception of a child may be influenced by such physical limitations, but abuse is not always founded upon such concrete problems. Kempe and Kempe (1978) pointed out that, given the experiences of a particular mother, the infant's sex or physical appearance (e.g., similarity to a disliked relative) could be an immediate elicitor of hostility and could eventually result in abuse. In addition, as a *result* of previous abuse, a child may develop behavior patterns that elicit more abuse. Harrington (1972) noted that abused infants have disturbances in sleep and feeding, cry excessively, and respond poorly to the caretaker's attempts to comfort them when they are distressed.

Although the perceived "difficulty" of some battered infants may be due to the abuse they have experienced, it may also simply reflect a more general breakdown in the development of the parent–child relationship and day-to-day interaction patterns (Burgess & Conger, 1978). Parke and Collmer (1975) have suggested several factors of interaction that, working separately or together, may promote a breakdown in the relationship. The failure or inability to sucessfully inhibit infant crying is one suggested factor. This failure may lead to maternal withdrawal from the infant and a further increase in crying (see, Bell & Ainsworth, 1972). The mother's attempts to inhibit crying may subsequently escalate to the level of abuse. In addition, the signals of abused infants may be generally unclear and/or the mother may be unskilled or unwilling to interpret them. Such infant unresponsiveness may also violate the expectations the mother has for normal development. The physical and preliminary behavioral evidence points to the conclusion that abused infants are indeed *difficult,* probably for a variety of individual reasons. But understanding the behavioral components of such "difficulty" necessitates direct observation of the abused infant's social interaction patterns.

Specific knowledge of early social interaction patterns is also critical to the therapeutic process. It has been well documented that abuse occurs in generational cycles (Curtis, 1963; Green, 1976; Kempe, Silverman, Steele, Droegenmueller, & Silver, 1962; Spinetta & Rigler, 1972; Steele & Pollock, 1968). Not every battered child becomes an abusing parent, but most abusing parents have themselves been abused. This intergenerational continuity of the battered child syndrome in itself suggests that intervention focused upon the young child is extremely desirable. Indeed, it seems surprising that, within the scope of child abuse intervention, the child had traditionally received so little attention. In our opinion, the success of childhood intervention will hinge upon a thorough understanding of the behavior of the child—an understanding that is initially rooted in rigorous observation and description of the child in his environment.

SOCIAL BEHAVIOR OF ABUSED CHILDREN: SUMMARY OF THE LITERATURE

The social interaction patterns of battered children are described in only a small fraction of the child abuse literature. Descriptions are predominantly residual observations from studies whose primary focuses were neither the behavior nor the psychological development of the child. Nevertheless, a general picture of the interactional style of battered children can be synthesized.

Some battered children have been described as passive and apathetic. Specifically, they have been described as inhibited, compliant, hypervigilant, and rarely crying or expressing distress or pain (Blumberg, 1977; Gray & Kempe, 1976; Johnson & Morse, 1968; Kempe & Kempe, 1978; Mirandy, 1976). Emotional expression is generally poor or lacking (Galdston, 1975; Gray & Kempe, 1976).

Others have described battered children as particularly aggressive and resistant in nature (Curtis, 1963; Galdston, 1975; Kempe & Kempe, 1978; Martin, 1976; Rodeheffer & Martin, 1976; Ten Broeck, 1974). In some instances, severe temper tantrums and anger have been observed (Green, 1978; Johnson & Morse, 1968; Kempe & Kempe, 1978), including episodes of self-destructive behavior (Blumberg, 1977; Green, 1978; In & McDermott, 1976). Violence seems to be a consistent pattern with many of these otherwise unemotional children—a pattern that diminishes but does not altogether disappear with treatment (Galdston, 1975).

Only one study however has attempted to directly compare the aggressive behavior of young abused children with that of matched controls (mean age was 6.4 years). Because abused children experienced extreme punishment by aggressive parental models, Reidy (1977) predicted that they would demonstrate more overt and covert aggression than nonabused children. Overt aggression was determined through observer and teacher behavior ratings, covert aggression was measured through responses given to the Thematic Apperception Test (TAT). The abused children were more aggressive in all respects—fantasy, free play, and the school environment. Thematic Apperception Test responses contained more themes of aggression and violence. More overt aggression was reported during free play and by teachers in the form of behavior problems. Reidy's predictions were clearly substantiated.

Given this descriptive summary, it is evident that battered children do not demonstrate a unitary style of social behavior (Martin, 1976). The existence of multiple typologies is clearly shown by Martin and Beezley (1976a, 1977). In a follow-up of 50 battered children between 22-months old and 13-years old, many of the "psychological wounds" of trauma were identified. Specifically, these investigators formally described personality characteristics observed in the course of their personal and clinical experience. Their work is most helpful as they give an indication of the frequency in their sample of the number of children showing particular types of behavior.

It is not surprising that their behavioral list is similar in many respects to the less systematic descriptions already available in the literature. Most striking in their sample was the childrens' inability to enjoy activities (66% of their sample): They instead accepted activities passively and without enthusiasm. Passivity was also reflected by a general lack of self-esteem, self-confidence, and feelings of worthiness. Behavioral passivity was frequently interspersed with episodes indicative of the childrens' extreme turmoil—temper tantrums, avoidance of peer interaction, withdrawal, and general socially inappropriate behavior. Aggressive behavior (24% of their sample) was also not unusual, typically reflected in one of two behavioral styles. Some children were consistently and openly aggressive. Others were usually passive but were highly aggressive and resistant in specific contexts. Other interesting behavioral characteristics also noted were hypervigilance (22% of their sample) and precocious, pseudoadult behavior (20% of their sample).

Utilizing a different approach in identifying the psychological correlates of trauma and neglect, Gaensbauer and his colleagues also identified a set of social and interactional behavior characteristics of abused and neglected children (Gaensbauer, Mrazek, & Harmon, in press; Gaensbauer & Sands, in press). Preliminary data analyses focused upon specific behavioral traits in the child that may, in fact, have elicited abuse or neglect from particularly "vulnerable" adults.

This approach to abuse and neglect was an extension of studies of affective behavior in normal infants. Abused and neglected infants between the ages of

12 and 26 months were observed in a standardized laboratory play session that was developed specifically for the study of social and emotional development. The 40-min session was composed of the following sequenced episodes: (a) mother–infant play; (b) stranger entrance and approach culminating in picking up the baby; (c) a similar approach by the mother and pickup; (d) administration of the Bayley developmental assessment; (e) mother separation and reunion; (f) mother–infant play; and finally (g) return of the stranger. The affective responses of abused babies observed in this context were characteristically different in both quality and range from normal infants (Gaensbauer et al., in press). In general, these infants appeared as sad, fearful, distressed, and often angry. Their play behavior was disorganized, aimless, and distinctly inhibited.

Clinical description provided the foundation for a subsequent study aimed at accurately depicting the range of "distorted affective communication" reflected in social interaction (Gaensbauer & Sands, in press). The single most likely interaction pattern observed was infant social and affective withdrawal. The abused and neglected infants failed not only to initiate contact, but also failed to respond to pleasurable interactions, isolating themselves to prevent social interchange. In addition, their affective communications were distorted, inconsistent, and unpredictable. Those emotions that did surface were notably shallow and resulted in ambivalent and ambiguous social signals. Interestingly, ambivalence was often demonstrated by the infant's conflicting communication. For example, the need for physical contact was expressed simultaneously with physical resistance, avoidance, and/or anger. However, proximity seeking and bids for attention occurred less frequently in these children than in normal samples.

Many of the abused children described in the literature appear to lack strong emotional bonds with specific individuals, most notably the parent. Mirandy (1976) noted that emotions were expressed indiscriminantly, and that there was no manifestation of anxiety upon separation from the mother. Other children have demonstrated acute anxiety when separated from therapists in contrast to parents (Green, 1978). In the laboratory session conducted by Gaensbauer and his colleagues, the majority of abused and neglected infants (60%) were as responsive to a strange adult as they were to the mother—an unusual behavior in normal infants. In fact 20% of the sample responded to the stranger in a *more* positive fashion than to the mother. Upon reunion after a brief separation, the mother was often avoided. Moreover, a handful of infants (6) showed more attachment behaviors to the stranger than to the mother (Gaensbauer et al., in press).

In summary, Gaensbauer and his colleagues elegantly demonstrated the specific disturbances in affective communication and social interaction that evolve from the mutually unsatisfying relationship of infant and parent. "Once established, such characteristics take on a life of their own and actively work in the environment [Gaensbauer & Sands, in press, p. 15]."

THE BEHAVIOR OF REJECTED INFANTS IN "NORMAL" SAMPLES

The laboratory play session used by Gaensbauer and his colleagues is highly similar to the Ainsworth Strange Situation—a laboratory separation observation we have employed in our own studies of medically normal, white, middle-class samples. This structured laboratory situation (developed by Ainsworth & Wittig, 1969) highlights the dynamics of the attachment behavioral system in 1-year-old infants. Bowlby (1969), in his theory of attachment, described a system of behaviors that serve to maintain proximity of the infant to the mother (e.g., crying, clinging, approach, seeking, calling, smiling). These behaviors serve to bring an infant and caregiver into proximity or contact on occasions of stress or uncertainty. In instances, however, when the need for security and/or maternal proximity is not activated by external "threat" to the infant, Bowlby postulated that infants would explore, venturing out to investigate and manipulate the external environment. The Ainsworth Strange Situation is designed to initially elicit exploration but then, through a series of mildly stressing events, to shift the baby's attention to seeking and maintaining proximity and/or physical contact with the mother.

Briefly, mother and infant are introduced to an unfamiliar but comfortable room filled with toys. A stranger enters the room and attempts to play with the baby; the mother leaves the infant in the company of the stranger (separation); the mother returns (reunion); the mother then leaves the infant alone (separation); the stranger returns; and finally the mother returns (final reunion). The experience of separation in a strange environment gradually heightens the need for maternal proximity and/or contact. The vast majority of infants observed in the Ainsworth Strange Situation in United States samples at first explore the strange environment in the security of the mother's presence. During and following separation, they seek proximity and contact, demand to be held, and express distress and even anger (Ainsworth, Bell, & Stayton, 1971; Ainsworth, Blehar, Waters, & Wall, 1979; Main, 1977; Matas, Arend, & Sroufe, 1978).

Of special interest to us here, however, are a small number of 1-year-old babies (about 20% in most white, middle-class samples) who appeared on the surface, unaffected by the stresses imposed during the Ainsworth Strange Situation (Ainsworth et al, 1979; Main, 1977; Main, 1979). The most striking characteristic of these infants is their superficial independence from the mother. Upon reunion after separation, they greet the mother by briefly averting their gaze, by turning or moving away, or by persistently ignoring and avoiding the mother's attempts to reestablish visual, vocal, or physical contact

(Ainsworth et al., 1979; Main, 1977; Main 1979). Many are friendlier to the stranger than to their mother.

This set of behaviors fits with the pattern of separation-related behaviors identified in the abused children described earlier (see, Gaensbauer et al., 1978; Mirandy, 1976). Babies behaving in this manner are classified as *insecure and avoidant,* using the classification system developed by Ainsworth (Ainsorth & Wittig, 1969). However, infants can also be assigned scores for the degree to which the mother is avoided during each of the two reunion episodes, independent of the formal classification system.

Avoidance of the mother upon reunion in the Ainsworth Strange Situation has been found to be associated with a set of behaviors that seem to comprise an entire avoidance syndrome (Main, 1977; Main, 1978).

1. Avoidance of the mother is strongly related to angry and uncooperative behavior. At 21 months, infants who had avoided their mothers in the Ainsworth Strange Situation at 12 months, attacked (generally unprovoked) or threatened to attack the mother in a play session (Main & Londerville, 1979). In addition, they engaged in episodes of nonexploratory hitting and banging. Similar bouts of inexplicable angry behavior have been seen in the home as well—bouts that in some instances culminated in attacks upon the mother ("baby creeps across the floor, veers toward the mother and strikes her legs, and crawls away"; Main, 1978). Avoidant infants also showed active disobedience to maternal commands and were described by their mothers as "troublesome."

2. Avoidant infants typically show less positive affect and enthusiasm (Main, 1979; Matas et al., 1978).

3. Main (1973) demonstrated that avoidance of the mother in the Ainsworth Strange Situation at 12 months predicted similar avoidant interactional patterns with an adult playmate 9 months later. Infants who had avoided the mother at 12 months tended to turn away or look away from an adult playmate attempting to initiate interaction. Moreover, they failed to approach the playmate when approach was expected. Infant avoidance of the attachment figure in the Ainsworth Strange Situation (either parent) was also strongly related to both avoidance of that same figure *and* poor social–emotional adjustment in daycare settings (Blanchard & Main, 1979).

4. Avoidant infants sometimes manifest behaviors that may index disturbance, although this correlate is not as strong as those just described. Specifically, stereotypies (e.g., rocking), hand flapping, echolalia, self-destructive behavior, inexplicable fears, inappropriate affect, and strange, tentative forms of establishing physical contact with the mother (e.g., patting the mother's feet or legs) are exhibited by some mother-avoiding 1-year olds (Main, 1977; Main & Waters, 1975).

This set of correlates of behavior in the Ainsworth Strange Situation certainly describes a "difficult" infant, and behavior in the Ainsworth Strange Situation itself directly resembles that of many abused infants. Surely 20% of the infants in normal samples have not undergone abuse—but what exactly are the characteristics of the mother who is avoided? Main (1977; in press; 1979) has discovered three strong maternal correlates of infant as evidenced under the test condition

1. The mothers of avoiding infants disliked and rejected physical contact. Main observed that often these mothers actively withheld physical contact, or even angrily pulled away in an effort to resist the infant's contact bid. On some occasions (for example, feeding the young infant) physical contact cannot be avoided, but behavior demonstrating maternal aversion to contact was still evident. One mother adopted extremely uncomfortable positions while holding the baby. Another mother held her infant's arms, harshly restricting his freedom of movement. In another instance, a mother was observed pinching the baby's cheek or physically shoving the baby downward. The mother's apparent aversion to physical contact in the first 3 months of life was found highly related to the infant's avoidance of the mother 9 months later.

2. The mothers of mother-avoiding infants also manifested a pattern of angry and threatening behavior. In free play sessions, some mothers mocked their infants; others spoke sarcastically or with undue irritation; and some stared the infant down.

3. Finally, these mothers demonstrated marked restriction in their expression of emotions. This was evident in their failure to express pleasure and even more strikingly in the absence of emotional change while being physically attacked by their infants. Main has summarized this syndrome as being one of rejection.

In summary, mother-avoiding babies somewhat resemble abused infants in their social and emotional behavior, and, although there is no reason to presume them abused by the mother, the syndrome *is* associated with rejection.

In an attempt to discover the correlates of more intense rejection, a pilot analysis was undertaken of the social interaction of an infant who was identified by her pediatrician as severely punished but *not* abused (George, 1975). The infant participated in the Ainsworth Strange Situation at 12 months and was found to be highly avoidant of her mother. She returned 9 months later for a videotaped play session with an adult playmate.

Three minutes of the play session were microanalyzed—specifically, a sequence in which the infant responded to the efforts of the adult playmate to engage her in a game of ball in the presence of her mother. The most striking characteristic of the behavior of this infant was avoidance. She avoided any direct social interaction with both the mother *and* the playmate by turning away from, moving away from, looking away from, and actively ignoring them.

Other behaviors indicative of her general avoidant style were indirect approaches. In one instance, for example, she used sidesteps rather than approaching the playmate face forward. On another occasion she gradually encircled the playmate and approached finally from behind with her face turned away as she reached the point of closest proximity. This toddler's avoidance and ambivalence was further indicated by her hesitancy toward social interaction. Interactional responses were never immediate and her movements were ambivalent: Approaches, for example, were immediately followed by backstepping slightly away.

Finally, there was little variety or enthusiasm in the play of this toddler. She said little and was overall devoid of facial expression. Interestingly, however, in the midst of such striking apathy, she also exhibited abrupt instances of angry behavior. Anger was expressed both in her facial expressions and by physical aggression. Without warning, for example, she suddenly attempted to hit her mother with the broom.

Avoidance: An Indicator of Conflict

Given a history of rejection and physical punishment, avoidance can most easily be "explained" as a direct index of fear. Fearful that an unpleasant interaction may result, the infant may have simply learned through past experience to prevent social interchanges entirely. In light of attachment theory, however, this view provides too simple an explanation. It assumes that the attachment behavioral system is minimally, if at all, activated when a rejected infant is reunited with the attachment figure in a strange environment. An alternative explanation is that avoidance is a manifestation of a *conflict* involving approach, withdrawal, and anger (George & Main, 1979; Main, 1977; Main, in press).

In instances of fear or stress of any kind (including threats from the mother) the attachment behavioral system is strongly activated and modulated only upon contact with the attachment figure (Bowlby, 1969). When the infant is threatened by a mother who simultaneously forbids approach he is placed in a situation of theoretically irresolvable conflict (Main, 1977; Main, in press). Two conflicting behavior patterns are aroused—to withdraw from the source of threat and to seek security and comfort from the mother. Because neither system can be terminated independent of the other, the infant's conflict is virtually irreconcilable.

If this situation of high activation remains unresolved, both angry behavior and conflict behavior should be expected in the infant. Indeed, both forms of behavior are associated with avoidance of the mother. Angry behavior does not appear in these infants in separation and reunion where it may be expected; rather it appears in stress free situations and, characteristically, it appears out of context.

One might predict that the experience of rejection and the resultant conflict would place the infant in a state of high anxiety and arousal, or even lead to behavioral disorganization. Yet, the behavior of the avoidant infant is not disorganized; it is rather definitively organized and simple in its appearance. Following Chance (1962), Main (1977, 1979, in press) suggests that behavioral organization is maintained by the rejected infant through shifting attention away from the attachment figure, particularly at moments when attachment, fear, and/or anger are most strongly activated. This may be accomplished through movements of avoidance—casting the eyes away, turning away, ignoring, or even "lack of recognition." Any of these acts of cutting off the source of arousal (the mother) may also be accomplished by superficially attending to the inanimate environment, behaviors seen in the avoidant infants in the Ainsworth Strange Situation (Ainsworth et al., 1971; Sroufe & Waters, 1977).

In summary, Main points out that avoidant behavior is observed in maternally rejected infants in stress situations where approach is normally expected. Through the attentional shift which "cutoff" permits, the conflict of approach, distress, and anger is attenuated. This allows the infant to regain and/or maintain behavioral control and proximity to the attachment figure.

BEHAVIOR OF ABUSED CHILDREN IN CAREGIVER AND PEER INTERACTION

Based on our knowledge of the social interactional styles of maternally rejected infants, we predicted that abused infants would demonstrate analogous forms of avoidance and aggression. Our study (George & Main, 1979) was initiated to both describe the behavior of abused children more generally and to substantiate our predictions. Abused children were observed in daycare settings, enabling us to observe their behavior with peers and with caregivers other than the mother. Note again that infants who had avoided their parents on reunion in the laboratory or in the Ainsworth Strange Situation had shown poor "social–emotional adjustment" in daycare settings (Blanchard & Main, 1979). Two therapeutic daycare centers in the San Francisco Bay Area were contacted seeking participants. As we were specifically interested in observing infants and toddlers, and because the majority of children in these centers were of school age, only 10 young, abused children (and 10 controls) participated in this study. The abused group was composed of 4 girls and 6 boys, ranging in age from 1- to 3-years old. The children had been physically battered (physical trauma ranging from severe nonaccidental bruises to burns and skull fractures). Neglect cases were excluded.

The 10 matched controls were sought in two other daycare centers. These centers were similar in both structure and philosophy to the abuse centers— serving families under stress in the community. Abused and nonabused young- sters were individually matched according to age, sex, and race—and, so far as possible, according to parental marital status, parental education and occupa- tion, and the adult predominantly caring for the child during the course of the study.

The social behavior of both groups of children was recorded by narrative records. After all observations were completed (a total of 2 hr per each child), the descriptive data were subsequently coded into mutually exclusive categories focusing on social interaction—approach, avoidance, approach–avoidance, and aggressive behaviors. Each category was conceptualized from both obser- vation of rejected children in normal samples and pilot work already com- pleted on the severely punished toddler. Behavior serving to decrease the distance between two individuals was coded as *approach* (but instances of aggressive behavior were excluded). Approach behavior was most frequently manifested by walking, running, or crawling toward a caregiver or peer (loco- motor approach). In some instances however a child simply turned his head toward another individual in a deliberate orienting response, initiating or re- sponding to a bid for interaction (head-turning approach).

The orientation or direction of an approach movement, particularly orien- tations which in a specific context seemed odd or unusual, provided us with other important information. A child's approach *orientation* was reflected by the following coding categories. *Direct* approaches were made if the infant moved toward a caregiver or peer in the most direct route possible—usually while facing the other person or in their full view. In contrast, *indirect* ap- proaches were oriented to the side (which occurred frequently) or from behind. Approaches to the rear or backward (e.g., backstepping) were particularly in- teresting in contexts where a more direct approach would have been possible.

Two other forms of affiliative behavior were also of interest. *Avoidance* was coded for any behavior serving to increase the distance between two individuals (e.g., walking away, backstepping, leaning away). *Approach- avoidance* was coded for conflict behaviors simultaneously manifesting both approach and avoidance: The category was mutually exclusive with *approach* and *avoidance*. One form of approach–avoidance behavior was focused on because it may be particularly indicative of internal conflict. This form in- cluded behaviors where locomotor approach appeared in conjunction with gaze aversion (e.g., walking toward a person with the head turned away from that person). It was particularly important to distinguish between behaviors initiated by the child and those behaviors occurring in response to initiations by caregivers and peers. Therefore, the incidence of behavior was summed separately for *spontaneous* acts and *responses to friendly approaches* by others. Caregivers or peers made essentially the same number of approaches per hour to the abused and to the control children.

The results of our data analyses were descriptively enlightening (see George & Main, 1979, for statistical details). Abused and control infants were similar in the number of peer approaches experienced, but abused children approached caregivers only half as often as controls. Most striking, however, was their differential response to spontaneous, caregiver- and peer-initiated friendly interaction. It certainly seemed reasonable to predict that under affiliative conditions cued as friendly, the abused child would feel safe and respond to the initiator by directly maintaining the relationship. Surprisingly, the reverse phenomenon was actually obtained. Abused and nonabused children were equally likely to walk or run toward a caregiver on their own initiative, but in response to a friendly advance, the battered toddlers failed to maintain the affiliation. Interestingly, it appeared that if approaches *were* made under these conditions, abused children would choose indirect routes. Approaches to the side or rear were observed in the majority of the abused children in contrast to the controls. For example, one, obviously distressed, abused infant came up behind an older child, then reached up to touch her. In addition, six of the abused children but only two of the control children used "backstepping" as a mode of approach. "Backstepping" is a particularly unusual approach. It cuts off mutual gaze by the child turning completely around; but approach continues as the child takes small backward steps in the direction of the target. An abused child was observed taking small backsteps as he approached a caregiver for a paint brush. In similar conditions controls were likely to approach more directly.

As predicted, abused toddlers generally avoided affiliative encounters with caregivers and peers. Avoidance comprised 25% of their responses compared with only 6% in the controls. The most prominent form of avoidance was physically moving away. Many of the abused children wriggled or pushed away from physical contact situations. In other instances, the children were observed to dramatically change course and walk away while being approached by another. Other forms of avoidance were reflected by simply turning the head away to cut off a potential interactor. Although the actual incidence of this form of behavior was small, it was our impression that the battered children were more hesitant in looking toward others. Gaze aversion was observed particularly in instances where physical contact was established or when a playmate or caregiver was looking directly at the child.

Potentially affiliative interactions resulted in conflict. *All* of the abused children but *none* of the controls were observed to respond to peer affiliations with approach-avoidance behavior. Only one nonabused infant engaged in a similar behavior in response to a caregiver (in comparison with seven of the abused). In addition, six of the abused children exhibited the approach-avoidance behavior most indicative of conflict—head moves in opposition to the body. In one instance, for example, a young battered child walked directly toward a peer as if interested in joining the play activity, but his head was turned away to the side, cutting off his sight of the social target. Often this form of approach-avoidance was observed as a child reached out to a caregiver but turned away or even closed its eyes to avoid eye contact. In similar situations, most nonabused children established eye contact to maintain the social interaction. Friendly initiations from both caregivers and peers were often responded to by abused children with indirect and tentative styles of social interaction, including avoidance and approach-avoidance.

The behavior of rejected infants in normal samples also led us to predict that abused children may be more aggressive, particularly exhibiting behavior indicative of conflict, frustration, and/or anger. A simple tabulation of the incidence of aggressive behaviors in both groups of children provided interesting insights, although the data were only partially substantiating of our predictions.

The most surprising differences arose when abused and nonabused children were compared with respect to aggressive behavior directed specifically toward the adult caregivers. Caregivers were the target of approximately a third of the aggressive acts observed in the battered children. Half the abused sample physically assaulted, or threatened to assault, caregivers, whereas no children in the control group exhibited similar acts. Acts of aggression against the caregivers occurred on an average of 6 times during the 2 hr of observation of the abused children. The control group engaged in aggressive acts against caregivers only once in the 2 hr of observation. Equally surprising, seven of the abused children chose to harass caregivers. "Harassment" is a form of aggressive behavior in which the specific intent appears to be to cause another person's discomfort or distress (Manning, Heron, & Marshall, 1977). Harassment of caregivers by battered children was likely to occur 4 times during the 2 hr of observation. In one instance, for example, an abused toddler suddenly and without apparent cause forcefully struck a caregiver with a toy. Another abused child inexplicably threw a rock at a caregiver and proceeded to hit him in the leg. In contrast, instances of harassment were not likely to be observed at all in the majority of control children.

The incidence of physical assault, threat, and harassment was a dramatic finding. We had predicted, however, that the battered toddlers would demonstrate an *overall* heightened aggressive syndrome. However, the aggression of the abused children exceeded that of the controls only when caregivers were considered as targets; the incidence of peer-directed aggression was comparable in both groups.

Despite this lack of group differences, it was our impression that the actual overall rates of aggressive behavior in *both* the abused and control toddlers was in fact quite high. Overall, the abused toddlers were likely to aggress in some fashion against someone an average of 18 times during 2 hr of observation; similarly, 10 aggressive acts were likely to occur in the matched (stressed) controls.

A Case Study

One participant in our study provides a particularly interesting example of the social interaction style previously described. Shelley, a toddler approaching 3-years old, had been raised in a consistently abusive atmosphere. Harsh physical punishment was the only mechanism her young single mother used to cope with the stresses of rearing her children. Although no specific traumatic incident was on record, Shelley was referred for therapeutic daycare. Shelly entered daycare a year prior to our observations. She was described at that time as withdrawn and particularly afraid of death. Her speech was inaudible and she spent a considerable portion of her day alone on the rocking horse.

Our first impression of Shelley was that of an energetic, self-sufficient, and happy little girl. Observations demonstrated however that she was a mature, avoidant, and angry child. Shelly particularly appeared to enjoy solitary activities and in this context she projected a creative and happy image. She could play with toys for long periods and use them imaginatively. Shelly spontaneously emerged from her solitary cacoon only to get something she needed, or to satisfy her curiosity. The majority of recorded approach behavior occurred, for example, when she had to go to the bathroom, was thirsty, or wanted candy or a toy. Although she initiated these approaches, it is interesting to note that Shelly chose, as often as not, to approach from behind or to the side of her social target.

Shelley actively tried to maintain her social isolation through avoidance and/or aggression against her intruders. Sometimes avoidance occurred subtly by actively ignoring the friendly advances of a peer or caregiver. More typically, however, she would simply move away to avoid the social interaction entirely. If solitude could not be regained, Shelley responded with obvious conflict. In one instance, an agemate intruded so far as to take some of her toys and Shelly did not hesitate to snatch them back. She subsequently manifested, however, odd approach–avoidance behaviors, specifically dumping a pail of sand on her intruder as she turned away to face the opposite direction. Her need to retaliate obviously conflicted with her need to move away.

In other instances aggression was used to maintain solitude. The entrance into her personal space by both caregivers and agemates was likely to stimulate threats or actual hostility. Shelley was observed to harshly glare at others, or even raise back her fist ready to strike. On other occasions she physically pushed her intruders away, oblivious to the consequences.

Although Shelley resented intrusion from others, she was frequently observed maliciously interfering with both peers and caregivers. She sometimes lashed out against her agemates, suddenly knocking over their toys, slapping them, and in one instance kicking them. Shelley also directed her anger against caregivers. Most typically she would suddenly run in their direction spitting at them or hitting them.

The same interactional style of avoidance and harassment was exhibited outside the daycare environment. During the course of our study, Shelley accompanied her mother to participate in our laboratory play session (the Ainsworth Strange Situation). As predicted, Shelley ignored her mother upon reunion after separation, totally self-sufficient in the playroom environment. Soon after her mother's return Shelley innocently engaged her mother in blowing soap bubbles. This pleasant interaction was doomed, however, for without explanation Shelley forcefully knocked the jar out of her hands. This act of harassment was performed with pleasure, seemingly knowing that punishment would have resulted in any other context. It was also an act of conflict, for as Shelley struck the jar, her head was turned away to the side thus cutting off her mother's image.

Throughout the course of our daycare observations we were struck by the determined, unhesitating quality of Shelley's behavior whether it was approach, avoidance, or harassment. In many ways she appeared very grown-up and precocious. She seemed fully aware of her behavior and its potential consequences, aware beyond the level normally attributed to a child not yet 3 years of age. This was further demonstrated in her behavior toward her sister. Shelley literally mothered her, taking over the function in which her natural mother was obviously deficient. She tended to her emotional needs and comforted her when distressed. In return, Shelley, rather than the mother, was the person this baby sought for security. Although we did not focus on this pseudo-adult quality of interaction in our study, it is interesting to note similar observances in the abused children described by Martin and Beezley (1977).

IMPLICATION FOR THERAPEUTIC INTERVENTION

The identification by Helfer and Kempe in 1968 of the battered child syndrome as a social problem precipitated a growing movement of description, identification, prevention, and treatment. Much time, energy, and money has particularly been invested in treatment programs. Traditionally, treatment has included parent-oriented programs—for example, psychotherapy, crisis nurseries, home counseling, and child care instruction (Parke & Collmer, 1975). There is, however, a growing concern over the "failure" of many of these approaches—they may or may not alter the abusive pattern established in an individual home (Martin & Beezley, 1977).

Exclusive emphasis on parental intervention has slowly begun to shift toward recognizing the importance of dynamic patterns of interaction in the parent–child relationship (Gaensbauer & Sands, in press; Gray & Kempe, 1976; Horenstein, 1977; Maden & Wrench, 1977; Martin & Beezley, 1977). Recognizably, the day to day interactions of infant and parent may have a more enduring psychological impact than the actual traumatic event (Gaensbauer & Sands, in press). The infant may be the target of rejection and threats of abuse, as well as the relatively rare incident of abuse itself.

Our data and that of others described earlier in this chapter suggest that the battered child is indeed a difficult child to handle. It seems reasonable to assume then that anomolous forms of social interactions would have been well-established before battering was actually detected. Thus, therapy centered on the parent–child relationship is a necessity, but as with any therapeutic intervention process, progress will be slow (Martin & Beezley, 1977).

A growing number of therapeutic programs have also specifically considered the psychological, as well as the physical needs, of the battered child. Despite the increase, it remains striking that child therapy is predominantly aimed at older children—children with at least preliminary skills in verbal communication and imaginary play. This is true of individual psychotherapy, particularly psychoanalysis and the adjunct therapy of play therapy.

Although individual psychotherapy for infants and toddlers is relatively infrequent, it does exist (Blumberg, 1977). For those few infants who do enter individual relations, the course of treatment is guided from the perspective that the infant is lacking basic trust and affection (Blumberg, 1977; Green, 1978; In & McDermott, 1976). Therapy is therefore designed to reshape the infant's view of the world through cuddling and nurturing (Blumberg, 1977).

Infant psychotherapy may indeed be a viable form of intervention but reliance on this method alone with infants has two foreseeable drawbacks. The most obvious concerns the availability of psychotherapy to most abused infants. These relationships are recognizably rare, leaving the majority of abused children untreated. Additionally, our data suggest that identifiable problems in social interaction are evident as early as toddlerhood. Modifications of social interactional styles (indirect approach, avoidance, approach–avoidance, and unwarranted hostility) may require active participation of therapists beyond the simple level of basic trust.

Recognizing these limitations several forms of alternate infant therapy have been initiated—most notably infant daycare and foster care (Martin & Beezley, 1976b; Mirandy, 1976). These methods of intervention are certainly available to greater numbers of abused children. In addition to providing respite for the parents and developmental stimulation for the child, an important aspect of these settings includes a focus on interpersonal relationships.

Providing the abused child with a stable therapeutic environment promoting the development of new social patterns should have both immediate and longterm effects on the child abuse syndrome. The obvious immediate result is a gradual change in the child's patterns of interaction with the parent. The entire pattern of social interaction must change: Changes in the parent alone only tackles half the problem. Alternate styles of interaction must also develop in the infant–styles that are less upsetting to the parent and therefore less likely to incite abuse. Still more importantly, battered infants must receive the opportunity to experience and model other relationships; and those relationships can be provided by sensitive and knowledgable caregivers in foster care or daycare settings. As models of relationships change, the child may seem less difficult to peers and caregivers as well. Immediate "successes," particularly in personality and social-emotional development, have been noted by a handful of investigators using foster care or therapeutic daycare facilities (see, Alexander, McQuistion, & Rodeheffer, 1976; McQuiston, 1976; Mirandy, 1976). Mirandy (1976) has stressed that "early preschool intervention should be able to prevent the need for special help at later ages for most abused children [p. 223]."

In the long run, the optimal goal of therapeutic environments for the child should be insuring the child against falling into the abused–abusing cycle. Our study has shown that as early as infancy, the behavior of the abused child bears some resemblance to that of the parent. First, of course, the child tends to engage in sudden bouts of inexplicable hostility to others. Second, she or he withdraws and avoids social affiliation in contexts where children normally seek or respond to interaction with others. It is possible that these behaviors are antecedents of the isolating mechanisms described in many abusing parents (Garbarino & Crouter, 1978; Melnick & Hurley, 1969; Parke & Collmer, 1975). Certainly part of the problem in the abuse syndrome may be the adult's reticence or inability to establish personal or community ties—ties that could potentially offer support in times of crises (Garbarino & Crouter, 1978; Merrill, 1962; Smith & Hanson, 1975). Early therapy may help these children to respond more positively to offers of support.

The relative lack of availability of infant therapeutic programs may in part be due to the failure to understand the early distortions that appear in the social behavior of the battered child. Our study points to the presence of such relative distortions in infancy, but many more investigations are needed to supplement our knowledge. Our study is only a beginning.

REFERENCES

Ainsworth, M.D.S., Bell, S.M.V., & Stayton, D. Individual differences in strange situation behavior of one-year-olds. In H. R. Schaffer (Ed.), *The origins of human social relations.* London: Academic Press, 1971.

Ainsworth, M.D.S., Blehar, M., Waters, E., & Wall, S. *Patterns of attachment.* Hillsdale, New Jersey: Laurence Erlbaum, 1979.

Ainsworth, M.D.S., & Wittig, B. A. Attachment and exploratory behavior of one-year-olds in a strange situation. In B. M. Foss (Ed.), *Determinants of infant behavior* (Vol. IV) London: Methuen, 1969.

Alexander, H., McQuiston, M., & Rodeheffer, M. Residential family therapy. In H. P. Martin (Ed.), *The abused child: A multidisciplinary approach to developmental issues and treatment.* Cambridge: Ballinger, 1976.

Bell, S. M., & Ainsworth, M.D.S. Infant crying and maternal responsiveness. *Child Development,* 1972, *43,* 1171–1190.

Blanchard, M., & Main, M. Avoidance of the attachment figure and social-emotional adjustment in daycare infants. *Developmental Psychology,* 1979, *15,* No. 4, 445–446.

Blumberg, M. L. Treatment of the abused child and child abuser. *American Journal of Psychotherapy,* 1977, *31,* 204–215.

Bowlby, J. *Attachment and loss. Vol. 1: Attachment.* New York: Basic Books, 1969.

Burgess, R. L., & Conger, R. D. Family interaction in abusive, neglectful, and normal familes. *Child Development,* 1978, *49,* 1163–1173.

Chance, M.R.S. An interpretation of some agonistic postures: The role of "cut-off" acts and postures. *Symposia of the Zoological Society of London,* 1962, *8,* 71–89.

Curtis, G. Violence breeds violence. *American Journal of Psychiatry,* 1963, *120,* 386–387.

Davoren, E. The battered child in California: A survey. *The San Francisco Consortium,* March, 1973.

Fontana, V. J. The neglect and abuse of children. *New York Journal of Medicine,* 1964, *64,* 215–224.

Friedrich, W. N., & Boriskin, J. A. The role of the child in child abuse: A review of the literature. *American Journal of Orthopsychiatry,* 1976, *46,* 580–590.

Gaensbauer, T. J., Mrazek, D., & Harmon, R. J. *Affective behavior patterns in abused and/or neglected infants.* In N. Frude (Ed.), *The understanding and prevention of child abuse: Psychological approaches.* London: Concord Press, in press.

Gaensbauer, T. J., & Sands, K. Distorted affective communication in abused/neglected infants and their potential impact on caretakers. *Journal of the American Academy of Child Psychiatry,* in press.

Galdston, R. Observations on children who have been physically abused and their parents. *American Journal of Psychiatry,* 1965, *122,* 440–443.

Galdston, R. Preventing the abuse of little children: The Parent's Center Project for the study and prevention of child abuse. *American Journal of Orthopsychiatry,* 1975, *45,* 372–381.

Garbarino, J., & Crouter, A. Defining the community context for parent-child relations: The correlates of child maltreatment. *Child Development,* 1978, *49,* 604–616.

George, C. *Microanalysis of the social behavior of a severely punished toddler.* Unpublished manuscript, 1975.

George, C., & Main, M. Social interactions of young abused children: Approach, avoidance and aggression. *Child Development,* 1979, *50,* 306–318.

Gray, J., & Kempe, R. S. The abused child at time of injury. In H. P. Martin (Ed.), *The abused child: A multidisciplinary approach to developmental issues and treatment.* Cambridge: Ballinger, 1976.

Green, A. H. A psychodynamic approach to the study and treatment of child-abusing parents. *American Academy of Child Psychiatry,* 1976, *15,* 414–429.

Green, A. H. Psychopathology of abused children. *Journal of the American Academy of Child Psychiatry,* 1978, *17,* 92–103.

Green, A. H., Gaines, R. W., & Sandgrund, A. Child abuse: Pathological syndrome of family interaction. *American Journal of Psychiatry,* 1974, *131,* 882–886.

Harrington, J. Violence: A clinical viewpoint. *British Medical Journal,* 1972, *1,* 228–231.

Helfer, R. E., & Kempe, C. H. (Eds.). *The battered child.* Chicago: Univ. Chicago Press, 1968.

Horenstein, D. The dynamics and treatment of child abuse: Can primate research provide the answers? *Journal of Clinical Psychology*, 1977, *33*, 563-565.

In, P. A., & McDermott, J. F. The treatment of child abuse: Play therapy with a 4-year-old child. *American Academy of Child Psychiatry*, 1976, *15*, 430-440.

Johnson, B., & Morse, H. A. Injured children and their parents. *Children*, 1968, *15*, 147-152.

Kempe, C. H. Pediatric implications of the battered baby syndrome. *Archives of Disease in Childhood*, 1971, *46*, 28-37.

Kempe, C. H., Silverman, F. N., Steele, B. B., Droegenmueller, W., & Silver, H. K. The battered-child syndrome. *Journal of the American Medical Association*, 1962, *181*, 17-24.

Kempe, R. S., & Kempe, C. H. *Child abuse*. Cambridge, Massachusetts: Harvard Univ. Press, 1978.

Klein, M., & Stern, L. Low birth weight and the battered child syndrome. *American Journal of Disease of Childhood*, 1971, *122*, 15-18.

Lynch, M. Risk factors in the child: A study of abused children and their siblings. In H. P. Martin (Ed.), *The abused child: A multidisciplinary approach to developmental issues and treatment*. Cambridge: Ballinger, 1976.

Maden, M. F., & Wrench, D. F. Significant findings in child abuse research. *Victimology*, 1977, *2*, 196-224.

Main, M. *Exploration, play, and level of cognitive functioning as related to child-mother attachment*. Unpublished doctoral dissertation, Johns Hopkins University, 1973.

Main, M. Analysis of a peculiar form of reunion behavior seen in some daycare children: Its history and sequelae in children who are home-reared. In R. Webb (Ed.), *Social development in childhood: Daycare programs and research*. Baltimore: Johns Hopkins Univ. Press, 1977.

Main, M. Avoidance in the service of proximity. In K. Immelman, G. Barlow, M. Main, & L. Petrinovitch (Eds.), *Behavioral development: The Bielefeld interdisciplinary project*. New York: Cambridge Univ. Press, in press.

Main, M. *Avoidance of the attachment figure in infancy*. Manuscript in preparation.

Main, M., & Londerville, S. *Compliance and aggression in toddlerhood: Precursors and correlates*. Manuscript submitted for publication, 1979.

Main, M., & Waters, E. *Autism and adaptation*. Paper given at the third biennial conference of the International Society for the Study of Behavioral Development, Surrey, England, July, 1975.

Manning, M., Heron, J., & Marshall, T. Styles of hostility and social interactions at nursery, at school and at home: An extended study of children. In L. Hersov & M. Berger (Eds.), *Aggression and anti-social behaviour in childhood and adolescence*. New York: Pergamon, 1977.

Martin, H. P. The child and his development. In C. H. Kempe & R. E. Helfer (Eds.), *Helping the battered child and his family*. Philadelphia: Lippincott, 1972.

Martin, H. P. Which children get abused: High risk factors in the child. In H. P. Martin (Ed.), *The abused child: A multidisciplinary approach to developmental issues and treatment*. Cambridge: Ballinger, 1976.

Martin, H. P., & Beezley, P. Personality of abused children. In H. P. Martin (Ed.), *The abused child: A multidisciplinary approach to developmental issues and treatment*. Cambridge: Ballinger, 1976.(a)

Martin, H. P., & Beezley, P. Foster placement. In H. P. Martin (Ed.), *The abused child: A multidisciplinary approach to developmental issues and treatment*. Cambridge: Ballinger, 1976.(b)

Martin, H. P., & Beezley, P. Behavioral observations of abused children. *Developmental Medicine and Child Neurology*, 1977, *19*, 373-387.

Matas, L., Arend, R., & Sroufe, L. A. Continuity of adaptation in the second year: The relationship between quality of attachment and later competence. *Child Development*, 1978, *49*, 547-556.

McQuiston, M. Crisis nurseries. In H. P. Martin (Ed.), *The abused child: A multidisciplinary approach to developmental issues and treatment*. Cambridge: Ballinger, 1976.

Melnick, B., & Hurley, J. Distinctive personality attributes of child-abusing mothers. *Journal of Consulting and Clinical Psychology*, 1969, *33*, 746-749.

Merrill, E. J. Physical abuse of children: An agency study. In V. DeFrancis (Ed.), *Protecting the battered child*. Denver, Colorado: American Humane Association, 1962.

Milow, I., & Lowrie, R. The child's role in the battered child syndrome. *Society for Pediatric Research*, 1964, *65*, 1079-1081.

Mirandy, J. Preschool for abused children. In H. P. Martin (Ed.), *The abused child: A multidisciplinary approach to developmental issues and treatment*. Cambridge: Ballinger, 1976.

Morse, W., Sahler, O. J., & Friedman, S. B. A three-year follow-up of abused and neglected children. *American Journal of Diseases of Children*, 1970, *120*, 439-446.

Parke, R. D. Some effects of punishment on children's behavior. In W. W. Hartup (Ed.), *The young child* (Vol. 2) Washington, D.C.: National Association for the Education of Young Children, 1972.

Parke, R. D., & Collmer, C. W. Child abuse: An interdisciplinary analysis. In E. M. Hetherington (Ed.), *Review of child development research* (Vol. 5) Chicago: Univ. Chicago Press, 1975.

Reidy, T. J. The aggressive characteristics of abused and neglected children. *Journal of Clinical Psychology*, 1977, *33*, 1140-1145.

Rodeheffer, M., & Martin, H. P. Special problems in developmental assessment of abused children. In H. P. Martin (Ed.), *The abused child: A multidisciplinary approach to issues and treatment*. Cambridge: Ballinger, 1976.

Sameroff, A. J., & Chandler, M. J. Perinatal risk and the continuum of caretaking casualty. In F. D. Horowitz, E. M. Hetherington, S. Scarr-Salapatek, & G. Siegel (Eds.), *Review of child development research* (Vol. 4) Chicago: Univ. Chicago Press, 1975.

Smith, S. M., & Hanson, R. Interpersonal relationships and childrearing practices in 214 parents of battered children. *British Journal of Psychiatry*, 1975, *127*, 513-525.

Spinetta, J. J., & Rigler, D. The child-abusing parent: A psychological review. *Psychological Bulletin*, 1972, *77*, 296-304.

Sroufe, L. A., & Waters, E. Attachment as an organizational construct. *Child Development*, 1977, *48*, 1184-1199.

Steele, B. F., & Pollock, D. A psychiatric study of parents who abuse infants and small children. In R. E. Helfer & CH. H. Kempe (Eds.), *The battered child*. Chicago: Univ. Chicago Press, 1968.

Ten Broeck, E. The extended family center: A home away from home for abused children and their parents. *Children Today*, 1974, *3*, 2-6.

Self, Teacher, Toy, and Peer-Directed Behaviors of Handicapped Preschool Children

INTRODUCTION

The developmental sequence of the child's early interactions with the world may proceed from parents to toys to peers. The innumerable Parent–Infant interaction studies support the idea that the primary interaction object during the first several months is the parent. Around 5 or 6 months, the infant begins to show more interest in toys or objects than in the parents (Trevarthen, 1974). The parent begins to experience more difficulty eliciting social behaviors, particularly in the typical Face-to-Face interaction situation. Peer interaction studies suggest that infants show little interest in peers or toys until the second half of the first year. At that time the primary interest appears to be toys, whereas afterward the principal interest is peers (Maudry & Nekula, 1939). A number of more recent studies have attempted to measure the infant's preferences for parent, toys, or peers by removing one or the other of the "competing" interaction objects. A study by our group, for example, suggested that mother was the primary focus of interaction from 10 to 14 months when both she and peers were present (Field, 1979a). However, when the mother was removed from the situation, infants directed an increasing number of social behaviors toward their peers. Other studies measuring the effects of the presence and absence of toys suggest that toys are preferred over peers during

313

HIGH-RISK INFANTS AND CHILDREN:
Adult and Peer Interactions

infancy, although their removal also facilitates peer interactions (Eckerman & Whatley, 1977; Ramey, Finkelstein & O'Brien, 1976).

Longitudinal studies have typically followed the sequence of first presenting the parent to the infant in a face-to-face situation, followed by the parent, and toys in a floor play situation, and finally by parent, toys, and peers in a floor play situation (Blurton-Jones, 1978; Field, 1977, 1979b; Goldberg, Brachfeld, & DiVitto, chapter 8 of this volume). Again the selected sequence of interaction situations probably represents a developmental shift in the infant's interests in interaction objects. Certainly, to observe the infant's emerging social skills, a developmentally appropriate situation is required.

A concurrent developmental sequence often noted during early peer interactions is that distal social behaviors precede proximal social behaviors. Proximal social behaviors are typically directed to the most familiar social object (e.g., the parent), whereas distal social behaviors are most frequently directed to less familiar social objects (e.g., the peer). Studies of infants 16- to 24-months old in which the familiarity of the setting (e.g., home versus lab) or the familiarity of peers were varied suggest that a prominent activity at all ages was watching the peer. Distal social behaviors (look at, vocalize, and gesture) tended to occur more frequently than proximal behaviors (touch, hit, proximity) at each age level (Eckerman, Whatley, & Kutz, 1975; Lewis, Young, Brooks, & Michalson, 1975; Rubinstein & Howes, 1976). In our study of peer interactions in the presence and absence of the mother, more proximal behaviors were directed towards the mother and more distal behaviors toward peers. Although, in the absence of mother and with increasing age, an increasing number of proximal behaviors were directed toward peers (Field, 1979a). Even though mothers and toys may be more salient stimuli, perhaps due to the infant's longer history of interactions with them than with peers, the salience of peers is also demonstrated by the previously mentioned studies, with the typical developmental progression being from mother to object to peer relatedness.

To establish the universality of developmental sequences, one could inquire whether children with sensorimotor handicaps and attendant developmental delays follow the same sequence and if they show similar interaction behaviors when matched by developmental age to normal children. A review of the sparse literature on the interactions of handicapped children suggests a very limited range of interactions, particularly when the children have been observed in nonintegrated classrooms. For example, Spradlin and Girardeau (1966) noted a general absence of social interactions amongst retarded children. In both structured and unstructured activities, most of these children remained isolated from neighboring children and adults while engaging in a variety of nonsocial and self-stimulating behaviors. The presence of self-stimulation and the absence of other-directed activity has been reported for groups ranging from autistic to Down's Syndrome to physically handicapped children. Typically, however, comparisons have been made between these children and chronologically age-matched children. Comparisons with developmental age-matched controls on the other hand, might be more appropriate and might reduce the differences between handicapped and normal children.

Hulme and Lunzer (1966) observed the interactions of subnormal and normal children matched for a mean mental age of 3.3 years (although the mean chronological age of the subnormal children was 7.5-years old versus, 3.4-years old in the normals). Although these groups were similar on a number of interaction measures, the subnormal children were markedly inferior both in the number and level of language responses. With the exception of language skills, then, this study suggests that matching for developmental age diminished many of the differences between the groups.

Lovell, Hoyle, and Siddal (1968) found that speech-delayed children developed fewer social interaction behaviors than their speaking peers. Gregory (1976) also observed almost exclusively solitary play among deaf children and related their impoverished interaction to the lack of communication skills necessary to sustain interactions. Cerebral palsy (CP) also has been noted to interfere with early development of interactions. Poor functional mobility in addition to intellectual deficits appear to be the limiting factors for this group (Hewett, 1970). Hewett suggests that children with physical and mental handicaps such as the CP child "need to be taught how to play and interact with other children."

Despite the delays in the development of interaction skills by these handicapped children, the children appear to follow a normal developmental sequence, at least in sensorimotor activities. Woodward (1960), for example, did a structural analysis of observations based on Piaget's levels of sensorimotor development. The children studied were severely retarded and at 7–9 years and 12–14 years had failed to achieve a 2-year mental level. Woodward found, however, that it was possible to classify the spontaneous activities of these children with Piaget's schema and showed that the sequence of development matched that described by Piaget.

To summarize, then, the literature suggests a developmental sequence in interactions so that the focus of these interactions progress from mother to objects to peers. In addition, early peer interactions may be characterized by distal followed by proximal interaction behaviors. The developmental delays in interaction behaviors typically noted in handicapped children may be attenuated when the handicapped children are compared to developmentally age-matched, nonhandicapped controls. Because handicapped children appear to follow the same developmental sequence as normal children in terms of their sensorimotor activities, we might expect that they also follow a normal developmental sequence in social interaction behaviors.

The present study is a comparison between the social behaviors of normal and handicapped children controlling first for chronological age and then for developmental age. The purpose was to investigate whether the proposed developmental sequence of adult, object, peer-related interactions might emerge by comparing groups of similar chronological but different developmental ages. Secondly, we wanted to determine whether comparisons between handicapped children and between handicapped and normal children at equivalent developmental, but different chronological, ages might suggest developmental, age-dependent social behaviors.

METHOD

Subjects

The children were 48 3 to 4-year olds ($M = 42$ months, $SD = 4$ months), 36 of whom were handicapped and 12 who were normal. The handicapped children had varying perceptual-motor handicaps including cerebral palsy (CP), mental retardation, and speech or hearing deficits. Their developmental ages as determined by standardized developmental assessments ranged from 10 months to 2 years ($M = 21$ months, $SD = 7$ months). The normal children were of the same chronological age with no developmental delays. Thus, their developmental age (3–4 years) was more advanced than that of the handicapped children. In addition, we observed a class of 12-handicapped children who were the same developmental age as the normal children (3–4 years) but were 1-year older chronologically (4–5 years).

The 3- to 4-year-old handicapped children had been assigned according to their developmental age or degree of developmental delay to one of three classrooms of 12 children each. In this way the three handicapped classrooms represented homogenous groupings of severely delayed (Group 1), moderately delayed (Group 2), or minimally delayed children (Group 3). Although the children of classroom or Group 1 had more severe degrees of CP, mental retardation, or speech and hearing deficits, the distribution of the type of perceptual-motor handicap was similar for each classroom, enabling classroom comparisons by degree of handicapping condition or developmental delay. Similarly, the distribution of socioeconomic background (low and middle class) was the same for all classrooms (handicapped and nonhandicapped).

Setting

Each class was held in carpeted rooms, measuring approximately 20' × 40', and featuring different play areas (sectioned off by standing toy shelves containing a variety of manipulative toys). The classrooms also featured floor-play equipment including slides, tumbling mats, balls, and forms, and crawl tunnels. The classes met 5 days per week for 5 hr per day with the day's activity divided into free play, gross and fine motor activities, language development, lunch, and naptime. Each of the classes was supervised by a teacher and teacher's aide.

Procedure

The children were observed by psychology graduate students assigned to separate classes. The students were unaware of the purpose of the study or the developmental and chronological ages of the children at the time of the observations. Each child was observed according to a randomly ordered roster of the class. Observations were weekly and for 5 min per observation. As the observations were continued over one semester (a 4-month period of 16 observations), the total observation time for each child was approximately 80 min.

TABLE 16.1
Operational Definitions of Observed Behaviors

Behaviors directed toward peer, teacher, or toy

Looking	— continuous visual regard
Smiling	— mouth upturned while looking
Vocalizing	— vocal sounds while looking or in response to vocalization by other
Proximity	— within 3' of person
Touching	— physical contact including patting, hugging, or rubbing
Offering toy	— holding out toy in direction of other person
Sharing toy	— mutual contact with an object
Taking toy	— physically tugging at or removing toy
Hitting	— forceful physical contact by hand, foot, or object
Crying	— loud, continuous wailing

Nondirected or self-directed behaviors

Looking	— at mirror or body parts
Smiling	— nondirected smiling
Vocalizing	— nondirected sounds
Moving	— nondirected movement including body rocking twirling, or aimless wandering
Touching	— stereotyped self-stimulation such as hand flapping, mouth rubbing, body tapping

Observations were made only during free-play periods in order to minimize the amount of adult directed activity observed. Each observer used a time-sample unit (TSU) sheet of operationally defined behaviors, observing for a 10-sec unit followed by recording for a 5-sec unit for a total of 30 TSUs or 5 min per observation.

Piloting revealed that most of the handicapped children were exhibiting fairly simple social behaviors. Although the simple behaviors approximated those of infants and would not characterize the sophistication and richness of normal preschool interactions, we focused on them to portray the behavioral repertoire of the handicapped child. The following distal and proximal behaviors were selected for coding: looking, smiling, vocalizing, moving toward, physical proximity, touching, offering toy, sharing toy, hitting, and crying. The operational definitions of these behaviors appear in Table 16.1. All of the behaviors were recorded for each target child as they were directed toward a teacher, a toy or peer. In addition, piloting revealed a number of self-directed, self-stimulation behaviors. We therefore observed looking-at-self (body parts or looking at face in mirror), nondirected smiling, nondirected vocalizations, nondirected movement (e.g., body rocking, twirling, or aimless wandering) and touching self (e.g., hand flapping, mouth rubs, ear taps, and other stereotypies). Interobserver reliabilities were assessed using videotaped observations of four sessions per classroom. They were calculated by K, a chance-corrected, percentage agreement measure with a statistical base (Bartko & Carpenter, 1976), and ranged from .78 to .93.

Hypotheses

Our hypotheses were as follows.

1. Proximal behaviors would be directed more frequently to teachers.
2. Distal behaviors would be directed more frequently to peers.
3. Self- and teacher-directed behaviors would appear more frequently in Group 1 (severely delayed) than in Group 2 (moderately delayed), Group 3 (minimally delayed) or Group 4 (normal).
4. Toy and peer directed behaviors would appear more frequently in Group 4 than in Groups 3, 2, or 1.
5. The children of Group 5 (handicapped children of older chronological but similar developmental age as that of normal children) would show interaction behaviors similar to those of Group 4 (normal).

Anlayses of Data

The raw data, number of TSUs per observation of the behaviors observed, were converted to proportions or percentage of the observation time. This conversion was necessary because some free-play observation periods were interrupted by teacher activities short of the 5-min observations.

Multivariate analyses of variance were first performed on the groups of behaviors which were (a) nondirective or directed at self, (b) directed at teachers, (c) directed at toys, and (d) directed at peers. Following these analyses Sex (2) by Group (4) analyses of variance were performed on each of the behaviors. Post hoc comparisons of individual groups were made by Bonferroni t tests (Myers, 1972). These tests were also performed separately on the data for Groups 4 (normal children) and 5 (older handicapped children).

RESULTS

The results will be presented by the separate groups of behaviors (i.e. self-directed, teacher-directed, toy-directed, and peer-directed behaviors). The means and F values for these appear in Table 16.2.

Self-Directed Behaviors

As can be seen in Table 16.2 the analyses yielded a significant effect for group on a number of variables including looking-at-self, smiling-at-self, nondirected moving-of-self in space, vocalizing, and touching self. All these differences were in the direction of there being more of these behaviors in the severely and moderately delayed groups. Post hoc comparisons suggested that Group 1 (severely delayed) and Group 2 (moderately delayed) showed more nondirected vocalizations than Group 3 (minimally delayed) and Group 4 (normal). Similarly, Groups 1 and 2 exhibited more touching-of-self (stereotypic hand-flapping, mouth rubs, and ear-tapping) than did Groups 3 and 4.

Teacher-Directed Behaviors

The analyses for this group of behaviors revealed significant group effects. However, contrary to our expectations, very few of the teacher-directed behaviors differentiated the groups. There were significant group effects only for vocalizing to the teacher and offering and sharing a toy with the teacher. Post hoc comparisons revealed that the normal children, more frequently than the handicapped children, vocalized to and offered and shared a toy with the teachers.

Toy-Directed Behaviors

The analyses for this group of behaviors revealed significant group effects. Post hoc comparisons suggested that Groups 3 and 4 (minimally delayed and

TABLE 16.2
Mean Proportions of Time Behaviors Observed, F values and p Levels ($df = 3, 43$)

Object-Group interaction

Behavior	Self						Teacher						Toy						Peer					
	1	2	3	4	F	p	1	2	3	4	F	p	1	2	3	4	F	p	1	2	3	4	F	p
Looking	13	13	5	4	3.21	< .05	32	35	38	35		n.s.	21	29	41	44	13.14	< .001	14	21	39	52	27.46	< .001
Smiling	12	9	3	.8	3.90	< .02	2	5	8	10		n.s.	.8	.8	.2	0		n.s.	1	2	2	13	3.93	< .01
Vocalizing	18	10	5	4	8.23	< .001	3	7	9	14	4.08	< .01	1	.6	0	.4		n.s.	2	2	6	37	14.98	< .001
Moving	22	13	.8	.5	4.15	< .01																		
Proximity							27	18	29	34	2.66	< .10							29	36	59	93	12.09	< .001
Touching	12	8	3	.6	19.70	< .001	4	5	2	7	2.41	< .10	17	21	36	41	9.11	< .001	2	.2	5	8		n.s.
Offering toy							.1	.3	.7	10	5.22	< .01							.3	.3	.5	8	4.79	< .005
Sharing toy							.6	.5	.8	11	4.64	< .01							.2	.6	4	21	20.35	< .001
Taking toy							.2	0	.4	0		n.s.	4	6	.3	.4		n.s.	.6	1	3	1		n.s.
Hitting							0	.2	0	0		n.s.							1	3	1	1		n.s.
Crying							9	7	2	.3		n.s.							0	0	0	0		n.s.

Groups: 1 = severely delayed; 2 = moderately delayed; 3 = minimally delayed; 4 = normal.

normal groups) spent more time looking at and touching toys. There were very low means for smiling at, vocalizing to, and hitting toys across all groups.

Peer-Directed Behaviors

Again the analyses suggested significant main effects for group. They were as follows.

1. There was more frequent looking at peers by the normal children than by the minimally and moderately delayed children, who in turn showed more peer-directed looking than the severely delayed children (Group 4 > Group 3 > Group 2 > Group 1).

2. The normal children smiled to peers more than did any of the handicapped children (Group 4 > Group 3 = Group 2 = Group 1).

3. The normal children also vocalized to their peers more frequently than did any of the delayed children (Group 4 > Group 3 = Group 2 = Group 1).

4. The normal children showed more moves toward their peers and were in close physical proximity more often than the minimally delayed children, who in turn differed significantly from the more delayed groups on these measures (Group 4 > Group 3 > Group 2 = Group 1).

5. The normal children offered and shared toys significantly more often than did any of the delayed children (Group 4 > Group 3 = Group 2 = Group 1).

As can be seen in Table 16.2, a number of behaviors occurred with such low frequency that no group differences were revealed. These included hitting and crying, irrespective of the target of these behaviors.

Comparison between Chronologically Older, Handicapped Children (Group 5) and Developmental Age-Matched Normal Children (Group 4)

The analyses for these groups suggested a number of differences despite the similar developmental ages of the groups. Group 5 (the handicapped group) showed more self-touching (or self-stimulating) behaviors (t (23) = 4.47, $p < .001$), less vocalizing toward teachers (t (23) = 4.30, $p < .001$), less vocalizing toward pers (t (23) = 3.96, $p < .001$), and less physical proximity to peers (t (23) = 4.11, $p < .001$). Thus, the handicapped children, in spite of their chronological age advantage and their equivalent developmental age, engaged in less developed social behaviors. Although they exhibited more self-stimulating behaviors, they directed fewer social behaviors toward peers and teachers.

Because it was not clear whether these differences between developmentally age-matched but chronological age-different children related to the handicapping condition of the older children, another group comparison was made. Here the 5-year-old handicapped children were compared to a smaller group of less severely handicapped 4-year olds (N = 8) who were of similar developmental age but chronologically younger.

Comparison between Chronologically Older Handicapped Children (Group 5) and Developmental Age-Matched Handicapped Children (Group 6)

The analyses for these groups suggested that the developmentally similar, but chronologically younger, children engaged in more self-touching (self-stimulating) behaviors (t (19) = 3.38, p < .001). However the chronologically younger children also engaged in more other-directed behaviors including vocalizing to teachers (t (19) = 4.11, p < .001), physical proximity to peers (t (19) = 3.94, p < .001), and vocalizing to peers (t (19) = 3.54, p < .001). Thus although the self-stimulating behaviors observed in handicapped children appeared to diminish with chronological age, their behavior remains impaired in terms of fewer other-directed behaviors.

DISCUSSION

Comparisons between the same chronological age but different developmental age handicapped and nonhandicapped preschool children yielded a number of differences suggestive of a developmental sequence. That is, with increasing developmental age, children demonstrate progressively fewer self-directed or self-stimulating behaviors such as looking-at-self, vocalizing-to-self, nondirected movement in space, and stereotypic touching-of-self (e.g., hand flapping and ear tapping). These are considered the least mature behaviors and appeared in the classsroom of the most delayed children. At the same time as developmental age increased, progressively more social or other-directed behaviors were observed, including physical proximity, looking, vocalizing, offering or sharing toys with teacher and peers. Thus, the most delayed children (moderately and severely delayed) engaged in more nondirected or self-directed behaviors than the least delayed and normal (nondelayed) children. In terms of teacher-directed behaviors, the groups were differentiated only on a few measures with the normal group showing more vocalizing (probably because their language skills were more developed) and offering or sharing toys with teachers (one of the more sophisticated social behaviors typically occurring at the age of 3 in normal children). Regarding toy-directed behaviors, the least delayed and the normal children again showed greater development by looking at and touching toys more than the other groups. Had more complex toy-related behaviors been measured, the normal children would have probably shown more advanced toy-related activity than the least delayed handicapped group. Regarding peer-directed behaviors, the normal children clearly showed an advantage over all the handicapped groups, including the minimally delayed, on most of the behavioral measures.

In support of our hypotheses, there appeared to be a developmental progression from self to teacher to toys to peer-related behaviors with (a) the moderately and severely delayed children's repertoire being comprised mainly of self-directed and some teacher-directed behaviors; (b) the minimally delayed and normal children not differing on toy-related behaviors; and (c) the normal (nondelayed) children moving ahead of the minimally delayed children in their socially oriented behaviors toward peers. Although the phenomena underlying this proposed developmental sequence remain unclear, in the Piagetian sense the adult requires less accommodation than a toy, which, in turn, requires less accommodation than a peer. Therefore, the sequence may be explained by the infant developing increasing accommodation skills. In the Watsonian sense, the adult provides more contingent responsivity than a toy, which, in turn, provides more contingency than a peer. In the Ainsworthian sense, the adult is a less strange or more familiar object than a toy, and the toy is a more familiar object than a peer. For whatever reasons, the saliency of these interaction objects appears to follow a progression of adults to toys to peers.

Similarly, there appeared to be more proximal behaviors directed toward teachers and more distal behaviors directed to peers, except for the normal children who differentially directed both proximal and distal behaviors more frequently toward peers. These data support the hypothesized developmental sequence of interactions, with interaction behaviors toward peers following those toward toys, in turn, following those toward teachers. Although self-directed behaviors were not included in the posited developmental sequence, they appeared to comprise a significant portion of the repertoire of the moderately and severely delayed children. These early nondirected behaviors have rarely been studied in the context of normal Mother–Infant interactions. However, body rocking, lip sucking, finger mouthing, and other sterotypic behaviors have been noted as naturally occurring stereotypies during the very early infancy of normal children (Field, Ting, & Shuman, 1979; Kravitz & Boehm, 1971). Thus, self-directed behaviors may be considered as an even earlier development than mother-directed behaviors.

It would appear, however, that these mannerisms persisted beyond the appropriate developmental stage in the handicapped children. For example, the 5-year-old handicapped children whose developmental ages (DA) were equivalent to the normal children (DA = 3 years) showed significantly more of the self-touching (hand flapping, body tapping) behaviors than did their DA matched normal peers. Our already mentioned comparison of stereotypies among normal and premature infants suggested that, when matched on DA, there were no significant differences between preterm and full-term infants in rhythmic behaviors such as these. In this way, stereotypies normally appear and disappear on a developmental schedule (Field et al., 1979). The persistance of stereotypies beyond an appropriate DA for handicapped children requires explanation. The stereotypies may provide stimulation necessary because of impaired skills in relating to and deriving stimulation from the environment and the resultant frustrations. In any case, these behaviors appeared to interfere with more varied, developed interactions with others, and if prolonged, they would be a serious barrier to other-directed interactions.

There may be a "sensitive" period for the development of social behavior, If self-directed behaviors interfere with that development, then even after stereotypies disappear from the child's repertoire, the child may not have rudimentary social behaviors to replace them. Although our 5-year-old handicapped group, for example, showed fewer self-directed behaviors, they also exhibited fewer social behaviors than the developmentally equivalent 4-year olds. The 5-year olds may have "outgrown" their stereotypies or gradually learned that these behaviors elicited negative reactions from their peers (White, Chapter 18 this volume). However, unlike the younger 4-year olds, they may have passed a "sensitive" period for developing a repertoire of social behaviors to replace the stereotypies.

In summary, then, although generalizing about behaviors of handicapped children may be questionable as each child presents a somewhat unique profile, these data suggest some reliable group differences. Although there appears to be a developmental progression from self to adult to toy to peer-related behaviors, and a progression from distal to proximal behaviors for both normal and handicapped children, there does not appear to be any DA dependent behaviors. The similar, social, developmental sequence for both normal and handicapped children is consistent with the similar, sensorimotor developmental sequence for these groups outlined by Woodward (1960).

These data do not support a number of studies that suggest isolation and strictly self-directed activity among handicapped children (Gregory, 1976; Spradlin & Girardeau, 1966), nor do the data suggest that these children, when matched on DA show only language response differences as suggested by Hulme and Lunzer (1966). Rather, the handicapped children appear to move beyond mere self-directed activity, although they do not match their normal peers when compared at the same DA.

It is not clear from these data how the development of social interaction behaviors compares with the development of motor–cognitive behaviors, which predominate in the assessments on which the DA assignments were based. The impaired social development of the severely delayed children may be more marked than their developmental lags in other areas.

Although some have suggested that social skills may require as much attention as cognitive, motor, and language skills, the focus of most remediation–intervention programs to date has been motor–cognitive–language skills curricula. Social gestures such as smiling, touching, offering, are not generally built into such curricula. In addition, teacher–child ratios are typically higher and teacher-directed activities are more frequent in classrooms of handicapped children, which may provide less opportunity for and less fostering social interactions. Data from other studies suggest that lower teacher-child ratios (Field, 1979c) and lesser amounts of teacher-directed activities (White, Chapter 18 this volume) are more conductive to social interactions. Tizard, (1964) and Mogford (1978) have illustrated that environments fostering social interactions among handicapped children appear to facilitate interactions at a level approximating their developmental age. White (Chapter 18 this volume) suggests that the social behaviors of handicapped children may be facilitated by integrating handicapped children with normal children. As Hewett (1970) and others have suggested, "These children may need to be taught how to socially relate to others," and other children who can model social behaviors may be good teachers.

ACKNOWLEDGEMENTS

I am grateful to the children and teachers who made this study possible and to the graduate students, Susan Widmayer, Lisa Lubin, Shelley Payne, and Wendy Stone who assisted in data collection.

REFERENCES

Bartko, J. J., & Carpenter, W. T. On the methods and theory of reliability. *The Journal of Nervous and Mental Disease*, 1976, *163*, 307–317.

Blurton-Jones, N., personal communication, 1978.

Eckerman, C. O., & Whatley, J. L. Toys and social interaction between infant peers. *Child Development*, 1977, *48*, 1645–1656.

Eckerman, C. O., Whatley, J. L. & Kutz, S. L. Growth of social play with peers during the second year of life. *Developmental Psychology*, 1975, *11*, 42–49.

Field, T. Effects of early separation, interactive deficits, and experimental manipulations on infant-mother face-to-face interaction *Child Development*, 1977, *48*, 763–771.

Field, T. Infant behaviors directed toward peers and adults in the presence and absence of mother. *Infant Behavior and Development*, 1979, *2*, 47–54(a).

Field, T. Interaction patterns of high-risk and normal infants. In T. Field, A. Sostek, S. Goldberg & H. H. Shuman (Eds.), *Infants born at risk*. New York: Spectrum, 1979(b).

Field, T. Preschool play: Effects of teacher/child ratios and organization of classroom space. *Child Study Journal,* 1979.(c)

Field, T., Ting, G., & Shuman, H. H. The development of rhythmic activities in normal and high risk infants. *Developmental Psychobiology, 1979, 12,* 97-100.

Gregory, H. *The deaf child and his family.* London: Allen & Unwin, 1976.

Hewett, S. *The family and the handicapped child.* london: Allen & Unwin, 1970.

Hulme, I., & Lunzer, E. A. Play, language, and reasoning in subnormal children. *Journal of Child Psychology and Psychiatry, 1966, 7,* 107-115.

Kravitz, H., & Boehm, J. Rhythmic habit patterns in infancy: Their sequences, age of onset and frequency. *Child Development, 1971, 42,* 399-413.

Lewis, M., Young, G., Brooks, J., & Michalson, L. The beginning of friendship. In M. Lewis & L. A. Rosenblum (Eds.), *Friendship and peer relations.* New York: Wiley, 1975.

Lovell, K., Hoyle, H. W., & Siddal, M. Q. A study of some aspects of play and language of young children with delayed speech. *Journal of Child Psychology and Psychiatry, 1968, 9,* 41-46.

Maudry, M., & Nekula, M. Social relations between children of the same age during the first two years of life. *Journal of Genetic Psychology, 1939, 54,* 193-215.

Mogford, K. The play of handicapped children. In B. Tizard & D. Harvey (Eds.), *Biology of play.* Philadelphia: Lippincott, 1978.

Myers, J. L. *Fundamentals of experimental design.* Boston: Allyn & Bacon, 1972.

Ramey, C. J., Finkelstein, N. W., & O'Brien, C. Toys and infant behavior in the first year of life. *Journal of Genetic Psychology, 1976, 129,* 341-342.

Rubinstein, J., & Howes, C. The effects of peers on toddlers' interactions with mother and toys. *Child Development, 1976, 47,* 597-605.

Spradlin, J. E., & Girardeau, F. L. The behavior of moderately and severely retarded persons. In N. R. Ellis (Ed.), *International review of research in mental retardation* (Vol. 1). New York: Academic Press, 1966.

Tizard, J. *Community services for the mentally handicapped.* London: O.U.P., 1964

Trevarthen, C. Conversations with a two-month-old. *New Scientist, 1974, 62,* 230-232.

Woodward, M. The behavior of idiots interpreted by Piaget's theory of sensorimotor development. *British Journal of Educational Psychology, 29,* 1960.

MELINDA A. NOVAK
J. GREGORY OLLEY
DEBORAH S. KEARNEY

CHAPTER **17**

Social Skills of Children with Special Needs in Integrated and Separate Preschools

INTRODUCTION

Early childhood education has had ambitious and diverse goals through-out its history in the United States. Early education as social reform, as therapy, and as compensation for a deprived environment have been well established themes since the early part of this century. The child study movement of the late nineteenth century added an extensive data base in the form of careful observations of children to these themes (Lazerson, 1972).

The last 20 years have brought a renewed interest in such topics accom-panied by an extensive growth of educational programs and research. The 1960s offered several approaches to compensatory education intended to offset the effects of poverty, and the outcomes of these programs have been thoroughly researched (e.g., Bereiter, 1972; Gray & Klaus, 1970; Weikart, 1972). In 1965, Congress authorized Project Head Start, a nationwide program of compensatory early education. in contrast to the earlier child study movement, which had based its data on observation, these modern research programs used objective measures of outcome, primarily IQ tests and achievement tests.

In Bronfenbrenner's (1974a) review of these evaluation studies, he pointed to the emphasis on intellectual measures and the absence of measures of social ability. Head Start and other compensatory education efforts may, indeed, affect "emotional security, self-esteem, . . . generosity, cooperativeness, re-sponsibility, and compassion [p. 2]," but there is little data to support this

HIGH-RISK INFANTS AND CHILDREN:
Adult and Peer Interactions

claim. Zigler and Trickett (1978) have emphasized this point and suggested that the social competence of preschool children could be measured by combining information from several sources (e.g., physical health, I.Q., school achievement, and several motivational and emotional variables). Because such concepts are not easily captured in objective measures, the older observational measures have also been reappearing as researchers attempt to assess the difficult nuances of social development (e.g., Peterson & Haralick, 1977).

In addition to the new interest in social–emotional development, the early 1970s was a time of rapid new development of services for young handicapped children. Whereas Head Start was originally aimed only at "disadvantaged" children, its mandate was revised to require the inclusion of handicapped children as 10% of its population. This trend toward new services for young handicapped children was reflected in the passage of new, comprehensive, special education laws in several states. In November 1975, President Ford signed the Education of All Handicapped Children Act (P.L. 94–142), and an emphasis on the early education of handicapped children in the least restrictive environment became national policy.

The policy of early education of handicapped children in settings that allow maximum contact with normally developing children is derived from widespread dissatisfaction with the performance of children in separate or "segregated" special classes (e.g., Dunn, 1968). It is also influenced by the normalization principle (Nirje, 1969), a view that supports the right of handicapped people to normal life experiences. Thus, children with a wide variety of handicapping conditions are being placed in early education classes with normally developing children on the assumption that they will benefit in their social development. The policy is persuasive on humanistic grounds, but the data base for such a broad policy is very limited. The traditional laboratory data of developmental psychology have been recently attacked from many quarters as lacking validity in real-life situations and, therefore, being inadequate for application to handicapped persons (Brooks & Baumeister, 1977), to public policy (Bronfenbrenner, 1974b), or to an adequate science of developmental psychology (McCall, 1977).

Such criticisms have led to a small explosion in the number of studies of social behavior of children in nursery schools and other early education settings. Most of these studies have retained traditional concern for strong methods while incorporating naturalistic observation in order to maximize ecological validity (e.g., Leiter, 1977; Lougee, Grueneich, & Hartup, 1977; Reuter & Yunik, 1973; Rubin, Maioni, & Hornung, 1976). Although social skills can be gained through many forms of interaction, the vehicle traditionally assumed to be most critical for the development of social behavior in young children is play (Vandenberg, 1978; Weisler & McCall, 1976). As Lazerson (1972) has pointed out, there is a long-standing belief that "childhood's uniqueness lies in its affinity for play [p. 34]."

Some research on the social behavior of autistic (Black, Freeman, & Montgomery, 1975; Richer, 1976), mentally retarded (Berry & Marshall, 1978), learning disabled (Bryan, 1978), and hearing impaired (McCauley, Bruininks, & Kennedy, 1976) children has been reported, but little of this burgeoning research effort has been directed at the practical issues surrounding the social skill development of young handicapped children during free play in integrated educational settings. Knapczyk and Yoppi (1975) and Wehman (1977) have endorsed the use of reinforcement procedures as a tool for teaching play skills to young handicapped children, but the fundamental research on handicapped childrens' natural acquisition of social behavior or social propensity during play has not been reported.

A cautious summary of the literature on handicapped children would seem to yield the following tentative conclusions. First, both the assessment and remediation of the problems of handicapped children are directed primarily at cognitive deficits and not at social deficits. Whether this is fortuitous (cognitive assessment traces its roots back to the general issues in learning which were a main focus of psychology in the 1950s) or by design (cognitive deficits may be easier to recognize, measure, and therefore remediate than social deficits) is not clear. In addition, of those studies that emphasize social behavior in handicapped children, the majority are directed to issues in remediation rather than assessment (Cooke & Apolloni, & Cooke 1977; Strain & Timm, 1974; Warfield, 1974). This is a rather surprising finding as one would expect that effective remediation of social deficits would depend upon the generation of precise information specifying the nature of the deficit. In this context, it is important to note that handicapped children will not necessarily imitate and learn appropriate social behavior as a result of exposure to normal peers in an integrated preschool setting (Snyder, Apolloni, & Cooke, 1977). Because children seem to prefer to interact with children who function at a similar developmental level (Ray, 1974), special therapeutic procedures may be required to facilitate such interaction (Cooke, Apolloni, & Cooke, 1977). The failure of passive remediation to lead to normal social behavior suggests the need, first, for an elaborate data base concerning the social abilities of handicapped children that can then be used to design effective forms of therapy. The purpose of this chapter is to provide some baseline information on the social behavior of handicapped children in preschool settings.

USING NATURALISTIC OBSERVATION TO MEASURE SOCIAL BEHAVIOR

The assessment of social behavior is a very complex task. One can not simply administer a test nor easily measure social behavior under highly artificial laboratory conditions. Perhaps the most effective, and yet, demanding way for the researcher to measure social behavior is to let the child behave naturally in a social setting, and then measure the temporal and spatial flow of such naturally occurring behavior. This technique has been referred to as "naturalistic observation" or the "ethological method".

The advantages of using naturalistic observation to study the social behavior of handicapped children are threefold. First, such studies are conducted in a natural setting to which the child has been adapted, in contrast to an environment structured by the experimenter into which a child is thrust for a short period of time. This serves to minimize the risk that the setting might be disruptive to the child. Second, the ethological method involves the measurement of freely emitted behaviors rather than responses that are structured or created by the experimenter. It thereby reduces the problem of differentiating between responses that the handicapped child can not perform from those that he will not perform. Finally, the ethological method can be classified as "holistic," as all of the actions of the child are recorded. In contrast to concentrating on a single response, researchers examine the interrelationships between behavior patterns. This reduces the possibility that the experimenter has selected an irrelevant behavior to measure.

There are, of course, disadvantages to using this method. One has to be able to construct a set of behavioral categories that captures ongoing behavior, social or otherwise. This construction can not be haphazard but must depend upon a set of criteria that can include such factors as the degree of stereotypy of a behavior in the normal population of children, the salience of a behavior, and the ability to define a behavior in terms of discernable discrete motor patterns. A second area of concern is that of data collection. Observers must be rigorously trained to recognize and record many different types of behavior patterns. In some instances, the flow of behavior is so fast, or the expression of behavior is so subtle that the observer becomes an unreliable instrument. Indeed, the multifaceted task of scanning, recognizing, and recording behavior patterns can be extremely difficult. Under certain circumstances, videotape equipment or microprocessing data acquisition units can alleviate some of these problems in observer reliability.

The development of a useful instrument for measuring behavior depends not only upon resolving the issues of reliability and validity but also upon recognizing and adjusting to the constraints created by the setting. In a preschool environment containing a number of children and teachers, problems concerning observer placement and mobility may arise. The observer's positioning in the environment and distance from the children, whether freely chosen or stipulated by the teachers, may influence the structure of the behavioral categories. For example, whether or not one decides to read facial expressions depends in part on one's distance from the subjects. The observer's degree of mobility may also be an important factor. As a child does not always face the observer or remain stationary, it may be necessary to move about in order to record all of the child's activities (a situation potentially disruptive to all concerned). Alternatively, one might elect to include a category of "not visible."

The three scoring instruments used in this research were carefully designed to enhance validity and reliability in the context of a preschool environment where observers remained stationary and at the periphery of the play groups. In our first system, the behavioral profile system, each child was watched individually for one 3-min period, 4 days per week, for 8–12 weeks, and all his or her activities were recorded. Names and definitions of the 20 social and nonsocial categories used in this system are shown in Table 17.1. These behaviors reflect whole body movements including locomotion, aggression, and social contact rather than finer elements of behavior that could not be readily coded by our observers such as facial expressions or types of verbal messages. The behaviors listed in Table 17.1 were measured both by their absolute and modified frequencies of occurrence in the standard observation period. The modified frequency score (MF Total) was obtained by dividing the observation period into 10 sec intervals and measuring the number of intervals in which the behavior occurred. Data were collected using a scoring sheet in which the x-axis consisted of 10 sec intervals and the y-axis consisted of behavioral categories. As can be seen in Figure 17.1, the MF total is obtained by summing the number of intervals in which the behavior occurred. The absolute frequency (AF total) of occurrence was obtained by summing the number of checks regardless of the intervals. Because behavior may start in one interval and continue through the next and subsequent intervals, checks separated by a dash are treated as a single frequency of occurrence. The behavioral profile system is used to generate information about the partitioning of a child's activity into social and nonsocial behaviors or into different types of social behavior.

When using the social interaction system, each child was watched individually for another 3-min period, on the same 4 days per week, for 8–12 weeks. However, only his/her social interactions were recorded. Social interactions were measured in three dimensions—the actual social behavior involved (in Table 17.1, asterisks denote social behaviors used in this system), to whom the social behavior was directed (a particular teacher or child), and whether this social behavior was initiated or received by the focal child. Observations were recorded on a data sheet in which the x axis consisted of social behaviors subdivided into the action categories of initiate and receive and the y axis consisted of particular children or teachers. Information concerning the absolute frequency of occurrence was placed into each cell. The social interaction system, as described in Figure 17.1, provides information about the types of social activities that are directed to particular children or groups (handicapped

TABLE 17.1
Behavioral Categories and Their Definitions

Tactile-oral explore:	Any touching or manipulating of objects or surfaces with the hands or mouth (not play)
Visual explore:	Child is not interacting or moving but is gazing at a person or object
Passive:	Child is neither interacting, moving, or gazing
Stereotypy:	Self-directed behavior of a ritualized nature. usually idiosyncratic and repetitive, includes thumb sucking, hair twirling etc.
*Social play:	Interactions with other individuals involving chasing, toy manipulation, acting out roles, or interacting in a game
Object play:	Solitary use of objects
*Social constructive activity:	Purposeful activity usually directed by the teacher, for example, passing out a snack, cleaning up the room—this activity is performed with peers
*Individual constructive activity:	Purposeful activity performed alone
*Social contact to teacher:	Passive physical contact not involved in play
*Social contact to peer:	Passive physical contact not involved in play
*Vocal behavior to teacher:	Sounds directed to the teacher
*Vocal behavior to peer:	Sounds directed to a peer
*Social aggression:	Any pushing, hitting, or pulling directed to another individual
Object aggression	Destruction or attempts to destroy objects
Cries and screams	
Locomotion	Movement, characterized by three steps in any direction, which is not a part of play or aggression
Not visible:	Child is out of sight of observer
Teacher direction:	Child receives a verbal command or physical prompt to action from the teacher
Praise:	Child receives a positive statement or touch from the teacher

NOTE: Asterisks denote categories used in the interaction as well as modified frequency system.

children) by the focal child. In addition, one can determine whether the child is more or an initiator rather than a receiver of social behavior, and if this varies by behavior and/or child.

Information on the social clustering patterns of all the children in the preschool was generated by recording the simultaneous locations of these children using a scan-all subject-sampling procedure. Spatial locations were recorded on a standardized diagram of the physical layout of the playroom. Five such scans were taken each day for 4 days per week. The data from each

MODIFIED FREQUENCY SYSTEM

SUB _Sally_ SIT _Clarke_ TIME _9:30_ DATE _3/9/79_ OBS _Nank_

BEHAVIOR	1	2	3	4	5	6	7	8	9	10	MF TOTAL	AF TOTAL
PASSIVE	✓					✓	✓				3	2
SOC PLAY			✓	✓	✓	✓			✓	✓	6	3
OBJ PLAY	✓	✓✓	✓				✓✓	✓			5	6
LOCOMO	✓	✓					✓	✓			4	3
VIS EXPL		✓✓					✓				2	3
TAC EXPL		✓									1	1
ETC												

INTERACTION SYSTEM

SUB _Sally_ SIT _Clarke_ TIME _9:45_ DATE _3/19/79_ OBS _Novak_

TO OR FROM WHOM	CONT I	CONT R	PLAY I	PLAY R	AGG I	AGG R	VOC I	VOC R	ETC I	ETC R	R	TOTAL I	TOTAL R
JEFF	/	/	//									3	1
BOB	/	/					//					3	1
LUCY			/	/								1	1
PAM												0	0
ETC													
TOTAL	2	2	2	1	?		2					7	3

FIGURE 17.1. Sample data sheets for the modified frequency and interaction systems.

sheet were summarized by examining each child, in turn, and recording the number and kind of children found within 18 in. (Zone 1), from 18 to 36 in. (Zone 2), or from 36 to 54 in. (Zone 3) of the focal child.

Because play interactions between young children may serve as an important vehicle for the development of social behavior, data were collected during free-play periods. An obvious advantage to the selection of this period for observation accrues from the fact that teacher direction and intervention were less common at this time. Therefore, spontaneous, naturally occurring interactions between peers could be recorded.

DESCRIPTION OF PRESCHOOL SITES

For over 3 years now, we have been observing children during free-play periods in five different preschool settings. As might be expected, these settings differed with respect to subject variables (age, sex, and handicap), teacher variables (numbers present and amount of contact between teachers and children during free play), environmental variables (amount of space and numbers and kinds of toys with which to play), and schedule variables (the timing of the free-play period and the presence of other activities). The ensuing description of each preschool setting will emphasize these variables and is summarized in Table 17.2.

Two of our preschools were not integrated. The Fort River Preschool 1, established as a preschool intervention project and especially designed for children with special needs, contained two female and seven male children with a variety of behavior problems. Only the seven males were selected for study. The majority of these male children possessed cognitive and attentional deficits as indicated by their difficulty in learning and comprehending language. In addition, one child was hyperactive and another very withdrawn. This preschool was staffed by three teachers who structured the children's activity in the following way. During the first part of the morning, the children were involved in a group participation session with a teacher. Subsequently the children were engaged in individual constructive tasks under the close supervision of a teacher. Then, at around 9:30 AM, children interacted in a free-play period during which observations were collected. Free-play activities were confined to a space measuring 15 ft. × 21 ft. and children had the opportunity to play with blocks, dolls, trucks, balls, construction toys, and other typical playroom items as well as with peers. During this time teachers interacted less frequently with the children although they would often try to engage an isolated child in play activities.

The Oakdale preschool contained 21 normally developing children (14 males, 7 females) supervised by three teachers. Seven males matched to the Fort River group were chosen for study. Children arrived at the preschool around 8:30 AM and were immediately allowed to play with each other. During this play period, children moved back and forth between two rooms measuring 560^2 ft. and played with a variety of toys, blocks, dolls, and other standard play items. Again, there was minimal teacher intervention during this early period so observations of the children were collected at this time. Approximately 40 min later, when the activity and exuberance of the children had waned, the teachers introduced more highly structured, individualized tasks.

Although the third site, St. Paul's preschool, was not integrated in any formal sense, administration on the Denver Developmental Screening Test (Frankenburg & Dodds, 1969) revealed that some of the children were developmentally delayed for their age group. In all cases, this represented a minimal delay of only one level of the Denver Screening Test. Thus, we were able to subdivide this preschool population into high- and low-risk subgroups. The St. Paul's preschool contained three separate classes of children divided on the

TABLE 17.2
Differences between Preschool Settings

	Preschool setting				
	Fort River 1	Oakdale	St. Pauls	Clarke	Fort River 2
Subject Factors					
Number of children in study	7	7	18	10	16
Number of children in class	11	21	37	10	16
Number of males	7	14	18	7	9
Class	lower-middle	lower-middle	lower-middle	middle	middle
Handicap	behavior problems	none	none	hearing loss	behavior problems
Teacher factors					
Number of teachers	3	3	3	3	3.5
Degree of direction	medium	medium	low	high	medium
Physical factors					
Amount of space	300^2 ft.	560^2 ft.	575^2 ft.	427^2 ft.	300^2 ft.
Type of Toys	small to medium	small to medium	large	small to medium	small to medium
Observation Factors					
Time of data collection	9:30 AM	8:30 AM	9:30 AM	9:30 AM	9:30 AM
Distinct free-play period	yes	yes	yes	no	yes
Presence of observers in room	yes	yes	yes	no	yes

basis of age. There were 6 males and 7 females in the 3-year-old class, 6 males and 7 females in the 4-year-old class, and 6 males and 5 females in the 4½-year-old class. We studied three high-risk and three low-risk children in each class.

Individual classes were located in separate rooms and were supervised by a single teacher. A large, additional room of 23 ft × 25 ft., designated as a playroom, was used by each class at separate times during the morning for a 40 min free-play period. Observations were collected during these periods, which began at around 9:15 AM. The playroom was unique in that it contained a variety of large gynmasium-like objects including two slides, a wooden boat, and other wooden riding toys in addition to smaller toys such as blocks and dolls.

The remaining two schools were formally integrated but differed from each other with respect to the nature of the handicap present in the special needs group. The Clarke preschool contained five normal (four male and one female) and five hearing-impaired (three male and two female) children, all of whom were studied. The normal group was matched to the hearing-impaired group on the basis of age and socioeconomic status. Children with hearing impairments arrived at 8:00 AM and were given individualized language instruction. Normal children arrived at 8:30 AM and began to interact with each other, after which the hearing-impaired children began to enter the classroom. Because the children were allowed to move freely throughout the entire morning with no well defined free-play period, observations of the group commenced around 9:30 AM. Teacher intervention was the highest in this preschool as indicated by the amount of time they spent interacting individually with the children and also involving them in group activities. In contrast to all other settings in which the observers were present in the room with the children, observers sat in another room and recorded data by looking through a one-way mirror.

The final preschool site, Fort River 2, contained eight normal children (three males and five females) and eight children (five males and three females) with behavior or language problems. All of the children served as subjects in this study. This preschool, under different supervision and involving different students than the Fort River 1 preschool, was staffed by three teachers. At the beginning of each day the children took part in a group participation session of singing and games, which was followed by a free-play period. Children interacted with each other as well as with a variety of standard play items and data were collected at this time.

Despite the substantial differences in preschool settings, we wanted to determine whether common behavioral differences between children with special needs and normal children could be identified. We analyzed the data from all of our settings separately using the analysis of variance and then looked for differences that were common to all settings. For these comparisons, presence of handicap and sex (where appropriate) were the between-subject variables and number of weeks was the within-subject variable.

In addition to this broad overview, we also examined the effects of three general variables on the behavior of our children with special needs and normal children. The first variable, type of free-play setting, was assessed by comparing the behavior patterns of the children in the St. Paul's and Fort River 2 preschools. The St. Paul preschool was designed in such a way as to favor rough, physical group play. This situation did not exist in the Fort River 2 school where space was broken up with tables and chairs and only small toys were available during play. We expected that marked differences in the play setting would at least alter the frequencies of various social behaviors. For this comparison, setting and sex were the between subject variables and number of weeks was the within subject variable in the analysis of variance.

Of special concern to researchers and teachers working with special needs populations is the issue of integration. Is immediate integration beneficial or should children be integrated after some form of treatment has been administered? We were able to study the effects of integration by comparing the behavior of our handicapped children in the segregated Fort River 1 school with the behavior of the children in the integrated Fort River 2 school. The room and play objects were similar for both schools. In this instance, the factors in the ANOVA were integration (Fort River 1 versus Fort River 2 handicapped children versus Fort River 2 normal children) as the between-subject variable and number of weeks as the within subject variable.

Very little is known about the teacher's effect on the behavior of preschool children because this is a variable that is difficult to manipulate. Teachers, for example, do not usually leave the free-play setting. In two of our preschools (Fort River 2 and St. Paul's), however, the teachers did agree to remove themselves a short distance from the free-play room for a 10- to 20-min period of time. In this way we were able to measure the effect of the presence or absence of the teacher on play activity. For this comparison, setting and sex were the between-subject variables and teacher presence and number of weeks were the within subject variables.

OBSERVATIONAL PROCEDURES

Although our preschool sites differed substantially, every effort was made to provide consistency in the procedures used to collect data. Subject control consisted of matching normal children to handicapped children on the basis of sex, age, and socioeconomic status. The ages of the children varied from 3 to 5 years, and children were matched to within 4 months of age. Although the majority of the children came from a middle-class background, several of the children had a lower-class background. In most instances, the lower-class children were matched to other children with a lower-class background. Whenever possible, the observers were kept ignorant of the nature of the handicap and the subset group (children having special needs or normal children) to which each subject belonged. Observers were not blind to these factors in the Fort River 1 and Oakdale settings; however, they were blind to the high- and low-risk groups at the St. Paul's preschool. Observers at the Clarke school could recognize the hearing-impaired child behaviorally and also because these children entered the classroom late. They were blind, however, to the degree of hearing impairment. The special needs children in the Fort River 2 school were also discernable as they were periodically removed from the classroom for additional therapy sessions. Observers did not have access to specific information about the children and conversations between the observers and the teachers about specific children were expressly discouraged.

Further experimental control was achieved by having the observers follow the same standard procedure in each site. A minimum of two observers were present at each preschool site, and they spent 3-6 weeks becoming familiar with the children and setting. Besides the necessity of having two observers present for the assessment of reliability, the time needed to sample all children twice, once for each of the two different scoring systems (modified frequency and interaction), was often longer than the free-play period itself. Therefore, while one observer would use the modified frequency system, the other used the interaction system. Observers alternated between scoring systems on successive days. In addition, observers never monitored the same child simultaneously with the exception of reliability checks, which were separate from the data collection. This period also allowed the children to adapt to the presence of the observers. Adaptation was indicated by a marked decline in interactions with, movements toward, and glances at the observers. Observers maintained a slack, emotionless countenance and ignored all attempts at interaction by the children. Formal data collection did not commence until the reliability scores between observers for each behavioral category reached 90% (as determined by a percentage agreement score). Reliability was subsequently assessed each week during formal data collection.

RESULTS

Assessment Across All Preschools

Despite the existence of qualitative and quantitative variation across preschool sites, consistent differences in the social behavior of handicapped and normally developing children were detected. Handicapped children played more with objects, played less with other children, and visually explored the environment more than their normal counterparts. By pooling the social interaction categories within each site, we discovered that handicapped children both initiated and received less social interaction than normally developing children, and received more teacher direction than their normal age-mates. These differences are depicted in Figure 17.2. Spatial clustering data were available for only two sites, but again, commonalities existed between these two sites. More children, especially normals, were found in Zones 1 and 2 when the focal subject was normal rather than handicapped. Normal children tended to cluster near to other children, most of whom were normal like

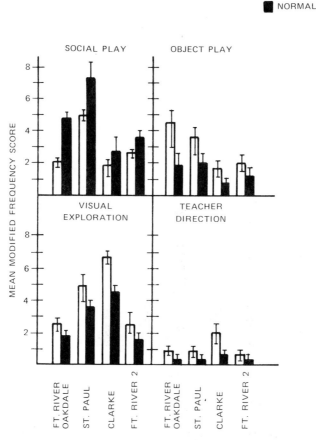

FIGURE 17.2. The graph illustrates behavioral differences between handicapped and normal children in diverse preschool settings.

themselves. These results suggest that the handicapped children do exhibit deficits in social behavior and that certain behavior patterns may be used to identify such deficits regardless of differences in setting or handicap.

Type of Free-Play Setting

The effects of this variable were assessed by comparing the behavior of the children in each of two preschool settings (i.e., St. Paul's school which has a large gymnasium-like playroom and the Fort River 2 school which utilized standard, preschool, play objects). As we expected, the children played somewhat differently in each setting. Vigorous social play and heightened activity characterized the children in the St. Paul's preschool. Besides showing higher levels of play, these children explored their environment, both visually and tactilely, more than the Fort River 2 children. In a subsequent analysis, we also included the data from the Clarke school because the absence of any defined free-play period constituted another interesting variation in the type of free-play setting. Because there is a confounding of type of handicap (hearing impairment) and type of free-play situation at the Clarke school, the results must be viewed with caution, however. Children in the Clarke school exhibited the

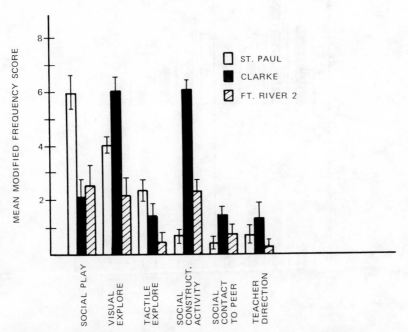

FIGURE 17.3. The graph illustrates the variation in preschool play behavior as a function of type of free-play setting.

lowest levels of social play and were more often involved in social constructive activity. These constructive activities which were led by the teacher included painting murals or carving pumpkins. Consequently, the Clarke school children also received the most teacher direction and social contact from peers. These results are displayed in Figure 17.3.

Although setting had an effect on social behavior, we were surprised to note that these differences were reflected equally in the handicapped and normal subjects (i.e., there was no interaction of play setting and the presence or absence of a handicap). This suggests that variations in free-play settings alone might not be sufficient to normalize the behavior of handicapped children.

Integration

The effects of integration were analyzed by comparing the behavior of the children in the Fort River 1 and 2 preschools. Spatial clustering data were not available for this analysis. As was depicted in the assessment of each site, children having special needs played more with objects and less with other

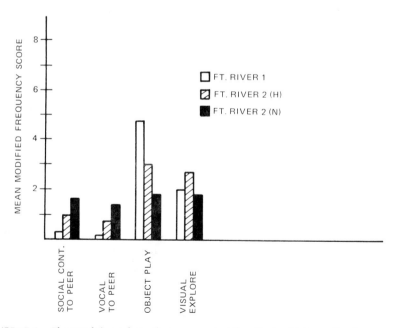

FIGURE 17.4.   The graph is a schematic assessment of the effects of intergration by comparing the handicapped children in our segregated preschool (Fort River 1) to the handicapped children (Fort River 2-H) and normal children (Fort River 2-N) in our integrated preschool.

children than their normal age-mates. In addition, social interaction scores were lower for handicapped children. However, when we compared differences in the two handicapped populations (Fort River 1 and 2) with the normal population (Fort River 2), the differences between normal and handicapped children were smaller in the integrated setting. As indicated in Figure 17.4, handicapped children in the Fort River 2 preschool showed more social contact with and verbal behavior directed toward peers and less object play than did their segregated counterparts. However, Fort River 1 and Fort River 2 handicapped preschool children displayed similar levels of visual exploration. These data suggest that at least a reduction in the degree of social deficits in the handicapped child may be associated with integrated settings.

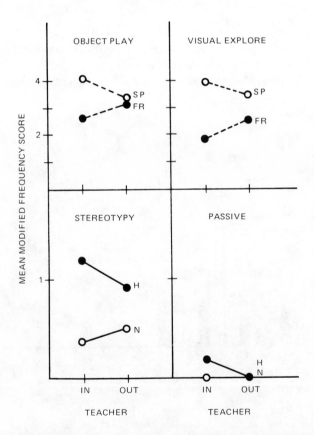

FIGURE 17.5. The graphs show the effects of teacher presence on preschool playroom behavior as a function of setting where (Fort River 2 appears as FR, St Paul is SP), and handicapped and normal subjects appear as H and N respectively.

Teacher Presence

We were very fortunate to be able to examine the effects of this variable in two preschool settings (i.e., St. Paul's and the Fort River 2 preschools). Overall, children played more and were less passive when the teacher was absent. Despite the increase in play behavior, close social interactions decreased on teacher's absence as indicated by the spatial-clustering data. There was a marked decline in the number of children found in Zones 1, 2, and 3 after the teacher left the room. The children were more likely to be found more than 4 ft from one another in the teacher's absence. There were differential effects of teacher presence in the two settings. For example, although visual exploration increased in the Fort River 2 children when the teacher left the room, no such increase occurred in the St. Paul children. In addition, object play increased in Fort River 2 children but decreased in the St. Paul children on teacher's absence. There were also differential effects of teacher's presence on the children having special needs and the normal children. Although handicapped children were more passive when the teacher was present in the room, these differences disappeared when she was absent. Stereotyped idiosyncratic patterns of behavior declined slightly in handicapped children but increased in normal children when the teacher left the room. These differences are depicted in Figure 17.5. Thus, the presence of the teacher had an effect on the social behavior of the children, and this effect interacted with both the setting and the handicap.

DISCUSSION

There is now evidence for the view that children suffering from sensory and cognitive deficits or behavior problems are likely to display social deficits as well. The goal of this research was to generate some information on the social patterns of handicapped children with an aim toward identifying particular patterns of behavior to be used for risk assessment and in the development of appropriate therapeutic manipulations.

As Hartup (1976) has indicated, perhaps the most sensitive indicator of developmental delay is inappropriate or reduced interaction with peers. The differences between our handicapped and normal subjects were therefore not unique or unexpected. These handicapped children played less with peers and more with objects, initiated and received fewer social interactions with peers, and spent less time in close proximity to other children. They also displayed heightened visual exploration, perhaps as a substitute for engaging in social play. It is especially important to note that these behavioral differences consistently appeared in very diverse settings. This suggests (a) that play patterns, social interactions, and physical spacing may be good markers for the assessment of social competency, and (b) that remediation should at least initially be directed toward minimizing the handicapped child's deficits in these key behaviors.

Given these findings, what kinds of educational therapeutic stretegies should we employ to facilitate social interaction in handicapped children? Historically, the first step in such thereapy has been the integrated classroom. Although the early hope that handicapped children might simply imitate their normal counterparts has not been realized, our study suggests that handicapped children probably behave somewhat more like normal children when placed in integrated rather than segregated settings. However, the persisting social deficits we observed seem to underscore the need for further manipulation of the physical or social environment.

Although the handicapped child's behavior did vary as a function of the setting, the behavioral differences between normal and handicapped children persisted. This would seem to suggest that simple changes in play setting will not have a strong therapeutic effect, unless these changes are accompanied by other modifications, perhaps in the normal children themselves.

The teacher's classroom behavior, as well as his mere presence, certainly influences the social responses of the special needs child. However, teacher-mediated attempts at social therapy have thus far been more successful at engendering teacher-directed sociality than interactions with age mates. As an alternative, Wahler (1967) and Patterson and Brodsky (1966) used manipulations of normal peers to induce social recovery in handicapped children. These and other experiments, though, are limited by their failures to examine all relevant behaviors and to include long-term follow-up studies. We would suggest the use of naturalistic observation to assess the social competency of handicapped children, focusing especially on the behavioral markers identified in our work. Subjects might be tested at the point of their entry into school, at periodic intervals throughout the period of cognitive and social rehabilitation, and afterward for some length of time. Follow-up observations should be particularly revealing if the child has been mainstreamed into the normal educational system because such children represent the most crucial test of one's therapeutic program.

REFERENCES

Apolloni, T., & Cooke, T. P. Integrated programming at the infant, toddler, and preschool age levels. In M. Guralnick (Ed.), *Early intervention and the integration of handicapped and nonhandicapped children.* Chicago: Univ. Park Press, 1978.

Bereiter, C. An academic preschool for disadvantaged children: Conclusions from evaluation studies. In J. C. Stanley (Ed.), *Preschool programs for the disadvantaged.* Baltimore: Johns Hopkins Univ. Press, 1972.

Berry, P., & Marshall, B. Social interactions and communication patterns in mentally retarded children. *American Journal of Mental Deficiency,* 1978, *83,* 44–51.

Black, M., Freeman, B. J., & Montgomery, J. Systematic observation of play behavior in autistic children. *Journal of Autism and Childhood Schizophrenia,* 1975, *5,* 363–371.

Bronfenbrenner, U. *A report on longitudinal evaluations of preschool programs. Vol. II: Is early intervention effective?* Washington, D.C.: Office of Human Development, 1974. (a)

Bronfenbrenner, U. Developmental research, public policy, and the ecology of childhood. *Child Development,* 1974, *45,* 1–5. (b)

Brooks, P. H., & Baumeister, A. A. A plea for consideration of ecological validity in the experimental psychology of mental retardation: A guest editorial. *American Journal of Mental Deficiency,* 1977, *81,* 407–416.

Bryan T. H. Social relationships and verbal interactions of learning disabled children. *Journal of Learning Disabilities,* 1978, *11,* 58–66.

Cooke, T. P., Apolloni, T., & Cooke, S. A. Normal preschool children as behavioral models for retarded peers. *Exceptional Children,* 1977, *43,* 531–532.

Dunn, L. M. Special education for the mildly retarded—Is much of it justifiable? *Exceptional Children,* 1968, *35,* 5–22.

Frankenburg, W. K., & Dodds, J. B. *Denver Developmental Screening Test.* Denver, Co: Univ. of Colorado Medical Center, 1969.

Gray, S. W., & Klaus, R. A. The early training project: The seventh year report. *Child Development,* 1970, *41,* 909–924.

Hartup, W. W. Peer interaction and behavioral development of the individual child. In E. Schopler & R. J. Reichler (Eds.), *Psychopathology and child development.* New York: Plenum Press, 1976.

Knapczyk, D. R., & Yoppi, J. O. The development of cooperative and competitive play responses in developmentally disabled children. *American Journal of Mental Deficiency,* 1975, *80,* 245–255.

Lazerson, M. The historical antecedents of early childhood education. In I. J. Gordon (Ed.), *Early childhood education.* Chicago: Univ. Chicago Press, 1972.

Leiter, M. P. A study of reciprocity in preschool play groups. *Child Development,* 1977, *48,* 1288–1295.

Lougee, M. D., Grueneich, R., & Hartup, W. W. Social interaction in same- and mixed-age dyads of preschool children. *Child Development,* 1977, *48,* 1353–1361.

McCall, R. B. Challenges to a science of developmental psychology. *Child Development,* 1977, *48,* 333–334.

McCauley, R. W., Bruininks, R. H., & Kennedy, P. Behavioral interactions of hearing impaired children in regular classrooms. *The Journal of Special Education,* 1976, *10,* 277–284.

Nirje, B. The normalization principle and its human management implications. In R. B. Kugel & W. Wolfensberger (Eds.), *Changing patterns in residential services for the mentally retarded.* Washington, D.C.: President's Committee on Mental Retardation, 1969.

Patterson, G. R., & Brodsky, G. A behavior modification program for a child with multiple behavior problems. *Journal of Child Psychology and Psychiatry,* 1966, *7,* 277–295.

Peterson, N. L., & Huralick, J. G. Integration of handicapped and nonhandicapped preschoolers: An analysis of play behavior and social interaction. *Education and Training of the Mentally Retarded,* 1977, *12,* 235–245.

Ray, J. D. *Behavior of developmentally delayed and nondelayed toddler-age children: An ethological study.* Unpublished doctoral dissertation, George Peabody College, 1974.

Reuter, J., & Yunik, G. Social interaction in nursery schools. *Developmental Psychology,* 1973, *9,* 319–325.

Richer, J. The social avoidance behavior of autistic children. *Animal Behavior,* 1976, *24,* 898-906.

Rubin, K. H., Maioni, P. L., & Hornung, M. Free play behaviors in middle- and lower-class preschoolers: Parten and Piaget revisited. *Child Development,* 1976, *47,* 414-419.

Snyder, L., Apolloni, T., & Cooke, T. P. Integrated settings at the early childhood level: The role of nonretarded peers. *Exceptional Children,* 1977, *43,* 262-266.

Strain, P. S., & Timm, M. A. An experimental analysis of social interaction between a behaviorally disordered preschool child and her classroom peers. *Journal of Applied Behavior Analysis,* 1974, *1,* 583-590.

Vandenberg, B. Play and development from an ethological perspective. *American Psychologist,* 1978, *33,* 724-738.

Wahler, R. G. Child-Child interactions in five field settings: Some experimental analyses. *Journal of Experimental Child Psychology,* 1967, *5,* 278-293.

Warfield, G. J. (Ed.) *Mainstream currents: Reprints from exceptional children 1968-1974.* Reston, Virginia: Council for Exceptional Children, 1974.

Wehman, P. *Helping the mentally retarded acquire play skills: A behavioral approach.* Springfield, Illinois: Charles Thomas, 1977.

Weikart, D. P. Relationship of curriculum, teaching, and learning in preschool education. In J. C. Stanley (Ed.), *Preschool programs for the disadvantaged.* Baltimore: Johns Hopkins Univ. Press, 1972.

Weisler, A., & McCall, R. B. Exploration and play: Resume and redirection. *American Psychologist,* 1976, *31,* 492-508.

Zigler, E. & Trickett, P. K. IQ, social competence, and evaluation of early childhood intervention programs. *American Psychologist,* 1978, *33,* 789-798.

Mainstreaming in Grade School and Preschool: How the Child with Special Needs Interacts with Peers

INTRODUCTION

Underlying the practices of mainstreaming and integration is the concept of normalization, of not depriving any individual of the privileges granted to the many. Because good peer relationships in childhood are believed to be important for later social and emotional adjustment (Hartup, Chapter 13 this volume), there is pressure to provide positive social experiences to all children as early as possible. There is an implicit assumption that children with special needs will derive the greatest benefit, academically and socially, from mainstreaming. Some further assumptions are made about mainstreaming during the preschool years. At very young ages children do not seem to have the negative attitudes toward the handicapped that appear at later ages. Before 4 years of age, children do not seem to notice physical disabilities (Jones & Sisk, 1967). Additionally, at this early age normal children can serve as models for imitation by handicapped children (e.g., Guralnick, 1976).

This chapter deals with the social repercussions and concomitants of mainstreaming and the factors that may facilitate or hinder social acceptance. Some researchers have differentiated between the term *mainstreaming* and the term *integration*—the former meaning that most of the child's education occurs in the regular class, the latter that most of it occurs in a special setting and the child spends time in the regular class only for special events (e.g., gym, movies,

347

art: see Fredericks, Baldwin, Grove, Moore, Riggs, & Lyons, 1978). In this chapter, we will use the terms interchangeably as the children we saw varied as to the locus of the major part of their education.

When we began our work, the literature contained a number of studies documenting the social nonacceptance of mainstreamed handicapped children at the grade school level (Bryan, 1974; Gottlieb & Budoff, 1973; Iano, Ayers, Heller, McGettigan, & Walker, 1974) and describing the behaviors of handicapped children in regular classes (e.g., Gampel, Gottlieb, & Harrison, 1974). Social acceptance was defined by the results of sociometric analysis. Social behaviors were derived from frequency counts on either very short or long complicated checklists or from teachers' ratings of a child's adjustment and behavior. These methods either gave too little information, were too cumbersome for broad use, or yielded information that seemed irrelevant to real life activity in the classroom. We wanted a method that combined the richness of clinical observation and the precision, reliability, and scorability of a more formal system. Following the trend of the time, a return to the study of children in their "natural environment," we wished to develop a systematic naturalistic observation scheme that would yield a reliable nonsociometric index of acceptability or popularity, and that would allow us to observe the kinds of behaviors that might be "turning off" the nonhandicapped children.

Other naturalistic observation systems for studying handicapped and nonhandicapped children in school settings include that of Bryan, Wheeler, Carey, and Croke (1976) for verbal communications of learning-disabled and control children and that of Ispa and Matz (1978) for comparing the social and emotional behaviors of integrated handicapped and nonhandicapped preschool children within a cognitively oriented program.

DEVELOPMENT OF THE ABC AND ABC-NK, NATURALISTIC OBSERVATION SCHEMES

A clinical rather than theoretical approach was used to develop our grade-school observation system entitled "Analysis of Behaviors in the Classroom (ABC)." We spent 6 months observing integrated classrooms and talking to teachers and children, trying to identify behaviors and situations that seemed related to poor acceptance and discomfort in the classroom. A second 6 months was spent designing and piloting observation techniques that would tap these behaviors. It is characteristic of the clinical approach that there is no fixed commitment to one particular way of looking at a child. As one observes in a classroom, one might notice critical incidents. At another moment, one might focus on the quality of verbal interactions or on a child's proximity to, or distance from, others. At other times, the observer's attention might be drawn to nervous or annoying habits of a child. The instrument that evolved was a multi-perspective one, rather than a single-strategy instrument.

Approximately 1 year after the development of the ABC we extended it for use in nursery and kindergarten schools—the Analysis of Behaviors in the Classroom–Nursery, Kindergarten Form (ABC-NK). Some categories of behavior were changed; a few were added. The ABC, ABC-NK system entails observing a target child for 20-min periods in any school situation. A single trained observer obtains a concurrent record of: (a) time spent alone or with others; (b) selected, mostly maladaptive or inappropriate, behaviors; (c) frequency of conversations with others; (d) critical, positively or negatively charged, emotional incidents (interactions); and (e), following the observation, the observer's rating of the child for activity level, amount of verbalization, and quality of play.

Each child is observed for 4–6 20-min periods, these periods being evenly divided between structured and unstructured settings. *Structured* settings are defined as those in which the child's work is clearly defined and he or she is not free to wander around the room. *Unstructured* settings are defined as those in which the child is free to move about the room, talk to other children, stop working, or change activity at will.

The format of this system was designed to allow for raw data to be reconstructed into a reasonably complete narrative of the observation period, regaining some of the richness of running accounts of classroom behavior. To determine the reliability of such reconstructions, a rater tabulated all agreements, disagreements, and unmatched statements between pairs of reconstructed narratives. One of each pair of narratives was written by the original observer; the other was written from the same data by an observer unfamiliar with the particular protocol being reconstructed. The percentage of agreement between paired independent reconstructions for each of four observation records was found to be 89 percent. A complete description of the system, the indices, and interobserver reliabilities of the ABC can be found in the manual (White, 1978). (Information about the ABC-NK can be obtained from the author.)

Reliabilities

Reliabilities were estimated by having pairs of observers concurrently, but independently, observing and recording the behaviors of the same children. Correlations were then computed between the scorings of the two observers. For the ABC, reliabilities for 23 indices were based on a total of 106 paired observations; for the ABC-NK, reliabilities for 27 indices were based on 59 paired observations. Pearson product-moment correlations were computed for paired raw scores for each index. For the ABC, 11 of the 23 reliability coefficients are .90 or better; 6 are between .80 and .87; 3 are in the .70s; and 3 are .54 or lower. These last three reliabilities rose to much higher values in a second reliability study with N of 53 paired observations. For the ABC-NK, 11 of the 27 reliability scores are .90 or better, and only 6 are as low as the .60s. In general, the reliability indices compare favorably with those yielded by other observation techniques (Boyer, Simon, & Karafin, 1973; Walker, 1973).

BEHAVIORS AND INTERACTIONS IN TWO GRADE-SCHOOL SETTINGS

The ABC was used to compare the behaviors and social interactions of handicapped and nonhandicapped children in integrated grade-school classrooms. We will discuss here the observational data for two groups of handicapped children: 12 children drawn from School 1 and 25 from School 2.

Systematic observations in School 1 were collected somewhat incidentally. The ABC was developed at that school and we revisited the school a year later to make systematic observations of the handicapped children in order to try to estimate whether the children had changed in the elapsed year. No observations of control children in School 1 were made. We include the School 1 observations in our discussions here because they offer an interesting supplement to the School 2 data. Many of the School 1 integrated children were quite disabled. All but one were bused to the host school, and they differed markedly from its upper-middle-class children in IQ, home background, and appearance. School 2 was chosen so that differences between children with special needs and control children would be minimal. School 2 was a working-class school in which the children with special needs had fairly mild disabilities. The children were from the local school district and were not very different from the nonhandicapped children in IQ, home background, or appearance.

Subjects

The subjects from School 1 were 12 children, all defined by Massachusetts Chapter 766 as having special educational needs. Their ages at the time of the observations ranged from 8 years and 4 months to 14 years and 1 month ($\overline{X} =$ 11 years, 6 months; SD = 2 years). IQ scores (primarily California Tests of Mental Maturity, occasionally Wechsler Intelligence Scale for Children and others) ranged from 35 to 90 ($\overline{X} = 77.2$; $SD = 14.3$). The subjects from school 2 were 25 children with special needs and 16 control children, matched for age and sex, from the same classrooms. Ages ranged from 6 years and 10 months to 13 years and 1 month ($\overline{X} = 10$ years, 7 months; $SD = 1$ year, 8 months for both groups). IQ scores for the group with special needs ranged from 61 to 121 ($\overline{X}$ = 86.6; SD = 13.4). The corresponding figures for the control group were: range, 80–111; $\overline{X}$ = 98; SD = 9.0.

Method

All children were observed according to the ABC manual directions (White, 1978). Children from School 1 were observed four times each. Handicapped children from School 2 were observed a minimum of six times each and control children a minimum of four times each. The data for each child were averaged. Thus, for each child there was one score for each of the ABC indices.

Results

Data obtained using the scoring categories of the ABC were analyzed, using 2-tailed t-tests and χ^2. For discussion purposes, the scoring categories were regrouped according to the type of data yielded in order to reflect a picture of (a) Social interactions with peers, (b) selected maladaptive or inappropriate behaviors, and (c) nonteaching interactions with teachers. Ratings were looked at separately.

SOCIAL INTERACTIONS WITH PEERS

The data shown in Table 18.1 reveal that children with special needs show a pattern of social isolation and reduced physical proximity to others. Significantly more of the children with special needs spent time isolated from others, and significantly fewer of them spent appreciable time with others. When time with others was broken into time spent at the periphery of groups, time spent centrally located, and time spent with teachers, the difference was found to be related to time spent centrally located. Significantly fewer of the children with special needs spent time with others, physically central to the focus of activity, and the amount of time they spent centrally located was significantly less than that of the control group. In addition, children with special needs received significantly more negative behaviors from their peers and significantly more of them were the recipients of negative behaviors (72% versus 31% of the control group). Significantly more of the children with special needs produced negative behaviors directed toward others. There were no differences between the groups in the production or receipt of positive behaviors, nor in the frequency of conversations with peers.

For the control children, significant correlations of selected ABC indices with age (see Table 18.2) revealed a pattern with increasing age of increasing peer conversation, increasing time spent with other children, and decreasing receipt of negative behaviors. This expected pattern of changes with age did

TABLE 18.1

Social Interactions with Peers: Grade School Special Needs (SN) and Control (C) Children

ABC index	School 1 Means (SN)	School 2 Means SN	School 2 Means C	School 2 t-test	School 2 χ^2
Percentage time spent isolated (not situation determined)	(6)	12	9	n.s.	$p < .02$
Percentage time spent with others (not situation determined)					
total	(15)	29	43	n.s.	$p < .01$
centrally located	(8)	23	38	$p < .05$	$p < .001$
at periphery	(.4)	3	2	n.s.	n.s.
Conversations with peers	(8)	10	13	n.s.	n.s.
Positive behaviors from target child	(.08)	.1	.2	n.s.	n.s.
Positive behaviors to target child	(.2)	.1	.2	n.s.	n.s.
Negative behaviors from target child	(.4)	.3	.1	n.s.	$p < .02$
Negative behaviors to target child	(.6)	.4	.1	$p < .01$	$p < .02$

TABLE 18.2
Correlations

| | School 1 | | School 2 | | | |
| | SN Children | | SN Children | | C Children | |
	r	p	r	p	r	p
r between age and:						
Percentage time with other children, central to focus of activity	.36	n.s.	.16	n.s.	.68	< .01
Amount of peer conversation	.45	n.s.	−.14	n.s.	.49	< .05
Frequency of negative behaviors to the child	.29	n.s.	−.15	n.s.	−.53	< .05
r between:						
Percentage time "centrally located" and amount of peer conversation	.85	< .005	.11	n.s.	.72	< .01

not occur for the children with special needs. In addition, a correlation between being centrally located and conversing with others, which was high and significant for the control group, did not exist for the handicapped children. These data taken together lead one to believe that, at least in School 2, the children with special needs as a group might not be developing comfortable peer interactions with increasing age.

The correlations of these indices with age for the children with special needs from School 1 were also not significant, suggesting that they too were not showing the developmental changes shown by nonhandicapped children. However, for this group, there was a high correlation between the time spent centrally with others and the frequency of conversation, suggesting that when the School 1 children with special needs spent time with their peers, they also conversed with them.

SELECTED MALADAPTIVE OR INAPPROPRIATE BEHAVIORS

Analysis of Behaviors in the Classroom data include four frequency counts of behaviors that might be classified as inappropriate or maladaptive. The correlation matrix for the control group suggests that these four indices were not related to each other, whereas they were intercorrelated for the handicapped children. In general, the incidence of these behaviors was low.

Table 18.3 reveals that children with special needs produced significantly more sounds and noises than control children and significantly more children with special needs produced such sounds as well as strange gestures and movements. There were no differences between the two groups in the amount of wandering or level of distractibility, although there is evidence from a different analysis of the data that aimless wandering was more characteristic of children with social problems than of children who were not negatively treated by others. It is interesting to note that, under conditions of listening, watching, or working as part of a group, children with special needs produced significantly fewer sounds and noises than they did under conditions of individual work, but significantly more strange gestures and movements than they did under conditions of individual work. Perhaps in a group situation they quickly learn to inhibit the production of noncommunicative sounds and noises, which are potentially more disruptive than unheard movements and gestures.

That all children, to some extent, inhibit potentially disruptive behaviors as they grow older is suggested by our data. For all three groups of children, age correlated negatively (though not significantly so) with all four of the indices of Table 18.3. There was also a suggestion in the data that both children with special needs and control children produced a fair number of gestures and movements when young. Although both groups decreased this production with age, the differences between the groups increased with age. In contrast, the

TABLE 18.3
Selected (Maladaptive) Behaviors: Grade School Special Needs (SN) and Control (C) Children

	School 1	School 2			
	Mean frequencies	Mean frequencies			
ABC index	(SN)	SN	C	t-test	χ^2
Distraction	(.95)	1.5	1.2	n.s.	n.s.
alone		.9	.7	n.s.	n.s.
in groups		.6	.5	n.s.	n.s.
Wandering	(.7)	.9	1.2	n.s.	n.s.
alone		.8	1.1	n.s.	n.s.
in groups		.1	.0	n.s.	n.s.
Sounds and noises	(1.4)	.8	.2	$p < .05$	$p < .02$
alone		$p < .05$ { .6	.1	$p < .05$	$p < .05$
in groups		.2	.1	n.s.	n.s.
Gestures and movements	(4.2)	2.0	1.1	n.s.	$p < .02$
alone		$p < .05$ { .7	.3	n.s.	$p < .02$
in groups		1.3	.7	n.s.	$p < .05$

355

differences between the groups with respect to sounds and noises seemed to decrease with age, with the older groups looking alike on this measure. This again gives some support for the idea that handicapped children adapt relatively quickly (in group situations and with age) by inhibiting the more disruptive of their unusual behaviors.

NONTEACHING INTERACTIONS WITH TEACHERS

These results, along with the results from the ratings scores, are presented in Table 18.4. The data show that a significantly higher proportion of children with special needs spent appreciable time alone with the teacher. Although the groups did not differ significantly in the amount of conversation with the teacher, the higher frequency of teacher conversation for the children with special needs, in conjunction with the nursery-school findings to be presented later, suggests that the factor of conversation with the teacher may be an important one to study further.

RATING SCALES

There were no differences between the groups in ratings of relative activity level or verbalization level. This indicates that, at least as a group, children with special needs were not presenting problems of hyper- or hypo activity, nor were they excessively talkative or quiet.

OTHER FINDINGS

The data discussed so far reveal nonacceptance of children with special needs by their peers as reflected by the physical proximity and isolation measures. The data also reveal rejection of children with special needs by the frequency of negative behaviors directed to them by others. We wondered what extraordinary behaviors on the part of the children with special needs were related to being the target of such negative actions. For the children with special needs, frequency of negative behaviors directed toward the child correlated with only unusual negative behaviors from the child to other children ($r = .473$, $p < .02$). The corresponding correlations for the control children showed that the frequency of unusual negative behaviors toward individuals within the control group correlated with the frequency of strange sounds and noises emitted by the children ($r = .677$, $p < .01$), frequency of aimless wandering ($r = .588$, $p < .02$), and frequency of conversation with the teacher ($r = .496$, $p < .05$). This suggested to us that once a threshold level of certain behaviors is reached, negative responses from others will be evoked, regardless of how frequent the behavior is and regardless of whether the child is handicapped or nonhandicapped. Perhaps high amounts of such behavior were the instigating factor in the rejection of children with special needs.

TABLE 18.4
Nonteaching Interaction with Teachers: Grade School Special Needs (SN) and Control (C) Children

ABC index	School 1 Means (SN)	School 2 Means SN	School 2 Means C	t-test	χ^2
Percentage time spent alone with teacher (not situation-determined)	(2.8)	3.3	3.0	n.s.	$p < .05$
Number of conversations with teacher	(3.7)	4.2	3.6	n.s.	n.s.
Rating of relative activity level	(1.9)	2.1	2.0	n.s.	n.s.
Rating of relative verbalization level	(1.6)	1.8	1.8	n.s.	n.s.

As a test of this idea, we selected, from the group of children with special needs, seven children who evoked *no* negative responses from other children. We then calculated the means of this subgroup for each of the indices above. As there was no correlation between these indices and negative behaviors from others for the special needs group, we would not expect this subgroup to differ from the total group unless our hypothesis of a threshold was correct. If this were the case, we would expect to find much lower means for this subgroup. The means of the nonrejected subgroup of children with special needs dropped dramatically on all three indices. This lends support to the notion that occurrences of sounds and noises, aimless wandering, and conversations with teachers are tolerated by other children until the frequencies cross some threshold. Once a child has crossed this threshold, he becomes the recipient of negative behaviors from others.

Discussion

The data suggest that grade school children with special needs were more isolated and rejected than control children and produced more strange (i.e., maladaptive, inappropriate) behaviors. We had hoped that, with a population of children who appeared to be not too deviant from nonhandicapped children, fewer indications of social nonacceptance and behavioral difference would be found. However, it must be emphasized that our data revealed low frequencies and small differences; differences that are significant, but that may not be important when one looks at the total picture.

The data also revealed some positive indications. There were improvements in some social behaviors with age (i.e., older handicapped children producing fewer sounds and noises and fewer gestures and movements than younger handicapped children). In addition, the data suggested that there are behaviors that serve as stimuli for rejection whether they are produced by children with special needs or by nonhandicapped children. Perhaps children with special needs and other children can be taught methods of controlling these behaviors. Certainly, they have shown signs of controlling some of them, such as noncommunicative sounds and noises. Concurrently, it is conceivable that nonhandicapped children can be taught to better tolerate these annoying behaviors.

Finally, the data suggested that some of the behaviors, characteristic of children with special needs at older ages, were more common among nonhandicapped children at younger ages. In fact, strange gestures and movements were just as common in both groups at young ages. Perhaps the behavior of mainstreamed handicapped children would not stand out beside the behaviors of nonhandicapped children at young ages. If the behaviors were not conspicuously different in younger age groups, they might not trigger a sequence of negative reactions.

BEHAVIORS AND INTERACTIONS IN TWO
NURSERY–KINDERGARTEN SETTINGS

Flavell (1977) discusses Piaget's observation that young children "center their attention on the present spatial field or stimulus stage to the exclusion of other relevant states and state-linking transformations in the 'temporal field' which consists of the recent past, the immediate present, and the near future [82]." Although Flavell (and Piaget) are talking about young children making inferences about physical experiences, much of the same can be seen when the very young adopt attitudes toward the personalities of the children with whom they interact. "I don't like Johnny," says Tom. When asked why, Tom replies that Johnny just hit him. But tomorrow, Tom will be playing with Johnny again, and when Johnny hits him again, Tom will cry and say he doesn't like him. It is as if Tom cannot yet make the generalization that Johnny hits. Evidence indirectly supportive of this idea can be found in studies of social cognition, such as Flapan (1968) and Lively and Bromley (1973). Perhaps the behaviors that "turn off" older children either will not be very unusual at nursery school age (as suggested by some of our grade school data) or will not be remembered over time (generalized) at young ages, so that preschoolers will be more accepting of the integrated children with special needs.

We collected data from two nursery schools that differed along two dimensions: proportion of children with special needs in the classroom and philosophy of nursery school education. The two factors are here confounded as the two schools differed on both dimensions.

A number of nursery schools take in one child with special needs and talk of integration. Lewis and Fraser (1978) speak of this as tokenism rather than integration, and claim that the single handicapped child mainstreamed without other children with special needs becomes more isolated by virture of his uniqueness in the class. We wondered, if they are right, will handicapped children in a school that mainstreams a relatively large number of handicapped children be more accepted than the handicapped children in a school that mainstreams not one per class but a small proportion of such children, or will all the handicapped children from both types of school be more accepted and less different in behavior from the nonhandicapped simply by virtue of their young age?

Subjects

Children were observed in two nursery schools. Subjects from Nursery School 1 were 16 children with special needs and 16 control children matched for classroom, sex, and race. At the time the observations started, ages ranged from 4 years and 1 month to 7 years and 8 months ($\bar{X}$ = 5 years, 9 months; SD = 1 year) for the handicapped children, and from 3 years, 3 months to 6 years

($\overline{X}$ = 4 years, 11 months; SD = 10 months) for the nonhandicapped children. School 1 mainstreamed an average of 17.8% handicapped children in each of its five classrooms. An approach designated as being "cognitive–developmental" was used. Observers noted a high level of teacher control of what transpired in the classroom during "free" time. There was a wide range of handicapping conditions represented in the sample, including one child with Down's syndrome, three who were mildly to moderately retarded, three with cerebral palsy (CP), four with speech and language delay or problems, and three with motor problems.

Subjects from Nursery School 2 were 25 children with special needs and 25 control children, matched for classroom, race, sex, and, as closely as possible, age. An additional 10 handicapped boys, for whom no sex matches could be found in their class, were included as a separate group. Because the boys were older than the rest of the handicapped children in the sample, we were interested in comparing their data with the data from the younger handicapped children. Excluding the 10 extra boys, ages at the time the observations began ranged from 3 years to 6 years and 11 months ($\overline{X}$ = 4 years, 11 months; SD = 1 year, 1 month) for the handicapped children and from 3 years to 6 years and 5 months ($\overline{X}$ = 4 years, 9 months, SD = 1 year, 1 month) for the nonhandicapped children. The extra group of 10 boys ranged in age from 5 years to 7 years and 5 months ($\overline{X}$ = 6 years; SD = 9 months). This school mainstreamed a high proportion of handicapped children—an average of 39.3% in each of its four classes. A vigilant but noninterfering and nondirective approach was used here during "free" time. The types and distribution of handicapping conditions were similar to those of Nursery School 1. The total of 35 children included 1 child with Down's syndrome, 8 who were mildly to moderately retarded, 2 with Cerebral Palsy, 8 with language delay or problems, and 3 with motor problems.

Method

In School 1, one round of data was collected (i.e., 6 20-min observations per child) during the early winter, and a second round in the late spring of the same year. In School 2, 11 handicapped children and 11 matched control children were observed in the spring of one year. Fourteen handicapped children and 14 matched, nonhandicapped children, plus the 10 additional handicapped boys, were observed the following autumn.

Data were collected according to the instructions for the ABC-NK. Each subject from School 1 was observed for 6 20-min sessions during each round of data collection. Proration was used to balance structured and unstructured time for two children who were observed only five times each. Each subject from School 2 was observed six times during the first data collection and a minimum of four times during the second data collection.

Data Analysis

The data from the two collection rounds in School 1 were combined, and the average of the 12 20-min observations was computed for each child for each index. The two rounds of data were also looked at separately. For School 2, the two data rounds were treated as separate studies (separate replications) as only six subjects were common to both data collections.

Results

As with the grade school data, these data were regrouped to separately examine three aspects of classroom behavior: social interactions with peers, selected maladaptive or inappropriate behaviors, and nonteaching interactions with the teachers. Ratings were looked at separately.

SOCIAL INTERACTIONS WITH PEERS

Table 18.5 suggests that the handicapped children from School 1, unlike those from School 2, showed a pattern of isolation and reduced physical proximity to others. Children with special needs from School 1 spent significantly more time alone, significantly less time centrally located, and significantly *more* time, than control children, at the periphery of groups.

The children with special needs were significantly more isolated whether one looked at self-initiated or other-initiated isolation. When we looked separately at self-initiated time with other children and other-initiated time with other children, we found that the groups differed significantly on only self-initiated time with other children. In other words, the children with special needs spent much time alone, both by choice and because they were left alone by others. Their reduced time with others seemed to be self-initiated rather than other-initiated.

Special needs children from School 1 were the recipients of significantly more negative verbal and physical behaviors from nonhandicapped children than were the control children, although they were not the producers of significantly more negative behavior. In contrast, the data from School 2 showed that children with special needs were no more negatively treated by their nonhandicapped peers than were the controls. However, it is interesting that School 2 handicapped children, during the second round of data collection, were the recipients of significantly more negative behaviors from other handicapped children than were their nonhandicapped control peers.

Children with special needs from both schools conversed significantly less with their nonhandicapped peers than did the control children. This agrees with the data reported by Ispa and Matz (1978) and perhaps is to be expected,

TABLE 18.5
Social Interactions with Peers: Nursery–Kindergarten Special Needs (SN) and Control (C) Children

	School 1			School 2						
	Collections 1 and 2			Collection 1			Collection 2			
	Means			Means			Means			Means
ABC index	SN	C	t-test	SN	C	t-test	SN	C	t-test	10 SN boys
Seconds alone[a]	145	81	p < .01	148	149	n.s.	157	143	n.s.	121
self-initiated	77	45	p < .02							
other initiated	68	36	p < .05							
Seconds with other children[a]	521	615	p < .05	361	409	n.s.	344	366	n.s.	475
centrally located	490	601	p < .02	351	406	n.s.	329	357	n.s.	466
self-initiated	149	242	p < .01							
other initiated	341	358	n.s.							
at periphery	31	14	p < .05	10	2	n.s.	15	8	n.s.	9
self-initiated	17	10	n.s.							
other initiated	14	4	n.s.							
Conversation with non-handicapped peers	6.4	12.2	p < .001	3.3	8.8	p < .01	3.3	6.1	p < .05	1.1

Conversation with handicapped peers	1.5	1.2	n.s.	3.5	1.1	n.s.	1.7	1.7	n.s.	8.1
Positive behaviors from target child	.10	.35	n.s.	.63	.45	n.s.	.70	.94	n.s.	1.01
to nonhandicapped peers	.07	.21	n.s.	.23	.33	n.s.	.42	.52	n.s.	.23
to handicapped peers	.03	.15	n.s.	.40	.12	n.s.	.28	.42	n.s.	.79
Positive behaviors to target child	.70	.10	n.s.	.46	.33	n.s.	.49	.46	n.s.	.56
from nonhandicapped peers	.68	.09	n.s.	.30	.27	n.s.	.33	.31	n.s.	.07
from handicapped peers	.01	.01	n.s.	.16	.06	n.s.	.16	.15	n.s.	.48
Negative behaviors from target child	.16	.19	n.s.	.54	.42	n.s.	1.17	1.38	n.s.	.92
to nonhandicapped peers	.12	.12	n.s.	.40	.37	n.s.	.78	.76	n.s.	.12
to handicapped peers	.04	.07	n.s.	.14	.05	n.s.	.39	.63	n.s.	.80
Negative behaviors to target child	.30	.15	n.s.	.25	.25	n.s.	1.25	.70	n.s.	1.19
from nonhandicapped peers	.26	.05	$p < .02$	.21	.18	n.s.	.84	.65	n.s.	.23
from handicapped peers	.03	.09	n.s.	.05	.08	n.s.	.41	.05	$p < .05$	.95

[a] Not situation determined

since the verbal ability of the children with special needs is probably less than that of the recipient children.

Differences between the schools, as revealed by the differences between the means for the different indices are interesting. Nonhandicapped children from School 2 spent much more time alone than did the nonhandicapped children from School 1. Additionally, the production of both positive and negative behaviors was greater for the children from School 2. This may relate to the lessened opportunity for the children in School 1 to move about and express themselves freely.

To briefly summarize the findings presented in Table 18.5, although all handicapped children conversed significantly less frequently with their nonhandicapped peers than did the controls, it was only in the school that mainstreamed a low proportion of handicapped children and had a high amount of teacher control (School 1) that handicapped children showed a significant pattern of isolation from their peers, reduced physical proximity to their peers, and increased negativity from their nonhandicapped peers.

When one looks at the School 1 data from the first and second rounds of data collection separately, the picture is a little less clear. During both winter and spring terms, the special needs children were significantly more isolated than their peers ($p < .05$ for each term). Only during the winter term did they spend significantly less time with other children ($p < .001$). However, it is not clear from the data whether the absence of a significant difference during the second data collection was due to the increased amount of time the handicapped children spent with others during the spring term or to the large drop in time spent by the control children with other children. In either case, there clearly was increasing similarity between the two groups in this respect as the year progressed.

SELECTED MALADAPTIVE OR INAPPROPRIATE BEHAVIORS

The grade-school data had suggested that many of the inappropriate behaviors observed were not particularly unusual for younger children, handicapped or nonhandicapped. As we had anticipated, there were few significant differences between children with special needs and the control children in the selected behaviors observed. The School 1 children with special needs evidenced significantly more distractibility and watching behaviors than the School 1 controls ($p < .02$ overall, $p = .05$ for each term separately). Children with special needs from School 2 were not sigificantly different from the controls on any of these measures.

NONTEACHING INTERACTIONS WITH TEACHERS

Table 18.6 reveals a pattern of significantly greater teacher interaction for the children with special needs of School 1, but not for those of School 2.

TABLE 18.6
Nonteaching Interactions with Teachers; Ratings: Nursery-Kindergarten Special Needs (SN) and Control (C) Children

ABC index	School 1						School 2			
	Collections 1 and 2			Collection 1			Collection 2			
	Means			Means			Means			Means
	SN	C	t-test	SN	C	t-test	SN	C	t-test	10 SN boys
Seconds alone with teacher[a]	131	43	p < .001	34	55	n.s.	133	70	n.s.	71
self-initiated	37	30	n.s.							
other initiated	94	13	p < .001							
Conversations with teacher	12.7	9.7	p < .02	4.4	3.1	n.s.	8.3	7.1	n.s.	5.4
Relative activity level	3.1	3.2	n.s.	2.9	3.0	n.s.	3.1	3.0	n.s.	3.1
Relative verbalization level	2.8	3.1	n.s.	2.4	2.8	n.s.	2.4	2.9	p < .02	2.7
Parten rating	3.0	3.3	n.s.	3.7	4.3	n.s.	3.5	3.9	n.s.	4.2

[a]Not situation determined

Relative to the control children, the children with special needs from School 1 spent significantly more time with the teacher, although it was interesting that there was no significant difference between the two groups in the amount of self-initiated time spent with the teacher. In other words, the handicapped children of School 1 were not overtly acting more teacher-dependent than the controls by seeking out the teacher. To the contrary, the handicapped children were more often sought out by the teacher than were the nonhandicapped children. Perhaps this relates to the greater teacher control at this school, or perhaps the children with special needs were indicating their need for the teacher in some way other than by approaching him or her. In either case, the net result was the same: The handicapped children of School 1 spent significantly more nonteaching time with the teacher. In addition, the children with special needs of School 1 engaged in significantly more conversation with their teachers than did the nonhandicapped children. In School 2, there were no differences between handicapped and nonhandicapped children in either the amount of time spent with the teacher, or in the amount of conversation with the teacher.

RATING SCORES

In both schools, there were no significant differences between the children with special needs and the controls on the Parten scores, indicating that the developmental level of the type of play the children with special needs engaged in, though lower than that of the control children, was not statistically different.

Although there were no significant differences between School 1 handicapped and nonhandicapped children on any of the ratings for the total year, the data revealed that, for the year-end data collection, children with special needs were significantly less active ($p < .05$) and significantly less verbally responsive ($p < .05$) than the control children. For the autumn data collection in School 2, children with special needs were significantly less verbally responsive; however, this was not true for the spring data collection.

OTHER FINDINGS: TEN OLDER HANDICAPPED BOYS

Data from the observations of 10 older handicapped boys, unmatched with controls, were collected to provide information about changes with age in the interactions and behaviors of handicapped children. Tables 18.5 and 18.6 show that the 10 older handicapped children from School 2 behaved, for the most part, more like the group of 14 control children than like the younger handicapped children. Most of their index scores either fell between the scores of the younger handicapped and nonhandicapped group or beyond those of the nonhandicapped children (in either case, implying a developmental trend that, though not significant, is quite consistent across indices). For some behaviors, it appears that the effect of age is very powerful. For example, the older handicapped group spent less time alone or on the periphery of groups and much more time centrally with others than all of the other children studied in that school. In addition, Parten scores were significantly higher for these children than for the younger handicapped group ($p < .05$) and higher, though not significantly so, than for the controls. Positive behaviors to and from the children of this group were higher than for the rest of the children studied and negative behaviors from the children were fewer.

However, scores on two indices did not fit this pattern. Children from this group of 10 boys conversed significantly less than the other handicapped children with nonhandicapped peers ($p < .01$) and significantly more with handicapped peers ($p < .001$). This finding is easily explained, however, by the fact that there were only two nonhandicapped boys in their classroom at the time of data collection.

OTHER FINDINGS: SOCIOMETRIC RESULTS

As most previous studies of the popularity of mainstreamed children with special needs had used sociometric techniques to judge children's acceptance in a classroom, we wondered how the ABC information relating to acceptance or rejection of children would compare with the results from standard sociometric methods. A sociometric procedure was administered to all the children in both schools. Each child was individually shown pictures of all the children in his or her class. After it was ascertained that the child could supply a name for or recognize each picture, he or she was asked which of the children he or she liked best of all (three names were recorded) and—in School 1 only—which of the children he or she did not like. The results support the observational findings by showing that in School 1 handicapped children were both rejected by their peers and not chosen as friends, whereas School 2 handicapped children were chosen as "liked" as frequently as nonhandicapped children.

Discussion

The nursery-school results were not as uniformly positive as we had hoped. Maladaptive inappropriate behaviors were not noticeably greater for handicapped than nonhandicapped children (with the exception of the greater frequency of distraction and watching behaviors for the handicapped children in School 1). In School 2, the hoped for pattern of acceptance and true intermingling of children did occur. Handicapped children in School 2 were not differentiated from nonhandicapped children by the amounts of time they spent alone and with other children, by the types of behaviors directed to them by their nonhandicapped peers, or by greater teacher interaction. However, the handicapped children from School 1, the school that mainstreamed a lower proportion of handicapped children and was higher in teacher control, showed a pattern of isolation, rejection, and high teacher interaction that was similar to (and even more extreme than) the pattern found at the grade school level.

Despite this, there were some positive social trends in School 1. There was improvement in the interactions of the handicapped and nonhandicapped children from mid year to year-end, though these changes were not statistically significant. The handicapped children received more positive behaviors and fewer negative behaviors from their nonhandicapped peers, and positive behaviors from the handicapped to the nonhandicapped also increased. Finally, handicapped children decreased the amount of time spent with the teacher and increased the amount of time spent with other children.

One gets the impression that in School 2, the handicapped children spent their days much like the nonhandicapped children, in terms of what they did and who they did it with (except that they did not converse as much with their nonhandicapped peers). One gets the impression of noninterfering teachers avoiding solitary interaction with the handicapped children when it was unnecessary and avoiding interference with ongoing activity. This, along with the larger number of such children in the classroom, might have the effect of not drawing attention to the handicapped children. Without attention drawn to them (by either their rarity in the population or by increased teacher attention), the children with special needs are not viewed as particularly different. That the children can learn and develop without constant teacher pressure is revealed by index scores for the 10 older handicapped boys.

CONCLUDING REMARKS

The results obtained in a given study may be due to specifics of the schools, teachers, and children involved, so one must generalize with caution. However, the results obtained at the grade-school level agree with the numerous findings reported in the literature (i.e., that mainstreamed handicapped children are not accepted by their nonhandicapped peers in grade school). Additionally, the data we obained suggested that certain patterns of behavior (i.e., producing noncommunicative sounds and noises, wandering aimlessly, conversing more than an average amount with the teacher, and being negative to others) were associated with being the recipient of negative behaviors from peers, whether the child was handicapped or not. We also found that some maladaptive inappropriate behaviors decreased with age for both handicapped and nonhandicapped children, suggesting that perhaps what looked like behavioral anomalies at grade-school level might look normative for all children at nursery school age.

The nursery-school results showed that handicapped and nonhandicapped children were not generally different on these inappropriate maladaptive behaviors. However, handicapped children in one school were isolated and rejected, showing a pattern very much like those handicapped children in the grade school. In the school that mainstreamed more children with special needs and had more nondirective teachers, the handicapped children showed few significant differences from the nonhandicapped children. It is impossible to separate out the influence of the number of handicapped children from the influence of the type of teacher activity (or the interaction of the two). Nonetheless, these studies present evidence that early integration of children with special needs with nonhandicapped children can be socially more successful than it is at the grade-school level. The data suggest that perhaps it is not age alone that allows for smoother mainstreaming in the nursery-school setting. Characteristics of the school itself apparently facilitate successful integration. A high proportion of handicapped children and/or minimal teacher structuring of free time seem to facilitate the social acceptance of handicapped children by their nursery-school peers. Perhaps the handicapped children stood out more in the first school because there were so few of them. Perhaps the children would have done better socially had the teachers not been so ready to help, shape, suggest, and be with the handicapped children.

However, one must not lose sight of other, perhaps more important, events and changes in the lives of mainstreamed handicapped children. Positive things are happening. Feelings of self-worth on the part of mainstreamed handicapped children subtly grow and affect the work the children do. In one of the grade schools in which we worked, we watched Rachel, rather severely retarded, painfully negotiating some stairs, two feet on each step. A child from her "regular class" whizzed by, calling out "Hi, Rachel!" The child beamed and proceeded to alternate feet the rest of the way up the stairs—a very dramatic and revealing little episode.

After 2 years of being mainstreamed in an elementary school, George was still fighting with other children or hiding in corners of the room during the time he spent in his "regular class." An interview with him revealed he hated being mainstreamed, hated the other children. A social worker was assigned to spend some time with him. One year later, we saw him again, now a happy outgoing child, participating quite actively in the ongoing events in his "regular class."

In a nursery school, an able-bodied child suggested a race to a child who could not walk. After identifying the finish line, he hesitated, then suddenly suggested the race be a swimming one (crawling on the floor) and the handicapped child happily participated. In another nursery school, a child, whose arms ended in deformed hands at the elbows, was asked by another child when they were all dressed and masked for Halloween, "Who are you? I can't guess."

Perhaps these are the important events in the lives of the handicapped children, not the few extra classroom minutes spent alone or the one or two extra attacks on them by the nonhandicapped children.

ACKNOWLEDGEMENTS

I would like to thank those who collected and coded the data, in particular Deborah Hird, Asunta Young, and Rena Mirkin. Great appreciation is expressed to the principals, directors, and teachers of all the schools involved for their patience and for making us feel more than just welcome. A particular debt of gratitude is owed to Dr. Milton Budoff whose valuable input and support influenced all phases of this research. Finally, I would like to thank the children whose cheerful and unselfconscious acceptance of us made our work possible.

This research was supported in part by Grant No. R01 HD08439 from the National Institutes of Health and Grant No. G0076-02459 from the Office of Education, Milton Budoff, Principal Investigator.

REFERENCES

Boyer, E. G., Simon, A., & Karafin, G., (Eds.) Measure of maturation: An anthology of early childhood observation instruments. Philadelphia: Humanizing Learning Program, Research for Better Schools, Inc., 1973.

Bryan, T. H. Peer popularity of learning disabled children. Journal of Learning Disabilities, 1974, 7, 621-625.

Bryan, T. H., Wheeler, R., Carey, R., & Croke, K. "Come on dummy": An observational study of children's communications. Journal of Learning Disabilities, 1976, 9, 661-669.

Flapan, D. Children's understanding of social interaction. New York: Teacher's College Press, 1968.

Flavell, J. H. Cognitive development. Englewood Cliffs, New Jersey: Prentice-Hall, 1977.

Fredericks, H. D., Baldwin, V., Grove, D., Moore, W., Riggs, C., & Lyons, B. Integrating the moderately and severely handicapped preschool child into a normal day care setting. In M. J. Guralnick (Ed.), Early intervention and the integration of handicapped and nonhandicapped children. Baltimore: Univ. Park Press, 1978. Pp. 191-206.

Gampel, D. H., Gottlieb, J., & Harrison, R. H. A comparison of the classroom behaviors of special class EMR, integrated EMR, low IQ, and nonretarded children. American Journal of Mental Deficiency, 1974, 79, 16-21.

Gottlieb, J., & Budoff, M. Social acceptability of retarded children in nongraded schools differing in architecture. American Journal of Mental Deficiency, 1975 78, 15-19.

Guralnick, M. The value of integrating handicapped and nonhandicapped preschool children. American Journal of Orthopsychiatry, 1976, 46, 236-245.

Iano, R. P., Ayers, D., Heller, H. B., McGettigan, J. P., & Walker, V. S. Sociometric status of retarded children in an integrative program. Exceptional Children, 1974, 40, 267-271.

Ispa, J., & Matz, R. D. Integrating handicapped preschool children within a cognitively oriented program. In M. J. Guralnick (Ed.), *Early intervention and the integration of handicapped and nonhandicapped children.* Baltimore: Univ. Park Press, 1978. Pp. 167–190.

Jones, R. L., & Sisk, D. A. Early perceptions of orthopedic disability. *Exceptional Children,* 1967, *34,* 42–43.

Lewis, E. G., & Fraser, K. M. *Integration—or "tokenism" in early childhood classrooms?* Submitted for publication, 1978.

Livesley, W. J., & Bromley, D. B. *Person perception in childhood and adolescence.* London: Wiley, 1973.

Parten, M. B. Social participation among preschool children. *Journal of Abnormal Social Psychology,* 1932, *27,* 243–269.

Walker, D. K. *Socioemotional measures for preschool and kindergarten children.* San Francisco: Jossey-Bass, 1973.

White, B. N. *Manual for the analysis of behaviors in the classroom.* Cambridge, Massachusetts: Research Institute for Educational Problems, RIEP Print #108, 1978.

Subject Index